PHYSICAL TECHNIQUES IN BIOLOGICAL RESEARCH

Volume III, Part B

Autoradiography at the Cellular Level

D0276227

PHYSICAL TECHNIQUES IN BIOLOGICAL RESEARCH

SECOND EDITION

Edited by

ARTHUR W. POLLISTER

DEPARTMENT OF ZOOLOGY
COLUMBIA UNIVERSITY
NEW YORK, NEW YORK

Volume III, Part B

Autoradiography at the Cellular Level

by

BRIGITTE SCHULTZE

INSTITUT FÜR MEDIZINISCHE STRAHLENKUNDE
UNIVERSITÄT WÜRZBURG
WÜRZBURG, GERMANY

NORTHWEST MISSOURI STATE
UNIVERSITY LIBRARY
MARYVILLE, MISSOURI 64468

 1969

ACADEMIC PRESS   New York and London

Copyright © 1969, by Academic Press, Inc.
ALL RIGHTS RESERVED.
NO PART OF THIS BOOK MAY BE REPRODUCED IN ANY FORM,
BY PHOTOSTAT, MICROFILM, RETRIEVAL SYSTEM, OR ANY OTHER
MEANS, WITHOUT WRITTEN PERMISSION FROM THE PUBLISHERS.

ACADEMIC PRESS, INC.
111 Fifth Avenue, New York, New York 10003

United Kingdom Edition published by
ACADEMIC PRESS, INC. (LONDON) LTD.
Berkeley Square House, London W.1

LIBRARY OF CONGRESS CATALOG CARD NUMBER: 54-11056

PRINTED IN THE UNITED STATES OF AMERICA

574
Q57p.2
V.3
pt B

PREFACE

Since J. H. Taylor contributed his article Autoradiography at the Cellular Level to the first edition of this treatise in 1956, a considerable amount of work has been done in autoradiography. The development of new techniques as well as the use of new types of emulsions have refined the autoradiographic method. The greater use of tritiated compounds in high resolution autoradiography has its advantages as well as limitations in quantitatively evaluating autoradiograms. The combination of autoradiography with electron microscopy has led to an improvement of autoradiographic resolution to 0.1 μ. Thus, today it is possible to demonstrate and localize labeled substances in subcellular structures. In addition, special techniques have been developed in recent years to detect diffusible, water-soluble substances with high autoradiographic resolution.

In this volume emphasis is placed on high resolution autoradiography with tritium. Since the first edition of this work, use of the autoradiographic method as a tool in studying metabolic processes has changed extensively. In earlier experiments, ^{32}P, ^{14}C, and ^{35}S were used as labels in studies of biological problems such as cellular metabolism and proliferation. Tritium did not play any role at that time, even though Fitzgerald et al. pointed out its advantages in autoradiography as early as 1951. Today the high resolution obtainable with tritium and the availability of so many tritiated metabolites make autoradiography a widely used method in investigating metabolic processes at the cellular and subcellular levels. Studies of the DNA, RNA, and protein metabolism of the cell are of major importance in autoradiography today, and consequently, are discussed at great length in this volume.

In this work, an attempt is made to review the different autoradiographic techniques and to supply information for their proper application. It demonstrates not only the advantages of the method but also its limitations and pitfalls. The book also deals with the difficulties in and the theoretical principles needed for the interpretation of autoradiograms. In addition, it makes accessible to the reader, in one source, the rapidly growing literature pertinent to the topics discussed.

Since publication of the first edition of this treatise, only a few reviews have been published on autoradiography: "Autoradiography as Histochemical Tool" by E. Harbers, "Autoradiography" by A. Ficq (which deals chiefly with track autoradiography), and "Radioautography, Its Use in Cytology" by P. J. Fitzgerald. Additional monographs and review articles related to special problems of autoradiography are referred to in the appropriate chapters of this book.

I am very grateful to all of my colleagues who have helped in the preparation of this work. I am particularly indebted to Dr. W. Maurer for many helpful suggestions and discussions, to Dr. J. H. Taylor for reading the manuscript and giving valuable advice, and to Dr. A. W. Pollister who accomplished the painful task of correcting the English text and bringing the manuscript into its present shape. I am also grateful to Drs. O. I. Epifanova and N. D. Gracheva who kindly directed my attention to the relevant Russian literature, so that it is as complete as possible. I also would like to express my gratitude to my co-worker, Miss M. N. Hasenfuss, whose constant and untiring help in preparing the tables, listing the references, reading the proofs, and translating the Russian literature has been of inestimable value.

March, 1969

B. SCHULTZE

Preface to Second Edition of Volume III

During the long period since the first edition was written there have been many improvements and innovations in every physical technique used in biological research on cells and tissues. This progress has made it imperative to present a new edition. The main chapter headings of the first edition have been retained since no widely useful methods have been developed that are different in principle from those current earlier. For one reason or another there have been a number of changes in authorship. All authors have been given freedom of choice in adherence to the original organization and in retention of the material of the first edition. However, in nearly every subject the revised manuscripts were considerably longer than those of the first edition. Therefore, it has become necessary to publish Volume III in three parts: A, B, and C. Volumes IIIA and IIIC cover all subjects except autoradiographic techniques; the latter is the subject of Volume IIIB.

March, 1969   ARTHUR W. POLLISTER

CONTENTS

1. General and Theoretical Aspects of Autoradiography

2. Autoradiographic Techniques

3. Application of Different Isotopes

4. DNA Synthesis

5. RNA Synthesis

6. Protein Synthesis

7. Lipid Synthesis

8. Electron Microscopic Autoradiography

9. Autoradiographic Methods in Cytochemistry 227

1. General and Theoretical Aspects of Autoradiography

I. Characteristics of the Different Types of Radiation

For autoradiographic purposes only α- and β-emitters, and in some cases isotopes that disintegrate by K-capture or isomeric transition, are suitable labels. γ-Emission generally has too great a penetrability and too little ionization to affect autoradiographic emulsions.

A. α-Particles

Since all α-particles of an α-decaying isotope have the same energy, they all have the same path length too, in tissue approximately 30–80 μ. α-Particles are positively charged helium nuclei. They are relatively heavy, have a short path, and produce many ionizations throughout their paths. In autoradiographic emulsions they appear as straight short lines of closely spaced grains (Fig. 1A). α-Tracks are easily traced through the autoradiographic emulsion to the point of their origin. The precision with which the point of origin can be determined is highest with α-radiation. However, the use of α-emitters in biological work is limited, since they are isotopes occurring mainly at the end of the periodic system.

B. β-Particles

Compared to the α-particles, the lighter β-particles have a longer path with fewer ionizations per unit path length and are easily deflected from their course. Their path is a random one compared to the α-particles, and the number of ionizations per unit path length increases with decreasing energy at the end of their path (Fig. 1B).

β-Rays that penetrate matter are absorbed. Absorption of the β-rays only depends on the thickness of the absorbing material, measured in milligrams per square centimeter, and not on the chemical characteristic of the absorber. In the range of high atomic numbers this relationship is not exactly accurate. Relatively small absorber layers absorb most of the β-particles. This is due to the continuous spectrum of the β-energy between zero and the upper energy maximum ($E_{\beta\,\mathrm{max}}$) of the β-emitters and to the fact that most of the β-particles have less energy than the maximum energy. Only a few β-particles have a much greater penetrability. The thickness of the absorber layer that is needed to absorb them completely is called the maximum range ($R_{\beta\,\mathrm{max}}$), measured as milligrams per square

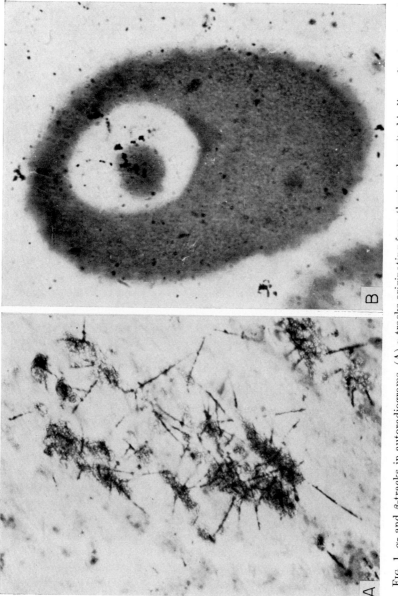

FIG. 1. α- and β-tracks in autoradiograms. (A) α-tracks originating from thorium deposited in liver after treatment with Thorotrast. (B) Three β-tracks emerging from the nucleolus of a starfish oocyte, tagged with adenine-8-¹⁴C. (From Ficq, 1959c.)

centimeter. This maximum range depends on the small number of β-particles with the highest energy, and only on those which by chance have a relatively linear path. Because of the spread of β-particles and of the continuous energy distribution of β-radiation, a much thinner absorber layer than $R_{\beta\,max}$ is sufficient to absorb most of β-particles.

The relationship between the maximum β-energy ($E_{\beta\,max}$) and the maximum range ($R_{\beta\,max}$) is demonstrated in Fig. 2. If $E_{\beta\,max}$ of an isotope is known, the maximum range $R_{\beta\,max}$ can easily be read from the curve. This maximum range of the isotope is important for the resolving power in autoradiography.

There is a great difference in maximum energy ($E_{\beta\,max}$) for the different β-emitters: for ^{32}P, it is 1700 keV ($R_{\beta\,max} = 760$ mg/cm^2, or 0.76 cm in H_2O); for ^3H, only 18 keV ($R_{\beta\,max} = 0.5$ mg/cm^2, or 5 μ in H_2O).

C. K-Capture and Isomeric Transitions

Isotopes decaying by K-capture are also suitable for autoradiographic experiments. Absorption of an electron from the K shell by the atomic nucleus leads to a hole in the K shell. This hole in the K shell is refilled by an electron from the next shell outward, resulting in the emission of X-rays. In elements with a low atomic number, up to about 50, these X-rays are absorbed most probably in the electron shell of the same atom. This leads to electron lines (Auger electrons) with an energy similar to that of tritium. Similar events occur in isotopes which decay by isomeric transitions. In this case, a low-energy γ quantum is emitted by the atomic nucleus. Part of the γ quanta are absorbed by the K shell of the same atom leading to electron lines with low energy. Furthermore, the hole in the K shell causes the emission of a K X-ray series connected with the emission of Auger electrons.

A systematic description of isotopes with electron capture or isomeric transition usable for autoradiographic purposes is given by Forberg *et al.* (1964). Isotopes with secondary electrons having energy as low as the β-energy of tritium will lead to a corresponding high autoradiographic resolving power. For examples of application in autoradiography, see Chapter 3, Section I, see also Schultze and Hughes (1965), Pentel and Tonna (1965), and Hammarström *et al.* (1965b).

II. Autoradiographic Emulsions

A. Characteristics

X-Ray films were used earlier in autoradiography for gross localization of isotopes in tissue. In general the sensitivity of photographic emulsions increases with increasing size of the silver bromide crystals. Fine-grain

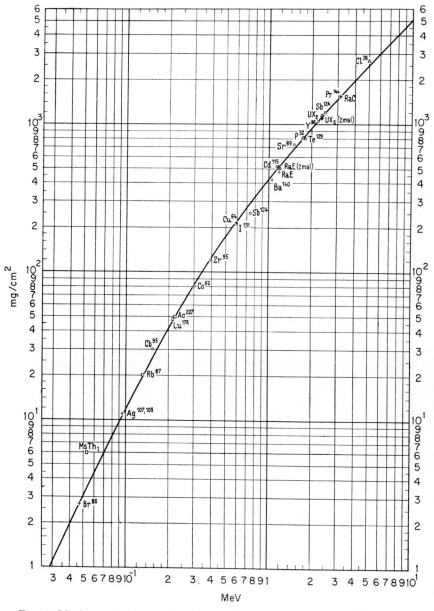

FIG. 2. Maximum range of different β-emitters as a function of their maximum energy. (From Meyer-Schützmeister and Vincent, 1952; see references therein.)

emulsions are needed for autoradiography at the cellular level since the attainable resolving power also depends on the size of the grains. For this reason, autoradiographic emulsions are relatively insensitive. Emulsions that have been developed for autoradiographic purposes have an average grain diameter of approximately 0.2 μ and less. In order to increase the sensitivity, the autoradiographic emulsions have a high concentration of silver bromide; 86% of the emulsion weight is AgBr, that is, half the volume of the emulsion. The sensitivity is also sufficient to register electrons at the minimum of their specific ionization at approximately 1 MeV.

Commonly used emulsions include nuclear research emulsions NTB, NTB-2, and NTB-3 from Eastman Kodak, USA; nuclear research emulsions G-5, K-2, K-5, and L-4 from Ilford, London; Scientia NUC 3.07 and 7.15 from Gevaert, Belgium; and the stripping film "Kodak autoradiographic plates AR 10" from Kodak, London. Their grain sizes are listed in Table I. Eastman Kodak NTB-3 emulsion has a higher sensitivity, but NTB-2 is usually preferred because of the lower initial background fog. Ilford G-5 emulsion with a grain size of approximately 0.3 μ is about 3–5 times more sensitive than stripping film AR 10 or Ilford K-2, but also has a higher background fog. Ilford K-2 corresponds to the stripping film AR 10, and Ilford L-4 with a grain size of 0.14 μ is used when finer grain sizes are desired, usually when autoradiography is combined with electron microscopy. Gevaert Scientia NUC 7.15 with a grain size of 0.15 μ (undeveloped) has a higher AgBr concentration and a relatively high sensitivity and is therefore suitable for registering particles of all energies, especially higher energy β-particles. Scientia NUC 3.07 with a grain size of 0.07

TABLE I

AUTORADIOGRAPHIC EMULSIONS AND THEIR GRAIN SIZE

Manufacturer	Emulsion	Grain size (in μ)
Kodak, London	Stripping-Film AR 10	0.2
Eastman Kodak, USA	NTB	
	NTB-2	
	NTB-3	
Ilford, London	G-5	0.27
	K-2	0.2
	K-5	0.2
	L-4	0.14
Gevaert, Belgium	NUC 3.07	0.07
	NUC 7.15	0.15

μ (undeveloped) registers strongly ionizing particles, as α-particles and low energy β-electrons (up to 100 keV). Stripping film AR 10 has an emulsion layer of 5 μ and a gelatin support of 10 μ. The use of stripping film has the advantage that the thickness of the emulsion is always constant; that is especially important in the case of quantitative autoradiography.

B. AUTORADIOGRAPHIC RESPONSE OF THE EMULSION

There is a fundamental difference between the response of a photographic emulsion to light and its response to particles. In the case of light as the radiation source there is a delayed response during an induction period, then grain density increases linearly with exposure, and with higher optical densities a flattening of the linear curve occurs. On the other hand, it is known that the grain density of emulsions increases linearly with the total amount of α-, β-, or γ-radiation as well as X-ray radiation in the region of small optical densities up to 0.05 (Lamerton and Harriss, 1954). If the autoradiographic emulsion is overexposed, the grain density approaches saturation.

C. FADING EFFECT

Linear relationship between grain density and exposure to β- and α-particles should be expected within certain limits, depending on the fading of the latent images. Herz (1951) reported 30% fading, and Ray and Stevens (1953) 80%, in 1 week for stripping film. The rate of fading depends on the emulsion (McLaughlin and Ehrlich, 1954), on the ionizing power of the incident particles (Herz, 1959), and especially on the humidity and presence of oxygen during exposure (Herz, 1951, 1959). Albouy and Faraggi (1949) found that fading is due to the oxidation of the latent image centers by the oxygen of the air whereby the humidity facilitates the penetration of the oxygen through the gelatin. Therefore they suggested exposure in dried inert gas. The curve of rate of latent image fading is a function of relative humidity, i.e., an exponential function of the moisture content of the emulsion. The observation that emulsion sensitivity is reduced at high relative humidities may be due to the increased rate of latent image fading (Norris and Woodruff, 1954). Messier and Leblond (1957) and Herz (1959) also found considerable fading if autoradiograms are exposed in a humid atmosphere. Herz (1959) suggested exposure of the autoradiograms in a CO_2 atmosphere. Ray and Stevens (1953) also observed considerable decrease of the fading effect if exposure occurs in the cold and in a dry atmosphere of CO_2 or N_2. However, obviously exposure in a dry atmosphere alone efficiently prevents fading. For Eastman Kodak NTB-2 emulsion, Leblond et al. (1963) and Kopriwa and Leblond (1962) found a linear relationship between grain density and exposure time up to 360 days if exposure is carried out in the cold (4°C) and in a dry atmosphere with Drierite (Fig. 3). The same relationship was found by Wimber *et al.* (1960), who did not even observe a significant difference between exposure with and without Drierite. On the other hand, linearity between grain density and exposure over long periods for stripping film was reported by Pelc but not found by other authors (Oja *et al.*, 1966; Schultze, 1968).

III. Photographic Process

Latent images are produced by the action of α- or β-particles on the silver bromide crystals of the photographic emulsion in a manner similar to the absorption of light. When passing through the emulsion the parti-

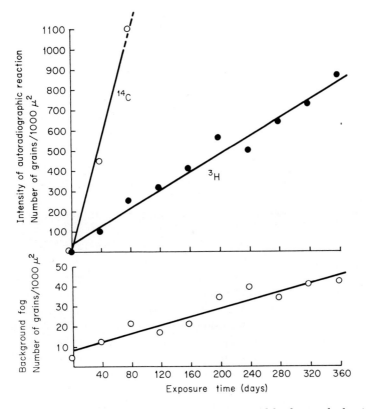

FIG. 3. Influence of the exposure time on reaction and background of autoradiograms of ³H- and ¹⁴C-labeled liver sections (with Drierite). (From Kopriwa and Leblond, 1962.)

cles cause ionizations and free electrons in the ionic lattice of the silver bromide crystal. The electrons are trapped at specific crystal irregularities, silver sulfide or metallic colloidal silver, which become negatively charged. Silver ions migrate to these spots and neutralize the electrons. At the end of the process, specks of neutralized silver atoms are formed preferentially at the border between the crystal and the gelatin. This deposition of elemental silver, so-called photolytic silver, forms the latent image. If the number of silver atoms in the crystal is adequate, the crystal is able to be developed. The reducing agents of the developer reduce the grains of the latent image to metallic silver. This first forms a filament growing into a coil of thread during development which appears as a silver grain in the light microscope. In comparison, the grains of the silver bromide crystals without latent images are reduced so slowly that they are almost unaffected by the time the grains of the latent image are reduced. The fixative dissolves the nonreduced silver bromide by forming soluble complexes without affecting the metallic silver, which then represents the autoradiographic grain.

IV. Autoradiographic Resolution

A. THEORY

The autoradiographic image of the radioactive source within the specimen is not strictly comparable to the photographic image produced by an optical system. With an optical system image a point source results in a pointlike image, while a radioactive point source in the specimen results in a more or less broad distribution of silver grains in the emulsion, since the particles are emitted in all directions and pass through the emulsion more or less diagonally. Only a small proportion of them hit the emulsion vertically.

Figure 4 schematically illustrates the autoradiographic conditions of resolution. The histological specimen contains a radioactive point source which emits particles in all directions, assuming that all the particles have a straight path and a constant density of ionization. The emulsion is situated above the source separated by a small protecting layer. The distribution of the grains in the emulsion then corresponds to the points in the figure. Looked upon from above, the grain density is highest directly above the point source and decreases quickly with increasing distance from the source. The curve in Fig. 4A represents the grain density. The dispersion of the curve at the point where the density is half the maximum density is a measure of resolution. The smaller this distance (b) the better the resolution and the sharper the autoradiographic image. The best resolution is obtained when the radioactive source is closest to the emulsion.

The shortest distance between two point sources—whereby they may
be recognized as two distinct points—has been defined as the "resolving
power." Two radioactive point sources in the histological section, as demonstrated in Fig. 4B (S_1 and S_2), can be distinguished as two sources only
if the distance between them is more than the width of the half maximum
density curve. The solid curve in Fig. 4B represents the sum curve of the
grain densities of both sources and shows two distinctly separated max-

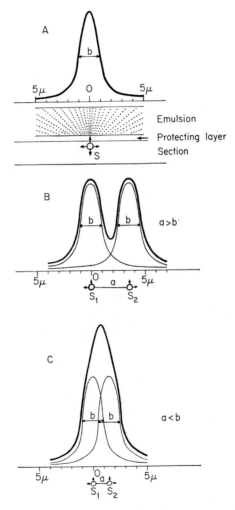

FIG. 4. Theory of the resolving power in autoradiography. S = point source of
radiation; a = distance between the two point sources S_1 and S_2; b = width of the
half-maximum curve of grains.

ima. If the distance between those two sources is smaller than the width of half the maximum density, the sum curve will show only one broad maximum (Fig. 4C).

B. FACTORS INFLUENCING THE AUTORADIOGRAPHIC RESOLUTION

The resolving power depends on (a) geometry, (b) energy of the particles, (c) characteristics of the emulsion, and (d) exposure.

1. Geometric Factors

The thickness of the section as well as of the emulsion, and especially of a separating layer (or more generally, the distance of the radiation source from the emulsion) strongly influence the resolving power. The shorter the distance between the radiation source and emulsion, the smaller the grain distribution. Theoretical and experimental studies demonstrate the importance of those different factors (Doniach and Pelc, 1950; Stevens, 1948, 1950; Gross et al., 1951; Nadler, 1951; Herz, 1950, 1951; Odeblad, 1952; Boyd, 1955; Harriss, 1956c; Pelc, 1956, 1957; Bleecken, 1961; Herrmann et al., 1961, 1962). Assuming that the β-emitter is distributed in rod-like fashion perpendicular to the section, the influence of the different layers of the source on the autoradiographic resolution may be calculated. The thickness of the protecting layer between section and emulsion influences the resolving power the most. Using ^{14}C, the direct contact of section and emulsion results in a resolution of approximately 2–3 μ. A layer of 3 μ between section and emulsion decreases resolution from 2.3 μ to 8.2 μ (Chapman-Andresen, 1953). According to the theoretical calculations of Doniach and Pelc (1950), the loss of resolving power by an interposed layer of less than 0.1 μ seems to be relatively small. In many cases the protecting layer can be omitted if test slides show that there is no chemical influence on the emulsion.

Less important is the influence of the thickness of the specimen, the reduction of which is limited by the content of radioactivity, as well as that of the emulsion, the reduction of which is limited by the decreasing sensitivity. To a certain degree the improved resolution of a thinner section may compensate for the decreased activity content (Falk and King, 1963). It should be noted that the values for section thickness in the literature are related to the adjustment of the microtome. The deparaffinized section, as it is actually used in autoradiography, is less thick than the paraffin section (water and lipids are extracted) and only the thickness of the dry material plays a role in resolution.

2. Energy of β-Radiation

Autoradiographic resolution also depends on the mean energy of the β-particles, i.e., their penetrability. Herrmann et al. (1962) theoretically and experimentally determined the relationship between maximal β-energy and resolving power. Their values obtained by test charts, analogous measurements, and calculations result in very similar curves: the resolving power above an energy of 0.6 MeV is strongly dependent on the β-energy, while between 0.6 and 0.2 MeV the curves show a constant lower limit value. Most of the β-emitters commonly used in autoradiography have an average β-energy of 0.6 MeV or less. For the β-emitters with a range of β-particles greater than the thickness of section and emulsion, the reduction of radiation intensity with distance from the source mainly depends on the inverse square law, the absorption being negligible. Therefore, the resolution is mainly due to the effect of geometry and does not improve greatly between ^{32}P and ^{14}C despite the great difference of β-energy. Bleecken (1961) also found that the maxima of the grain density curves of ^{35}S and ^{32}P have the same shape; but with increasing distance from the radiation source the grain density curve for ^{35}S declines faster than for ^{32}P. The width of half-maximum density is almost the same for both isotopes. The similar shape of the grain density curves of both radiation sources is explained by the fact that the average range in both cases is great compared to emulsion thickness and diameter of the source. With ^{32}P toned test pictures it could be shown that β-energy has little influence on the autoradiographic resolution within the range of high energies (Bleecken, 1967).

With β-energies of less than 0.2 MeV, however, absorption has to be taken into account. For low β-energies with β-traces ending in the emulsion, the resolving power increasingly depends on the energy and increases with decreasing energy, since the range of the β-particles in the emulsion is shorter. Tritium with a maximum energy of 18 keV corresponding to a range of 6–7 μ in water and the mean β-energy of 5.7 keV has an effective range of approximately 1 μ in material of unit density. Therefore, the grains are situated in a small layer of the emulsion of about 1 μ which faces the section, and only a small layer of the section facing the emulsion contributes to the autoradiographic picture. The factors that influence the resolving power of tritium have been studied by Robertson *et al.* (1959). Based on curves of ^{3}H-radiation doses as a function of the distance from the radiation source and on derived radiation isodoses curves, they calculated the decrease of radiation intensity with increasing distance from the center of the point source. It was found to be steepest in sections 0–1 μ thick; i.e., those extremely thin sections yield the sharpest autoradiographic picture with a width of half the maximum density of only 0.2 μ. D. K. Hill (1959, 1962) found experimentally and by calculation the resolving power for tritium to be 0.24–0.34 μ for sections thicker than than about 0.5 μ. He also found that there is only a slight loss of resolution, or gain in grain count, in thicker sections (1.5 μ) compared to thinner ones (0.5 μ).

Because of this high resolution power of tritium, this isotope is best suited for autoradiography in studies at the cellular and subcellular level, as was pointed out already by Fitzgerald *et al.* (1951) and Fitzgerald and Engström (1952).

3. Grain Size of the Emulsion

It is obvious that the resolving power further depends on the grain size of the emulsion. Therefore, the less sensitive emulsions with fine grains yield the best resolution in autoradiography. Tzschaschel (1959) examined the resolution of different types of emulsions. Grain size, and consequently resolution, are influenced also by developmental conditions.

4. Exposure

If the exposure is extended over long periods, the grain density over the radiation source will approach saturation, which leads to a broadening of the grain density curve, i.e., to a decreased resolution.

V. Dosage of Isotopes

A. GENERAL ASPECTS OF REQUIRED DOSAGE

For satisfactory autoradiographic pictures to be obtained at the cellular level with good resolution, the specimen has to be very thin. Compared to that in biochemical studies it contains only a small amount of biological substance. Therefore the concentration of the isotope within single small cell constituents has to be rather high compared to biochemical tracer studies, where many of those cell components can be pooled. In principle, the photographic emulsion is not less sensitive than the counter in biochemical work insofar as with the usual techniques about 1/10 of all β-particles result in an impulse or silver grain, respectively. As compensation for the small radioactive specimen in autoradiographic studies, about 100 times more radioactivity is used than in biochemical work. Futhermore the photographic emulsion permits much longer times for measurement than are usually used for activity measurement with the counter. In this way it is possible to register radioactivity even in subcellular structures.

The amount of remaining radioactivity in the tissue depends on many factors, such as the biological behavior of the labeled substance, availability time of the precursor, dilution by nonradioactive isotopes already present in the organism, time between administration of dose and sacrifice of the animals, or incubation time in cell cultures and preparation of the tissue. Furthermore, the dosage depends on the autoradiographic technique used (grain or track method) and on the sensitivity of the autoradiographic emulsion. Therefore, no general rules can be given for the required dosage of the isotope. When one is working for the first time with a particular labeled substance, the dosage has to be determined empirically in order to obtain good autoradiographic pictures in reasonable exposure times. Calculations based on similar experiments or tracer work can then be very useful.

Labeled substances that are used for autoradiographic studies should have a high specific activity. On the one hand, the amount of substance administered should not exceed physiological limits, and on the other hand—as mentioned previously—the isotope concentration in tissue has to be rather high. The limits for autoradiographic work are often set by the ability to prepare precursors with sufficiently high specific activities, especially if isotopes with a long half-life are used. Isotopes with a very short half-life are not qualified for autoradiographic investigations, because there is not enough time left for preparation and exposure of the autoradiograms.

B. Effect of Radiation Dose

Because of the relatively high amount of radioactivity administered, special attention has to be focused on the possible radiation damage. If the distribution pattern within the organism and the excretion of the labeled substance are known, the radiation dose produced by the emitted α- and β-particles can usually be estimated. This is true for gross distributions.

C. Microdose Distribution

In order that the radiation dose does not exceed the tolerable dose at the cellular level, knowledge of the microdistribution of the radiation dose is necessary. The radiation dose of a certain spot in the tissue is due to all β-particles that reach this spot. Since β-particles in the environment with a distance greater than the maximum range do not contribute to the radiation dose, to obtain a distribution scheme of the microdose of β-radiation, a section of the thickness of the maximum range of the isotope used should be prepared. The distribution of the grain density in the autoradiogram of this section then corresponds to the local β-radiation dose, and this represents an unsharp image of the known autoradiographic isotope distribution in the section.

Radiation can be kept much lower if the method of track autoradiography is applied in which the radioactivity administered may be 10 to 100 times less than would be required for grain autoradiography.

D. Radiation Dose with Tritium

For very low energy β-emitters like tritium, it is difficult to calculate the exact radiation dose. With specific precursors like ^{3}H-labeled thymidine, the β-particles are mostly absorbed within the cell nucleus. Considering the high specific ionization, the radiation dose for the single cell nucleus may be quite high. Robertson *et al.* (1959) calculated that the average radiation dose per disintegration in the case of tritium decreases by a factor of 12 at a distance of 0.5 μ from the ^{3}H-point source and by a factor of 60 at 1.0 μ from the source. However, an exact estimation of the radiation dose in a single nucleus is problematic.

Variation of the radioactivity of the administered compound allows critical examination of whether or not there is influence of radiation or radiation damage on the effect under study. Diverse organisms as well as various metabolic processes may differ in their sensitivity to radiation damage. Furthermore, possible radiation damage may be excluded by considering other parameters like morphological ones that indicate radiation damage. For instance, Kisieleski *et al.* (1964) compared the decrease of spermatocytes in mice injected with variable doses of tritiated thymidine with the estimated amount of incorporated tritiated thymidine per nucleus of primary spermatocytes. The threshold value for demonstrable morphological radiation damage was found to be about 125 disintegrations per nucleus using combined chemical and autoradiographic methods.

VI. Background and Artifacts

A. Factors Influencing the Background Fog

Not all grains in the emulsion are produced by exposure to radioactive material. To a certain degree this background fog is inevitable, since it is produced during the preparation of the emulsion. Sensitive emulsions have a higher background. Background fog increases with the age of the emulsion, improper storing at high temperature, exposure to cosmic rays, overexposure to safety light, mechanical influences during handling, such as distortion and pressure (Moore, 1951), chemical influences, e.g., reducing agents used during the preparation of the specimen or contained in the tissue, and exposure of the autoradiograms at too high temperature.

The background fog can be kept low by proper storage (at 4°C) and proper handling of the emulsion. It has to be checked each time a new batch of emulsion is used. The chemical effects can be avoided by proper preparation of the specimen and careful elimination of reducing agents by washing. If the tissue itself reduces the silver bromide crystals of the emulsion, as unfixed tissue may (Boyd and Board, 1949), a protecting layer of celloidin, silicone, or nylon may be helpful. However, if tritium is used for labeling, even a celloidin layer of 1 μ interposed between section and emulsion absorbs most of the β-particles (see also Chapter 1, Section VII, D). The reducing capacity of tissue was mainly attributed to the SH-groups (Board, 1951). However, Everett and Simmons (1953) and Tonna and Cronkite (1958) could show that a chemographic effect occurred even after saturation or blocking of the SH radicals. Everett and Simmons (1953) also found that an interposing layer of celloidin did not prevent the reducing effect on the emulsion. According to their results, the reducing agent should be water soluble, because excessive washing of the sections removed those substances. The background fog caused by chemical effects of the specimen should always be evaluated by testing with nonradioactive specimens of the same kind.

B. DETERMINATION OF THE BACKGROUND

In quantitative autoradiography the background should be determined near the site where counts are made and should be subtracted from the total number of grains. It is incorrect to determine the background outside of the specimen over the margin zone of the autoradiogram only, since the background of the emulsion that is not covering the tissue, compared to the one over the tissue but not over the radioactive source, may differ (Tonna and Cronkite, 1958). If, for instance, with radioactive thymidine only some of the cell nuclei are labeled, the background should be counted over the unlabeled nuclei.

C. ARTIFACTS

Besides the mentioned effect of nonradioactive tissue on the film, many artifacts may occur during handling. In most cases those artifacts can easily be distinguished from the effect of the isotope or the background. Flashing by static electricity, which occurs by handling stripping film in a dry atmosphere, can produce grains (see Chapter 2, II, A, on stripping film technique). Distortion of the film at margins of tissue or interspaces leads to developable grains and can cause misleading interpretation (Doniach and Pelc, 1950; Levi, 1951). Clusters of grains that occur in very dilute emulsion are easily recognizable (Oehlert et al., 1962c). In contrast to those effects that produce grains, oxidizing agents in the tissue lead to extinction of the latent image. This effect can be ascertained by exposing nonradioactive tissue to preexposed film with an equally high background fog.

Other artifacts may occur during development and fixation. Loosening of the film and displacement may simulate a radioactive effect at sites where no radioactive material is localized. Proper attachment of the film, such as wrapping the film around the slide, prevents these dislocations. If the stripping film or the emulsion, which is usually dried in air or in a cold air stream, is dried too fast (in warm air) a higher background may appear. During the fast shrinkage the pressure within the emulsion obviously leads to sensibilization of the silver bromide crystals (Sawicki and Pawinska, 1965). Furthermore, staining of the specimen after photographic processing can lead to artifacts by dissolving silver grains (see Chapter 2, Section V, on staining).

More detailed information concerning possible artifacts in autoradiography are given by Doniach and Pelc (1950), Odeblad (1953), Boyd (1955), Niklas and Maurer (1955), Pelc (1957), Harbers (1958), and Oehlert et al. (1962c). See also Rogers (1967).

VII. Quantitative Autoradiography

A. PROBLEM

Theoretically it is possible to use the autoradiographic method as a quantitative tool for measuring the radioactivity per cubic micron at the level of subcellular structures as is known from biochemical methods at the level of whole organs or tissues. In the case of autoradiography the emulsion replaces the counter. However, there are two problems in applying quantitative autoradiography: (1) the quantitative response of the emulsion, i.e., the absolute calibration of the emulsion as discussed in Chapter 1, VII, C and (2) the influence of β-self-absorption in the specimen on the autoradiographic response. β-Self-absorption factors are not significant when using high β-energy emitters; however, they are of great importance in tritium autoradiography.

B. QUANTITATIVE ANALYSIS OF AUTORADIOGRAMS

There are three methods described for quantitative analysis of autoradiograms: (a) determination of the grain density by counting single grains, (b) track counting, and (c) photometric determination of the optical density.

1. Grain Counting

The visual counting of single grains with an ocular with a square micron grid is time consuming but a simple, useful, and very sensitive method. With oil immersion, the single grains are clearly visible. In the case of tritium, the grains are confined to an emulsion layer of about 1 μ or less and are easily counted. More energetic electrons produce grains in different emulsion layers and they can only be counted by focusing up and down with the oil immersion objective. Nadler (1953b) described a grain-counting method that takes into account only those grains of specific layers in a given area over the center of the source. If the grain density is very small, the statistical error of the number of β-incidents hitting the emulsion and the number of latent images per electron have to be considered. The influence of the absorption factor and self-absorption coefficient applies only to very low energy isotopes (tritium) and will be considered in the next section. Stillström (1963,1965) described a mathematical grain count correction for autoradiography which also includes cells with a very small grain number, the effect of background and exposure time upon the true grain count distribution, and also the transformation of the grain count distribution by varying cell size.

Since visual grain counting is rather tedious, Dudley and Pelc (1953) developed an automatic electronic grain counter built on the principle of the flying-spot scanner that automatically examines the microscopic area and registers the counted grains. Also Mazia *et al.* (1955) described an automatic counting apparatus that works by forming band patterns of the grains and photoelectric recording of the distribution of band intensities. Recently Stubblefield (1965) described a new technique that allows repeated autoradiograms to be made of the isotope distribution in the chromosomes of a single cell. After photographic combination of the separate autoradiograms into a single composite and conversion of the grain images to lines, the densities were measured with a recording microdensitometer. A similar method of flying-spot scanning and image-plane scanning was described by Tolles (1959). Ostrowski and Sawicki (1961) recommended a grain-counting method based on photographs of the different levels in the emulsion. By pricking the individual grains with a needle and counting the pinholes on the reverse side of the photograph the number could be determined. Comparison with the method of direct counting resulted in lower values for statistical deviations in the case of the photographic method.

2. Track Counting

The advantage of track autoradiography requiring much smaller quantities of radioactivity has already been mentioned. The counting of α-tracks is simple because of the closely spaced grains and of the fact that α-particles have a straight path. They are best counted in an emulsion that is thicker than the path length of the α-particles. Since each α-particle that enters the emulsion causes a track, the content of radioactivity in the underlying specimen can be estimated from the number of tracks per square unit. The calculation can be complicated by the fact that α-emitters may disintegrate to radioactive daughter elements that also emit α-particles. Thus, the autoradiographic response might be due not only to the administered substance, but also to the radioactivity of the daughter elements.

It is much harder to count β-tracks. Because of their low initial specific ionization, it is difficult, sometimes impossible, to determine the origin of the β-track. High energy β-electrons produce grains that are farther apart in the origin of the track, but the tracks are relatively straight. Lower energy β-electrons produce more grains per unit path length near the origin, but the tracks are more tortuous. Close contact between specimen and emulsion are especially required in track autoradiography. In contrast to grain counts, the counting of β-tracks only results in a statistical value for many cells without information on individual cells.

Details on track counting are described by Boyd and Levi (1950), Campbell (1951), Campbell and Persson (1951), Levi (1951, 1953, 1954), Levi and Hogben (1955), Levi and Nielsen (1959), and Ficq (1953, 1955b, 1959c).

3. Photometric Determination of the Optical Density

With this method the optical density of the emulsion is measured by a microphotometer. The enlarged image is focused by a photomicrographic apparatus at the level of the search unit of a densitometer. The measured density can be related to the isotope content in the tissue by comparison with optical densities of emulsions exposed to standards of known radioactivity. The photometric method has several disadvantages for autoradiographic work at the cellular level. The densitometer operates best at relatively low magnifications and at grain densities greater than those desirable for highest autoradiographic resolution. Furthermore, the unevenness of the histological structure and the impossibility of adjusting the aperture of the densitometer to the different shapes of the cell structures cause difficulties. Another disadvantage lies in the fact that the total absorption of light is due to the sum of emulsion, specimen, and slide. In order to be able to subtract the absorption caused by the specimen, it is necessary to measure spots without radioactivity in the autoradiograms. However, absorption by the specimen which varies from spot to spot introduces a great factor of uncertainty. Furthermore, this method necessitates a rather complicated apparatus. Thus, the method of grain counting is preferable.

Recently Dörmer et al. (1966) worked out a method for quantitative determination of the silver grains by incident light microscopy. This method avoids the absorption effects mentioned above and obviously leads to reproducible results. See also Dörmer (1967).

Detailed descriptions of quantitative autoradiography employing the photometric method is given by Marinelli and Hill (1948), Axelrod and

Hamilton (1947), Dudley and Dobyns (1949), Odeblad (1952), Domingues *et al.* (1956), and Dörmer *et al.* (1966).

C. Number of Grains Produced per Disintegration Process

The goal of quantitative autoradiography consists in the absolute determination of radioactivity in the various cell structures. The correlation between the number of developed grains in the autoradiographic emulsion and the concentration of isotope atoms in the underlying specimen can be estimated if the efficiency of the isotope for the particular emulsion used is known. The number of grains per disintegration process was measured for different isotopes and various emulsions; Table II contains the values found in the literature. Herz (1951), Lamerton and Harriss (1954), and Cormack (1955) determined the grain yield per incident electron for stripping film. For ^{35}S a grain yield of 1.8, for ^{32}P of 0.8, for ^{131}I of 1.8, and for ^{59}Fe of 1.6 grains per electron was found. Corresponding values for tritium depend very much on the geometric factors and are valid only for the special experimental conditions used by the author referred to. According to Hughes (1958) and Hughes *et al.* (1958), 5 β-electrons of tritium are required to render developable 1 grain in the case of labeled bacteria, and 20 disintegrations are required for 1 grain in labeled nuclei of smears of mammalian cells. Lajtha and Oliver (1959) found the required β-disintegrations to be 20 per developable grain. Wimber *et al.* (1960) determined in squash preparations that 10.9 electrons (stripping film AR 10) and/or 19.3 electrons (NTB-3) are necessary to produce 1 developable grain. Kisieleski *et al.* (1961b) reported that 200 ^{3}H-β-electrons are required for 1 grain. Maurer and Primbsch (1964) counted the mean grain density in autoradiograms of 3 μ thick sections (stripping film AR 10), incinerated the sections, and simultaneously measured the ^{3}H-activity in the scintillation counter (TriCarb, Packard). They found 16 disintegrations per grain. Considering that only half of the β-electrons are emitted in the direction of the emulsion and that the β-self-absorption coefficient for the methacrylate sections of 3 μ has a value of 0.3, the number of *incident* electrons per 1 grain is $16/2 \times 0.3 = 2.4$.

If the efficiency is known for a particular circumstance, the isotope content in the specimen can be calculated. On the other hand, the grain density can be compared with test autoradiograms from a source with known radioactivity content (Beischer, 1953; Dudley and Dobyns, 1949; André, 1956).

D. Quantitative Autoradiography with Tritium

Because of the high resolving power, tritium is preferred for quantitative autoradiography at the cellular and subcellular level. However,

TABLE II
DECAY PROCESSES PER DEVELOPABLE GRAIN FOR THE DIFFERENT ISOTOPES AND VARIOUS TYPES OF EMULSION

Isotope	Stripping film	Liquid emulsion	β/grain	References
^{32}P	Kodak AR 10	—	1.3	Herz (1951)
^{32}P	Kodak AR 10	—	1.3	Lamerton and Harriss
^{35}S	Kodak AR 10	—	0.6	(1954)
^{32}P	Kodak NT2a	—	1.3	Cormack (1955)
^{131}I	Kodak NT2a	—	0.6	
^{59}Fe	Kodak NT2a	—	0.6	
^{3}H	Kodak AR 10	—	5.0 (bacteria)	Hughes et al. (1958)
^{3}H	Kodak AR 10	—	20.0 (smears)	
^{32}P	Kodak AR 10	—	1.3	Lajtha and Oliver
^{14}C	Kodak AR 10	—	0.5—0.6	(1959)
^{3}H	Kodak AR 10	—	20.0	
^{3}H	Kodak AR 10	—	10.9	Wimber et al. (1960)
^{3}H	—	Kodak NTB	19.3	
^{3}H	Kodak AR 10	—	100—200!	Kisieleski et al. (1961b)
^{3}H	Kodak AR 10	—	16.0	Maurer and
^{3}H	Kodak AR 10	—	2.4 (see text)	Primbsch (1964)
^{3}H	—	Ilford L-4	1.3^a	Caro and Schnös (1965)
^{3}H	—	Ilford L-4	5.0^b	Caro and Schnös
^{32}P	—	Ilford L-4	40.0^b	(1965)
^{3}H	—	Kodak NTE	3–4	Bachmann and
^{3}H	—	Ilford L-4	12.0	Salpeter (1965)
^{3}H	Kodak NTE, Ilford L-4	—	8.0	Bachmann and
^{35}S	Kodak NTE, Ilford L-4	—	21.0	Salpeter (1967)
^{3}H	—	Kodak NTB-3	5.8	Hunt and Foote (1967)

^{a} Overall efficiency in thick emulsion
^{b} In a monolayer of photographic grains

because of the low energy of the ^{3}H-β-electrons, self-absorption and absorption strongly influence the quantitative data. Thus, in drawing conclusions from the grain density about the local absolute ^{3}H-activities in the cell structures, one has to consider that the density of the dry mass is different for the different cell structures and that any absorbing layers may lead to misinterpretations.

1. Influence of β-Self-absorption

Maurer and Primbsch (1964) studied the influence of β-self-absorption for tritium in the different cell structures under the geometric conditions of autoradiography. For this purpose, mean grain densities were counted over the different cell structures on autoradiograms of sections of varying thickness from 0.3 to 6.0 μ (embedded in methacrylate, which was removed afterward). Grain counts over cytoplasm and karyoplasm were made after labeling with ³H-labeled amino acids and corresponding counts over the nucleolus after labeling with cytidine-³H; the curves in panels A–C of Fig. 5 show the results. For all three cell structures, the curves increase linearly at very small thicknesses and then show saturation. The nucleolus curve begins to flatten at a few tenths of a micron. For the same thickness, β-self-absorption is much smaller for the cytoplasm and even less for the karyoplasm. Thus, corrections have to be made for the different amounts of β-self-absorption in the different structures. It

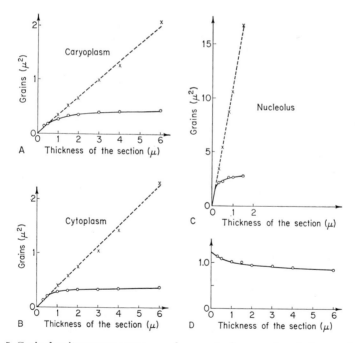

FIG. 5. Grain density curves over caryoplasm, cytoplasm, and nucleolus as a function of the thickness of the ³H-labeled histological section (methacrylate embedded, AR 10 stripping film). (A and B) Mouse liver labeled with tyrosine-l-³H; (C) mouse liver labeled with cytidine-³H; (D) quotient of B and A, ———, counted grain density; --------, calculated grain density without self-absorption. (From Maurer and Primbsch, 1964.)

is only at a section thickness of about 0.1 μ that the grain density over the three cell components represents the actual ^{3}H-activity content of the different cell structures.

While the curves in Fig. 5A–C are related only to the special tissue under study, the curves in Fig. 6 derived from those in Fig. 5 are of general importance. Figure 6A demonstrates that the grain density curves for the three different cell constituents (Fig. 5A–C) result in the same curve if the section thickness in microns is replaced by the dry weight

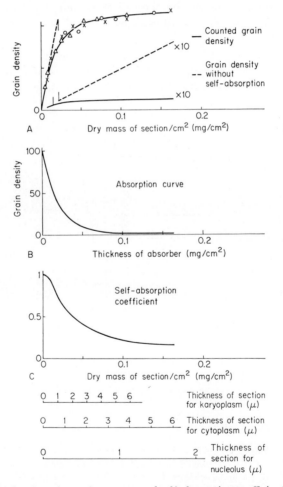

FIG. 6. Grain density, absorption curve, and self-absorption coefficient as a function of mg/cm² dry weight of the ^{3}H-labeled section for autoradiographic geometry (micron values represent the thickness of methacrylate sections and are valid for the liver investigated). (From Maurer and Primbsch, 1964.)

in milligrams per square centimeter, and the curves are shifted in their height. This is expected since self-absorption depends only on the absorbing mass (mg/cm²)—at least in the range of small atomic numbers.

Figure 6C gives the self-absorption coefficient which shows to what fraction the grain density is reduced because of the β-self-absorption. As shown in Fig. 6C, the self-absorption coefficient is very different for the different cell structures. For example, for a liver section of 1 μ, the self-absorption coefficient is 0.2 for the nucleolus, 0.6 for the cytoplasm, and 0.8 for the karyoplasm, i.e., over the nucleolus only 20%, over the cytoplasm 60%, and over the karyoplasm 80% of the grains are present that would be produced without self-absorption. Without considering these differences the number of grains cannot be taken as a measure for the incorporated activity in these cell compartments. The values demonstrate that β-self-absorption has an important influence on grain counts in tritium autoradiography. Therefore, for quantitative analysis of tritium autoradiograms, the mass density (dry mass in mg/cm²) must be known and from this the self-absorption coefficient can be derived from the curve in Fig. 6C.

Pollister (1965) measured interferometrically the dry mass in mg/cm² per micron for the different cell structures of the salivary gland in *Drosophila*. The values measured are in good agreement with those for liver cells determined by Maurer and Primbsch (1964). Using the self-absorption coefficient of those authors, Pollister calculated correction factors which by multiplication with the grain density measured lead to the actual grain density. For application of those correction factors in studies of the RNA synthesis in the different cell compartments, see Schultze and Maurer (1963) and Arnold (1965).

2. Influence of β-Absorption

The curve for β-absorption in Fig. 6B was derived from the curve in Fig. 6A (Maurer and Primbsch, 1964). It represents the influence of absorption on the ³H-β-radiation in case an inactive absorbing layer covers the radiation source. According to this absorption curve, the grain density decreases to 10% of the actual value by means of an absorbing layer of only 0.05 mg/cm², which corresponds to a layer of about 0.5 μ wet tissue of unit density. This is of special importance for grain counting in smears and squashes, since a cytoplasmic layer of half a micron lying over a labeled cell nucleus reduces the grain count to about 10% of the actual value. The existence of a cytoplasmic layer of 0.5 μ (wet tissue), however, may be difficult to exclude. Thus, an uneven layer of cytoplasm or serum covering the cells, as it may occur in smears, can lead to misinterpretation of the results.

For quantitative tritium autoradiography see also Perry (1962a).

2. Autoradiographic Techniques

I. Preparation of Tissue

A. FIXATION OF TISSUE FOR AUTORADIOGRAPHY

1. Influence of the Fixative on the Content of Radioactivity

In preparing specimens for autoradiography, fixation is the first step in the routine histological procedure. The choice of a fixative depends on the labeled compound used and the autoradiographic goal. If the distribution of water-soluble substances is to be investigated, most of the radioactive substances will be lost during the usual fixation process and a special technique has to be employed (see below). On the other hand, if metabolic studies of proteins, nucleic acids, and polysaccharides are performed, the possibility of fixing the higher molecular substances but dissolving the water-soluble labeled precursor or metabolites is of great advantage. In these studies, common chemical fixatives like formalin (pure, or with alcohol and acetic acid), Carnoy, Bouin, or alcohol are used and are assumed to make proteins, nucleic acids, or polysaccharides insoluble for all subsequently applied solutions. Precaution has to be taken that the fixatives do not affect the photographic emulsion. Any fixative having a reducing or oxidizing action (fixatives with metallic salts) must be carefully removed prior to applying the film. Unfixed tissue may also contain such substances. Reducing agents cause fogging of the film, oxidizing agents may cause fading of the latent image. Zenker's fixative, for example, is known to desensitize the photographic emulsion (Kopriwa and Leblond, 1962) (Table III). The above-mentioned fixatives do not usually affect the film, but it is always advisable to test the influence of the fixative by control slides.

Many authors have reported that various fixatives result in different losses of radioactivity (Lamerton and Harriss, 1951; Taylor and McMaster, 1954; Hagmüller and Hellauer, 1955; Kaminski, 1955; Sano et al., 1957; Harbers, 1958; Kopriwa and Leblond, 1962; Baserga and Kisieleski, 1963; Baserga and Nemeroff, 1962a; Linnartz-Niklas et al., 1964). This problem is even more complex, because the amount of radioactive compound that is removed by fixation may depend also on the experimental time and may even be different for different cell structures.

24

TABLE III
EFFECT OF FIXATION ON INTENSITY OF AUTORADIOGRAPHIC REACTION[a]

	Cytidine-^{3}H-injected mouse liver[b] (grains/1000 μ^2)
Carnoy	124.4 ± 3.8
Bouin	116.6 ± 5.1
Formalin	105.5 ± 1.9
Zenker	3.1 ± 0.2
Zenker (iodine and cysteine)	75.1 ± 2.1

[a] From Kopriwa and Leblond (1962).
[b] Unstained sections.

Studying the incorporation of tritiated cytidine into HeLa cells, Feinendegen et al. (1960b) found that with a variety of fixatives different amounts of activity are removed at different times after short-term incubation of the cultures. It is possible that after a short incubation, the precursor is only partly incorporated into macromolecular RNA and is still partly in the acid-soluble fraction. The amount incorporated into macromolecular RNA increases with time, and the amount in the acid-soluble fraction decreases. That means that a different fraction of activity can be eliminated by the fixative, depending on the experimental time. Harbers and Neumann (1955) reported loss of RNA of liver sections due to fixation with Carnoy. According to Schneider and Maurer (1963), neutral formalin fixation yields highest grain counts over cell structures of mouse tissue after injection of tritiated cytidine. Varying losses of activity (determined by grains counts) by the different fixatives were found when compared to grain counts obtained after fixation with neutral formalin. Furthermore, the authors observed that different fixatives remove different amounts of activity from the various cell structures. This may account in part for the discrepancies in results of incorporation studies of tritiated cytidine by some authors. Using different fixatives, Antoni et al. (1965) examined biochemically the loss of radioactivity and the loss of mass of RNA, DNA, and protein in liver tissue and ascites tumor cells after short-term labeling with ^{3}H- or ^{14}C-labeled cytidine, thymidine, and lysine, respectively. They found a loss of activity and of mass of RNA with methanol, Carnoy, and some fixatives containing perchloric acid. According to their results, neutralized formalin or formalin with 0.5% trichloroacetic acid (TCA) are the most suitable fixatives for RNA. Methanol removes more than 50% of the ^{3}H-RNA-activity, while the loss of RNA mass is much less. With decreasing experimental time (10 min) the loss of ^{3}H-activity increases, i.e., more than two-thirds of the ^{3}H-activity is removed. The authors doubt that the effect of the methanol is due to retained non-denatured ribonuclease, since they could not find any enzymatic ribonuclease activity in the tissue after methanol fixation. There was a loss neither of activity nor of mass of DNA or protein by most of the fixatives examined.

For quantitative losses of nucleic acids during the preparation of frozen sections, see Komender et al. (1965).

2. Differential Fixation

As mentioned above, the fixation of protein by fixatives containing protein-precipitating substances has the advantage that the proteins are quantitatively precipitated and the precursor, the free amino acid, is eliminated. Droz and Warshawsky (1963) using leucine-^{14}C reported that at least 91–97% of the radioactivity retained in histological sections after application of labeled amino acids is firmly bound to protein, presumably by peptide bonds. They did not find any loss of activity in pancreas, liver, kidney, and brain of the mouse after fixation with Bouin. Schultze et al. (1960) subjected formalin–TCA (6% formalin and 0.5% TCA) fixed and paraffin-embedded sections of liver and brain after application of ^{14}C-labeled amino acids to the isolation procedure of nucleic acids according to Schneider's method (1945) and found an activity loss of only 0% to 3%, measured with the Geiger counter. Ostrowski et al. (1961) found a 1% loss of protein mass in liver and kidney after fixation with 4% formalin, and Merriam (1958) reported 6–12% weight loss in liver, muscle, and brain with the same fixative.

In order to eliminate the labeled free amino acid from the tissue as completely as possible it is advisable to add the corresponding nonradioactive amino acid in excess to the fixative and all solutions subsequently used. This way the specific activity of the free amino acid may be lowered, on the one hand, and, on the other, labeled molecules possibly absorbed by tissue constituents may be exchanged with unlabeled ones which are ineffective in autoradiography. Artifacts due to binding of free amino acids to the tissue by different fixatives were described by Peters and Ashley (1967).

In the case of polysaccharides, fixation at acidic pH leads to selective autoradiographic demonstration of sulfomucopolysaccharides, while the sulfate is removed. On the other hand, basic fixatives remove sulfomucopolysaccharides at least partly (Dziewiatkowski, 1952b; Boström and Gardell, 1953).

B. Differential Extraction of Tissue

1. Nucleic Acids

Demonstration of incorporation of a labeled precursor into one particular compound can be achieved, if biochemical or enzymatic extraction of this compound in the histological section leads to elimination of the autoradiographic effect compared to controls. But biochemical extraction methods are limited in their applicability to histological sections, which must be carefully treated in order to preserve the tissue structure. Extraction methods have been applied mostly in incorporation studies of precursors into *nucleic acids*. In contrast to those extractions used in unfixed tissues or homogenates, application to fixed tissue sections involves special difficulties, depending on the fixative used.

a. *Extraction with ribonuclease.* According to biochemical investigations ribonuclease specifically digests ribonucleic acid. For ribonuclease treatment histological sections are usually incubated in a solution of 1 mg of ribonuclease per milliliter of distilled water for 4 hours at 40°C. The efficiency of ribonuclease depends strongly on the fixative used. Some authors found that ribonuclease removes all ribonucleic acid from tissue fixed in Carnoy, 10% formalin, 80% alcohol, or cold acetone, but not in Zenker's fixative, which is known to inactivate ribonuclease (Stowell and Zorzoli, 1947; Brachet and Shaver, 1948; Kaufmann et al., 1951a,b; Korson, 1951; Kurnick, 1952; Lagerstedt, 1956; Quay, 1957; Walker and Leblond, 1958; Jonsson and Lagerstedt, 1959; Schwarz and Rieke, 1963; Baserga and Kisieleski, 1963). Harbers and Neumann (1954, 1955) claimed that it is impossible to remove RNA quantitatively with ribonuclease and reported simultaneous loss of DNA. In an extensive study of the influence of different fixatives on the radioactivity of mouse tissue after incorporation of cytidine-^{3}H, Amano (1962) was able to confirm the above-mentioned findings for Carnoy, but he did not find complete removal of ribonucleic acid in tissue fixed in formalin containing fixatives. Also Baserga and Kisieleski (1963) reported that formalin fixation makes tissue more resistent to ribonuclease and deoxyribonuclease. Furthermore, Amano (1962) found some loss of ^{3}H-RNA activity by incubating the sections in distilled water, if the tissue was fixed in Carnoy for 3 hours only. He did not find ^{3}H-RNA activity loss after Carnoy fixation for 24 hours. He explained this effect by an observation of Lagerstedt (1956), who demonstrated that tissue fixed in Carnoy for a short time retains some of the ribonuclease contained during life, and to this is attributable the loss of activity even in distilled water. Alfert and Das (1962) also could show that survival of ribonuclease activity is a definite fact that leads to digestion of RNA after fixation.

   b. Extraction with deoxyribonuclease. Although the action of deoxyribonuclease is known to be less specific and complete than that of ribonuclease, deoxyribonuclease removes DNA from the tissue, as demonstrated by the Feulgen reaction. Amano (1962) found very satisfactory removal of DNA by incubating the tissue sections for 24 hours at 37°C in a solution containing 0.05 mg of crystallized deoxyribonuclease per milliliter of Gomori's Tris buffer with 0.2 M $MgSO_4 \cdot 7H_2O$ at pH 5.7 (activity optimum of deoxyribonuclease at pH 6; see Schmidt, 1955). The reaction of deoxyribonuclease depends still more on the type of fixative used. There is good agreement in the literature that deoxyribonuclease removes DNA in tissue fixed in Carnoy, 80% alcohol, and acetic acid–alcohol, but not after fixation in formalin or Zenker's solution (Brachet and Shaver, 1948; Daoust and Clermont, 1955; Jackson and Dessau, 1955; Kaufmann *et al.*, 1951b; Korson, 1951; Kurnick, 1952; Quay, 1957; Stowell, 1946; Schwarz and Rieke, 1963; Baserga and Kisieleski, 1963). In all these experiments it was often observed that incubation with deoxyribonuclease leads to considerable loss of RNA from the cell too. Amano (1962) found that Carnoy is the best fixative for incubation with deoxyribonuclease and that all formalin-containing fixatives like Bouin make DNA more resistant to deoxyribonuclease treatment. In his studies he used grain counting on autoradiograms of mouse tissue 24 hours after application of cytidine-³H to show that subsequent treatment with ribonuclease and deoxyribonuclease quantitatively removed the radioactivity from the sections in the same way as did treatment with 5% TCA at 98°C for 30 min. This means also that all autoradiographically measured activity is due to tritiated cytidine incorporation into both nucleic acids. Amano prevented simultaneous loss of RNA in deoxyribonuclease digestion by raising the concentration of Mg^{2+} in the buffer solution to 0.2 M. A concentration up to this degree does not yet inhibit the deoxyribonuclease activity.

   c. Extraction by acid hydrolysis. Differential extraction of nucleic acids by acid hydrolysis (trichloroacetic or perchloric) has been utilized by many investigators. Schneider's (1945) hot TCA extraction for total nucleic acids was applied to tissue sections by Pollister and Ris (1947) and Taylor and Taylor (1953). Extraction for 15–30 min at 90°C removes both RNA and DNA from most types of cells, presumably without removing proteins. However, the quantitative separation of the two types of nucleic acid is more difficult. Although RNA is more rapidly hydrolyzed than DNA, the end point for extraction of RNA may not be reached before DNA is lost. Harbers and Neumann (1954) reported that it is not possible to obtain reliable quantitative results for the extraction of nucleic acids in fixed tissue by Schmidt and Thannhäuser's method (1945). Atkinson (1952) reported considerable alteration of the acid extractability of RNA by the fixation methods used. Also Taylor and McMaster (1954) following the loss of ^{32}P-labeled RNA and DNA from tissue sections (*Lilium longiflorum*) by acid hydrolysis did not get a good quantitative separation. Feinendegen *et al.* (1960b, 1961c,d), on the other hand, reported good results with PCA extraction of RNA and DNA from HeLa cells. Baserga and Kisieleski (1963) found that extraction in 10% PCA in the cold for 12–18 hours gives results comparable to those obtained with ribonuclease. Since they observed that cells treated with PCA looked better morphologically than those digested with ribonuclease and considering that PCA extraction is a much simpler procedure than ribonuclease digestion, they prefer the PCA extraction for the removal of RNA.

d. *Extraction of* ^{32}P-*labeled nucleic acids.* As long as specific precursor for incorporation studies into nucleic acids, e.g., labeled thymidine, cytidine, or uridine, were not yet available, ^{32}P as water-soluble phosphate was mostly used. Even after extraction of the acid-soluble fraction with 5% TCA and of the lipoid fraction with ether–alcohol and chloroform, the remaining activity cannot be accounted for by labeled nucleic acid only, since there may still be labeled phosphoproteins present. Such phosphoproteins are not extractable by methods that maintain the histological structure and the nucleic acids. Taylor and McMaster (1954) discussed the problems of separating RNA, DNA, and phosphoproteins in tissue sections of *Lilium longiflorum* by enzyme digestion and acid hydrolysis. They also reported a loss of DNA after ribonuclease treatment and assumed that it is due to the action of a retained active deoxyribonuclease, which is capable of hydrolyzing intracellular DNA when RNA has been removed from the cell. Concerning the action of deoxyribonuclease, they found that this enzyme removes as much ^{32}P from cells of lily anthers as hot TCA does following ribonuclease digestion and concluded that deoxyribonuclease must completely remove DNA from some types of cells at least.

2. Proteins

It is very difficult to separate different kinds of proteins by special extraction methods like those that were described for nucleic acids. Histones can be extracted from fixed tissue sections without the removal of other proteins; but none of the available methods can separate the proteins more precisely than into histone and nonhistone types. For extraction of histones, nucleic acids may first be removed by treatment with hot TCA. This reagent does not remove the histones from fixed tissue sections (Pollister, 1952). Kurnick (1950) used 0.1 N HCl for 5 min on formalin-fixed tissue and got an increased methyl green staining, which he attributed to the removal of histones with consequent increase in stainable groups of the DNA. Purified pepsin has been shown to cause considerable shrinkage of salivary gland chromosomes without disrupting their structural continuity (Mazia *et al.*, 1947; Kaufmann *et al.*, 1949). Mazia attributed the shrinkage to the removal of nonhistone proteins, since in his tests pepsin failed to digest fibers of histone or nucleohistone, but digested fibers of more acidic proteins. Attempts to fractionate the ^{35}S-labeled proteins of fixed sections of lily anthers by digestion in pepsin met with some success (Taylor and Taylor, 1953). Most of the nuclear bound sulfur was retained, while the labeled proteins of the cytoplasm were removed. However, the interpretation of the action of pepsin on basic and acidic proteins in various kinds of tissue requires additional work to be useful in autoradiography.

3. Sulfomucopolysaccharides

Differential extraction of different types of sulfomucopolysaccharides by hyaluronidase treatment was studied by Bélanger (1954a). Chondroitin sulfate A, which is found mostly in hyaline cartilage, is hydrolyzed by testis and *Pneumococcus* hyaluronidase while chondroitin sulfate B is resistent to both types of hyaluronidase. Chondroitin sulfate C, on the other hand, is hydrolyzed only by testis hyaluronidase. These differences provide possibilities for differential demonstration of the various sulfomucopolysaccharides.

In all fixation methods and differential extraction of tissue sections and smears, the fixative has an important influence on the substance to be examined.

C. Preparing Smears and Squashes

Preferably in hematology and tissue cultures, smears from blood, bone marrow, lymph node fluid, or cultured cells are prepared. In most cases those smears are fixed in methanol. Thus, one has to be aware of the influence of this fixative on the substrate under investigation.]

A special preparation of cells for autoradiography consists in producing squash preparations by flattening cells between two rigid plane surfaces, usually by thumb pressure. Cells of the same preparation should have similar thickness. Such thin nuclei are very valuable for studies with tritiated compounds, especially tritiated thymidine, because of the short range of the β-rays of tritium. Wimber *et al.* (1960) tested the variance of thickness of a great number of nuclei by cutting paraffin-embedded squashed material perpendicular to the plane of the squashes. They found an average thickness of mouse intestinal cell nuclei of 1.18 μ and of *Tradescantia* cell nuclei of 2.97 μ. A variation of even this thickness may cause differences in autoradiographic efficiency due to different self-absorption. Testing this effect by preparing a series of squashes under varied pressure, they did not find a marked correlation. However, there still may be a possibility that a very thin layer of cytoplasm lies between nucleus and emulsion, the absorption effect of which is not negligible (see Chapter 1, Section VII, D, 2). Jona (1963) described a technique for preparing squashes by using Scotch tape, which is more readily removed than is a coverslip. However, freezing on Dry Ice, as proposed by Conger and Fairchild (1953), provides a very good method for removal of glass coverslips.

D. Preparing Sections of Undecalcified Bones

The preparation of sections of decalcified bones does not differ from the usual method of preparing histological sections, but several procedures have been described for preparing undecalcified bone sections for autoradiography. These methods are used in cases where decalcification would lead to the loss or complete removal of the isotope. Axelrod (1947) suggested that the bones be fixed in alcohol, embedded in celloidin, and cut with special precautions. A variation of this technique—securing the section with transparent adhesive tape during cutting—was used by Duthie (1954). Arnold and Jee (1954a,b) described two techniques: with the first, celloidin embedding under high pressure, undecalcified adult bone of all types was easily cut to sections of 5.8 μ; with the second method, which eliminates all contact of bone with aqueous solutions, 200-μ sections are simultaneously embedded and mounted on glass slides by means of a clear thermoplastic cement. The mounted bone sections are then ground to 5–25 μ on fine silicon carbide paper. In all these methods the microscopic resolution will be poor compared to conventional decalcified and embedded bones.

E. Thickness of the Sections

Usually sections between 3 and 5 μ are used. The thinner the section, the better the resolution and the coordination of grains to the corresponding cell structure. A limiting factor in diminishing the section thickness is the reduction of activity which decreases linearly with decreasing thickness of the section. In the case of tritium labeling, only the uppermost layer of the section contributes to the autoradiographic reaction. Figure 5A–C demonstrates that the number of grains does not increase linearly with the increasing thickness of the section of the same tritium-labeled material. Linear increase occurs only in a very small region, and the curve very soon reaches saturation. This means that there is not a great difference in the grain yield between 2 and 6 μ (Maurer and Primbsch, 1964).

Furthermore, because of the geometry within a 4–5 μ section, a small nucleus may produce no detectable autoradiographic reaction even when it contains the tracer atom, and thus it may be incorrectly scored as negative. In order to improve the recording of labeled cells and of the number of grains, Pickworth et al. (1963) described a modified technique placing the 2 μ methacrylate section on a slide, which was dipped in liquid emulsion beforehand. Then the slide with the section on top of the emulsion was dipped once more. The authors found 1.4 times more labeled cells in the double-emulsion group compared to the single-emulsion group.

II. Techniques for Applying Photographic Emulsions

All procedures concerning the application of emulsion are done in a completely lightproof darkroom about 3 feet from a Wratten safelight No. 1. A survey of the autoradiographic techniques including tissue preparation was given by Boyd (1955) and Rogers (1967). There are several techniques for applying the emulsion which have been used in autoradiography but have now been replaced by improved methods. With the *"apposition technique"* (Heller and Hamilton, 1950) the section is placed on a slide and pressed against the emulsion surface. After exposure the slide with the section and the emulsion are separated, the section is stained, and the emulsion is developed. Because of relatively loose contact, this method is used only when approximate localization of radioactive compounds is desired. With the *"mounting technique"* (Endicott and Yagoda, 1947; Evans, 1947; Boyd et al., 1950), the histological section is mounted directly on the photographic emulsion. Section and emulsion remain permanently in contact throughout photographic processing and tissue staining. A modification of this technique is the sandwich technique, in which the emulsion with the section is covered by another emulsion.

The current techniques, particularly in autoradiography with tritium, will be described in more detail in the next section.

A. STRIPPING FILM TECHNIQUE

This technique introduced by Pelc uses a thin photographic emulsion with a permeable gelatin base which has to be stripped from a glass plate or celluloid strip (Kodak Ltd., London; Ilford, London; Eastman Kodak, USA) (Pelc, 1947, 1956; Boyd and Williams, 1948; MacDonald et al., 1949; Doniach and Pelc, 1950; Bogoroch, 1951; Pelc and Howard, 1952).

Prior to application of the stripping film, the slides are dipped briefly into a very dilute gelatin solution with the addition of chrome alum (0.5% gelatin and 0.05% chrome alum dissolved in distilled water). In the dry state this gelatin layer has an approximate thickness of $1/1000$ to $1/100$ μ and, thus, does not influence the penetration of the short-range β-rays of tritium. This thin gelatin layer on both sides of the slide prevents the loosening or loss of the film. The slides can be processed through all photographic procedures of development and fixation as well as staining afterward without dislocation of the film, provided the film is allowed to dry completely between the photographic and staining steps.

Kodak Ltd., London, provides a most satisfactory stripping film with a 5-μ layer of fine grain emulsion (diameter of grains approximately 0.2 μ) and a gelatin base of 10 μ, attached emulsion side up to a glass plate. Conveniently big pieces of film are cut, stripped off the glass plate, and floated with the emulsion side down on top of a 20°C distilled water bath. After 2–3 min the film has stretched. It is placed on the slide by picking up the film with the slide, which is immersed and brought close to the film. The film drapes itself around the slide as the slide is withdrawn from the water.

In order to prevent electrostatic flashing which easily occurs while stripping the film off the plate—especially in a dry climate—and which may raise the background to intolerable levels, stripping should be carried out in a darkroom with 55–65% relative humidity. Mazia and Bucher (1960) recently recommended a modified technique for removing the film from the plate. The plate is briefly immersed in 100% alcohol and then transferred to 95% ethanol, where strips of requisite size are peeled off while submerged in alcohol. The pieces are then placed on water, emulsion side down, and processed as described before.

Maurer and co-workers (1961) changed the stripping technique during the last years as follows: Cuts are made that will yield strips of the desired size, then the whole stripping film plate is placed in a shallow dish of distilled water. One side of the strips is loosened and wrapped around one edge of the slide kept with the section side down. On removal of the slide from the water, the remaining film will drape itself around the slide. By this method flashing is completely avoided and background is considerably diminished (Fig. 7).

B. LIQUID EMULSION TECHNIQUE

In order to improve the contact between section and photographic emulsion Bélanger and Leblond (1946) used liquid emulsion dropped on the slide with the histological section and spread evenly with a brush or

FIG. 7. Covering the slide with stripping film.

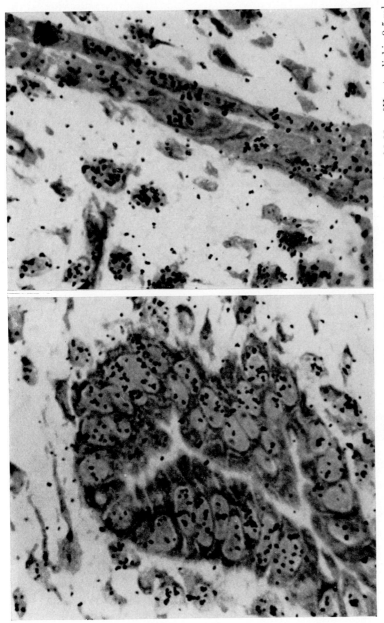

FIG. 7A. Autoradiogram of uterus from 24-day-old rat, 2 hr after subcutaneous injection of 0.63 μg ³H-estradiol in 0.5 ml saline. Concentration of radioactivity in cell nuclei of uterine glands and lamina propria. One-micron sections stained after photographic development for DNA and RNA with methyl-green-pyronin. ×1200. Exposure 42 days. (From Stumpf and Roth, 1968.) For discussion, see p. 44.

glass rod (Leblond *et al.*, 1948a; Gross *et al.*, 1951). Bélanger (1950, 1952c) modified the liquid emulsion technique and obtained "inverted auto-radiographs."

1. Thin Emulsion Layer (Dipping Technique)

Introduced first by Joftes and Warren (1955), this technique has the advantage of being easy to handle and permits processing a large number of slides in a short time (Messier and Leblond, 1957; Joftes, 1959, 1963; Prescott, 1964a). The liquid emulsion in bulk (Eastman Kodak NTB, NTB-2 and NTB-3; Ilford G-5, K-5, K-2 and L-4) is melted in a water bath at 40°C. Whether it is used undiluted or diluted depends on the type of emulsion and on the purpose of the investigation (Falk and King, 1963). A diluted emulsion yields thinner layers than an undiluted one. Some authors recommend the addition of a wetting agent like Duponol C to the distilled water for dilution (Joftes, 1959; Meyer-Arendt, 1962). It should be noted that diluting the emulsion with more than 2 parts of distilled water to 1 part of emulsion may lead to artifacts, mainly clustering of grains (Oehlert *et al.*, 1962c). The prewarmed (and wet) slides are dipped into the emulsion, withdrawn after some seconds, drained on tissue paper, and dried standing vertically in a clean air stream. Air bubbles, must be removed from emulsion by careful stirring with a glass rod and eventually filtering the emulsion through cotton. The slides must show a uniform coat. This uniformity is of less importance for autoradiography with tritium provided the emulsion layer is thicker at every spot than the practical range of tritium-β-particles, i.e., 1–2 μ, but β-emitters with higher energy produce grains throughout the emulsion covering the specimen. Leblond *et al.* (1963) and Kopriwa and Leblond (1962) found that the emulsion of autoradiograms processed in the usual manner was not uniform. The same was found by Bleecken (1961) whose grain density curves for liquid emulsion (using ^{32}P) show a saddle-shaped depression over the maximum thickness of the specimen due to a thinning of the emulsion. Leblond *et al.* (1963) and Kopriwa and Leblond (1962) performed very extensive and careful experiments in order to find the optimum conditions for applying a uniform liquid emulsion layer. They describe a technique improved by drying the dipped slides at 28°C and at a constant relative humidity of 80%.

A pouring device with which numerous easily reproducible preparations of emulsion of predetermined thickness can be made in a short time was described by Tzschaschel (1958a,b). A semiautomatic instrument for the autoradiographic coating technique has also been devised by Kopriwa (1967a).

2. Thick Emulsion Layer

Liquid emulsion is also used for track autoradiography (Ficq, 1953, 1955b, 1959c; Boyd and Levi, 1950). The emulsion is applied undiluted or diluted only with one-third distilled water to two-thirds emulsion by dropping several drops on the slide and spreading it evenly with a brush or a glass rod. This way the thickness of the emulsion can be controlled. The time required for drying of the thick emulsion layer is much longer than for thin ones. This is important since exposure time of the autoradiogram is counted only from the time when the emulsion is completely dry. Latent images produced in the wet emulsion are erased immediately by fading. In thick emulsions, tracks of β- or α-emitters can be followed to their origin in the specimen. The time for developing and fixing is considerably longer than for the thin emulsions.

A modification of the liquid emulsion technique was introduced by King et al. (1951), who added ^{32}P-labeled *Paramecium* cultures to liquid Ilford G-5 emulsion. The intimate contact between specimen and emulsion permits better distinction between the tracks of the specimen, which are emitted in all directions, and the background tracks from contamination of the emulsion with α-emitters.

C. DOUBLE-LABELING TECHNIQUE

The method of double labeling recently introduced is of great advantage for certain studies. It enables the investigator to study the dynamics of special metabolic processes by applying the same but differently labeled substance at different time intervals. For instance, the length of the DNA synthesis period in a cell can be measured by application of ^{3}H-labeled thymidine first, and ^{14}C-labeled thymidine second, after a certain time interval. Furthermore, with this technique it is possible to trace the metabolic behavior of two different substances in the same cell simultaneously. By application of thymidine-^{14}C and simultaneous injection of ^{3}H-labeled amino acids or RNA precursors, protein or RNA metabolism can be studied in cells that are synthesizing DNA and in those that are not. Biological variations from animal to animal can be avoided in this way.

1. Thick Emulsion Layer

This double-labeling technique also makes use of a thick emulsion layer. Applying isotopes of different energy like ^{3}H- and ^{14}C-labeled substances (simultaneously), it is possible to distinguish the two labels within the thick emulsion. ^{3}H-labeling, for instance, with its weak energy β-particles produces grains in a very thin layer of the emulsion close to the specimen, while ^{14}C-labeling with a β-energy ten times higher produces tracks in the thick emulsion (Gerbaulet et al., 1961, 1963; Hilscher and Maurer, 1962; Pilgrim and Maurer, 1962, 1965).

2. Two Emulsion Layers

The double-labeling technique has led to further modifications of the stripping film and the liquid emulsion technique with the aim of registering tritium grains in the first layer and, for example, ^{14}C-tracks in the second. If two emulsion layers are applied in order to obtain the most accurate distinction between ^{3}H grains and tracks of β-particles with higher energy, they may consist of a combination of stripping film and liquid emulsion or of the application of 2 stripping film layers or two layers of liquid emulsion. The latter may be applied by dipping twice or dropping and spreading the second emulsion with a brush. In all cases the first layer is developed after relatively short exposure times prior to the application of the second layer. The first layer should have such a thickness that after photographic processing the weak energy β-particles do not reach the second emulsion layer ($\sim$0.5 mg/cm^2 = saturation thickness of ^{3}H-β-radiation). Depending on the thickness of the second emulsion layer, either grains or tracks are registered. With this technique, even at long exposure times of the second emulsion layer, no additional grains are produced in the first layer, so that way a quantitative evaluation by grain counting of the ^{3}H-labeling in the first emulsion is possible practically without interference by ^{14}C-labeling. One disadvantage of this method lies in the lesser resolution of the ^{14}C-labeling in the second emulsion. The distance between the specimen and the autoradiographic reaction in the second emulsion is often too great to allow an exact determination of the radiation source in the specimen. Thus, it is easier to trace a track back to the specimen in a single thick emulsion layer.

Plaut (Krause and Plaut, 1960) used two layers of stripping film for double labeling studies with ^{3}H- and ^{14}C-labeled thymidine. The first layer was a very thin stripping film, the gelatin base of which prevents tritium β-particles from penetrating into the second layer of normal AR 10 stripping film.

Dawson et al. (1962) also described a method using two layers of stripping film. The first stripping film has no gelatin supporting layer, and a color coupler in this layer results in blue dye-coupled grains after photographic processing. After a cover of 0.1 μ celloidin is laid, normal AR 10 stripping film is applied. For further details on autoradiographic differentiation between various β-emitters by a combined color-coupling and double-stripping film technique see Field et al. (1965).

Baserga (1961) and Baserga and Nemeroff (1962b) using thymidine-^{3}H *dl*-leucine-³H thymidine-¹⁴C and uridine-¹⁴C tested different double-layer techniques with liquid emulsion and stripping film of which part of the gelatin layer was digested with trypsin. They found that the combination of 2 NTB liquid emulsion layers provided the most satisfactory results.

Wimber (1963), Wimber and Quastler (1963), and Davies and Wimber (1963) used a double coating of Kodak NTB liquid emulsion by the dipping technique, where the slides with the first emulsion layer were allowed to dry for 30 min prior to the application of the second emulsion.

Lennartz *et al.* (1964) and Pilgrim *et al.* (1966) working simultaneously with ³H- and ¹⁴C-labeled thymidine used a thin stripping film (5 μ thick without gelatin base, experimental scientific plates V 1062, unbacked) for the first layer and liquid emulsion Ilford G-5 for the second layer (ca. 30 μ thick in dry state).

Sandwiching sections between a highly sensitive and a low sensitive emulsion was recommended by Trelstad (1965).

Buckaloo and Cohn (1956) described a method for distinguishing two or more isotopes by the different energy of their particles. In multilayer color film, the β-particles are absorbed in different film layers depending on their energy, which leads to different colors of the grains.

Stripping film and liquid emulsions are usually air-dried or dried with a cold fan. Using unexposed blanks from Kodak AR 10 Sawicki and Pawinska (1965) recently found that fast, open drying with a fan for 25 minutes resulted in more background grains than slow drying in a desiccator for 6 hours. Even more background could be avoided by drying very slowly in a desiccator for 24 hours. The higher background after fast drying is assumed to be caused by the rapid shrinkage of wet emulsions, which results in an increase in the intraemulsion pressure that in turn sensitizes the silver halide crystals, leading to an increase in the number of developable grains.

III. Exposure

As mentioned above the exposure times, which depend on the type of isotope, the injected dose, time between application and sacrifice, and the type of emulsion used, have to be determined empirically with test slides. In order to get an autoradiographic reaction which enables the investigator to observe details microscopically, about 10^7 to 10^9 β-particles should hit 1 cm² of the emulsion (Wainwright *et al.*, 1954; Marinelli and Hill, 1948). Certain estimates of the exposure time required may be obtained by measuring the activity of the section in a suitable counter and calculating the β-particles/cm². However, since the activity distribution in the section may be very irregular, those estimated exposure times may be quite different from the ones actually necessary. In most cases, especially with tritium labeling, it is advisable to ascertain the correct exposure time with test autoradiograms. A series of sections are covered with emulsion and exposed. By developing autoradiograms after different time intervals, the correct exposure time can be determined. Also, application of a very sensitive emulsion may lead more quickly to the correct exposure time for the emulsion to be used in the actual experiments, if the factor for the different sensitivity is known. For different purposes different exposure times may be necessary. For grain counting exposure should be short, the number of grains not too high, less than 1 grain per μ^2. Slightly overexposed negative autoradiograms are preferable for positive prints. Exposure time should be kept low for quantitative autoradiography, because all disturbing secondary processes, like increasing background and fading of the latent image, increase with time. In general, exposure time should not exceed the half-life of the isotope used, since half the activity has disappeared at that time and additional exposure does not add much to the autoradiographic effect. Exposure in low humidity reduces fading; therefore, Drierite (anhydrous calcium sulfate) is placed in the slide boxes during exposure. For more details on fading see Chapter 1, II, C.

IV. Development and Fixation

Manufacturer's recommendations should be followed for development. For most of the thin emulsions usable for autoradiography and stripping film 4–6 min development in Kodak D-19 is suitable. Leblond *et al.* (1963) and Kopriwa and Leblond (1962) have determined the influence of different developers and of developing time on grain counts in autoradiograms of ^{3}H-labeled sections. They found that there is no marked difference in grain counts with the various developers. Since the background increases slowly during the first period of development, but later on rises quickly with increasing time, the development time should be kept short. Time for development, of course, depends on the thickness of the emulsion layer and the temperature of development. For thick emulsion layers 20–30 min of development may be required, depending on the temperature. In some cases it might be necessary to soak the thick emulsion in distilled water prior to development to make it penetrable to the developer. Yagoda (1955) described a special isothermal processing of thick nuclear emulsion that provides uniform development throughout the entire thickness. A similar procedure was recommended by Guidotti and Setti (1956). This temperature-development method facilitates the work with electron tracks. The commonly applied development should be carried out at a constant temperature, in temperature-regulated water baths. Stripping film and thin emulsions are usually developed at 18°C; for thick emulsion layers lower temperatures (12–14°C) are preferable. An automatic slow shaking of the dishes during development has proved to be very useful. Constant developing conditions are absolutely necessary for comparative quantitative autoradiography.

After development the autoradiograms are rinsed in water—a stop bath is not necessary—and fixed in acid fixer for 3–10 min, thick emulsions for 20–40 min. The hypo has to be removed very carefully by washing in running tap water for 15 min, or 30–60 min for thick emulsions, respectively. For prestained specimens washing should not be extended more than necessary in order to prevent the leaching out of the soluble dyes. Kodak Hypo clearing or other similar products are also very useful in removing traces of hypo.

For immediate mounting the slides are dehydrated in alcohol, cleared, and mounted in the usual fashion. If specimens are to be stained through the emulsion, the autoradiograms should be allowed to dry completely after photographic processing in order to prevent loss or dislocation of the emulsion during the staining procedure.

V. Staining

A. Staining prior to Applying the Emulsion

If the specimens are stained prior to applying the emulsion, they should be slightly overstained, since there will be some loss of the water-soluble dyes during photographic processing. Leblond et al. (1963) and Thurston and Joftes (1963) described some valuable staining procedures that are performed prior to dipping or in combination before and after application of the emulsion. Precaution has to be taken that staining does not dissolve the radioactive substance under investigation. Hydrolysis during Feulgen staining, for instance, may lead to loss of DNA. Walker and Yates (1952) and Woods (1957) found a consistently lower content of DNA by the Feulgen method than is estimated from the same nuclei in the living state. Experiments of Lang and Maurer (1965) with thymidine-^{3}H showed for different mouse tissues that there is ^{3}H-activity loss of 15% by hydrolysis at the point of optimum staining (1 N HCl at 60°C for 12 min, of 10% PCA at 20°C for 20 hours, respectively). If the sections were washed after hydrolysis, the activity loss amounted to as much as 50%. Baserga and Nemeroff (1962a,b) also found a loss of 15% of the radioactive label (^{3}H- and ^{14}C-labeled thymidine) by Feulgen staining. See also Taylor (1958b). A method for vital staining with neutral red and trypan blue of thymidine -^{3}H-labeled cells prior to autoradiography which does not cause spurious grains was described by Sawicki et al. (1967b).

For quantitative evaluation of autoradiograms tissue sections should be stained after photographic processing, because labeled substances may be dissolved during the staining procedure. However, Feulgen-staining has to be performed prior to autoradiographic procedure, because acid hydrolysis that is necessary affects the emulsion.

B. STAINING THROUGH THE EMULSION

Staining through the photographic emulsion requires longer staining times; and it is advisable to differentiate after staining with HCl–alcohol in order to remove the stain from the gelatin layer. Simmel et al. (1951), Fitzgerald (1959), Bélanger (1961), Thurston and Joftes (1963), and Linnartz-Niklas et al. (1964) described some of the staining procedures that leave the film mostly free of stain. Baserga and Banks (1962) recommended digestion of the gelatin layer by trypsin. Most of the common histological staining procedures may be used for staining through the film: hemalum, hematoxylin and eosin, Mayer's hematoxylin, basic fuchsin, methylene blue, azure blue, cresyl violet, Giemsa. Also hematological stains have been satisfactorily applied to autoradiograms through the film (Lajtha, 1952, 1954; Everett et al., 1960; Gude et al., 1955; Berman and Newby, 1963).

It has to be kept in mind that some staining procedures applied through the emulsion may lead to a loss of developed silver grains as was observed for gallocyanin (Stenram, 1962a; Linnartz-Niklas et al., 1964).

A new method for better recognition and photographic reproduction of human chromosomes in tritium autoradiograms by removing the silver and/or digesting the gelatin of the film was described by Bianchi et al. (1964) and Froland (1965).

VI. Autoradiography of Water-Soluble Substances

A. PRECIPITATION METHOD

In order to prevent the leaching of radioactive water-soluble substances, several methods have been used in autoradiography. In plant tissue, ^{32}P was precipitated in situ by fixation in absolute alcohol with the addition of basic lead acetate (Russell et al., 1949). ^{82}Br was precipitated by alcoholic silver nitrate (Winteringham et al., 1950). Hempel (1963a, 1965) studied the occurrence of catecholamine storing cells after application of ^{3}H-DOPA to mice. For fixation of the water-soluble ^{3}H-catecholamine he used chromate precipitation. All these methods are applicable only for certain specific substances. However, autoradiography of water-soluble substances has become more and more important, since the behavior of water-soluble compounds in the tissue and especially within the cell gives valuable information about metabolic processes. For this reason, many investigators looked for suitable methods to prepare autoradiograms of specimens containing water-soluble radioactive substances.

B. Freeze-Drying Method

If all the radioactive material is to be retained, fixation of the tissue by freeze-drying (see Volume IIIC of this series, Chapter 1) the specimen is the best method and was first applied in autoradiography by Leblond (1943b). Since then this has been a routine method for many purposes (Holt et al., 1949; Holt and Warren, 1950, 1951, 1952, 1953a,b; Winteringham et al., 1950; Harris et al., 1950; Williams, 1951; Mellgren, 1952; Jennings and Krakusin, 1952; Andresen et al., 1953; Gallimore et al., 1954b; Passalacqua, 1954a; Canny, 1955; Edwards, 1955; Freed, 1955; Sterling and Chichester, 1956; Pallas and Crafts, 1957; Andros and Wollman, 1965). After freezing in isopentane cooled to − 170°C with liquid nitrogen, the tissue is vacuum dehydrated and embedded in paraffin. The dry emulsion is then pressed against the sections. In order to avoid contact with water, Harris et al. (1950) recommended picking the section from a surface of warm mercury. Recently Wilske and Ross (1965) recommended fixing frozen-dried tissue in the vapor phase with osmium tetroxide or paraformaldehyde and vacuum-embedding it in Epon. One-micron sections can then be used for coating with emulsion in the conventional manner.

C. Freeze-Substitution Method

A modification of this technique is the freeze-substitution method (Blank et al., 1951; Feder and Sidman, 1958; Russell et al., 1949). Vacuum dehydration is replaced by dehydration in alcohol. Gielink et al. (1966) described a method by which the leaching of water-soluble and exchangeable calcium (^{45}Ca) in histoautoradiography of oat tissue can be prevented by using acetone as the dehydration fluid and by keeping the tissue sections, while stretching on water, embedded in the methacrylate matrix.

However, the method of freeze-drying does not prevent a partial loss or diffusion of the labeled water-soluble substance within the tissue, since after freeze drying the samples have to be embedded in order to be cut.

D. Techniques Using Cryostat Sections and Low Exposure Temperatures

In recent investigations cryostat sections have been used for tracing water-soluble substances autoradiographically.

Oster et al. (1955) first introduced a method of cutting unfixed frozen tissue with the freezing microtome, applying the emulsion without thawing, and exposing the autoradiograms at −20°C. Further attempts have been made to prevent loss or diffusion of water-soluble substances by cutting the tissue in a cryostat (Taugner *et al.*, 1958; Taugner and Wagenmann, 1958; Huang, 1960; Reinholz *et al.*, 1960; Novek, 1962).

Fitzgerald (1961) described a similar method for the investigation of the intracellular incorporation of thymidine-^{3}H and cytidine-^{3}H. In his technique, tissue is frozen in isopentane (about $-170°C$), cut in the cryostat ($-20°$ to $-30°C$), dehydrated by freeze-substitution ($-70°C$) or by vacuum freeze-drying below $0°C$. Only for the small moment of mounting with dry stripping film are the sections exposed to room temperature. The autoradiograms are then exposed at $-20°C$. In order to prevent loosening or loss of the stripping film during the photographic procedure, autoradiograms are immersed in a 10% solution of formaldehyde for 5–10 min before development.

Recently a number of authors described the pressure-mounting of cryostat- or freeze-dried and paraffin-embedded sections on a dry photographic emulsion with exposure at low temperatures (Branton and Jacobson, 1962; Smitherman *et al.*, 1963; Stumpf and Roth, 1964, 1965a,b, 1966, 1967; Stumpf and Lester, 1966; Hammarström *et al.*, 1965a; Werner *et al.*, 1966; Gahan and Rajan, 1966).

Special emphasis should be placed on a method developed by Stumpf and Roth (1964, 1965a,b, 1966, 1967, 1968; Stumpf and Lester, 1966; Kleine, 1967; Höbel and Lehrnbecher, 1967; Buscher *et al.*, 1968; Sander and Attramadal, 1968) using dry-mounted, freeze-dried frozen sections. With this method the most reliable results are obtained and diffusion or translocation of the radioactive tracer within the tissue seem to be eliminated. Furthermore, tissue preservation and autoradiographic resolution are comparable to that obtained with standard methods, as can be seen in Fig. 7A. (See p. 35.) The following steps are necessary for this technique:

1. Freezing of tissue in liquefied propane at $-180°C$ with simultaneous mounting on tissue holder for cryocutting.

2. Cryocutting of tissue at 1.0 μ or thinner performed at knife temperatures at or below $-60°C$.

3. Vacuum freeze-drying of thin, frozen sections utilizing a portable cryosorption pump.

4. Dry-mounting, preferably in a low-humidity darkroom, of unfixed, unembedded freeze-dried sections on emulsion-coated slides (Kodak NTB-3) previously stored over Drierite.

5. Exposure in a freezer at $-15°C$.

6. Photographic development with staining as final step.

With this method and special procedures to make the sections adhere to the emulsion during the photographic process, tissue preservation and autoradiographic resolution comparable to that obtained with standard methods were achieved.

A simple and effective method for autoradiographic detection of water-soluble substances was elaborated by Appleton (1964) and Pelc and Appleton (1965). Cryostat sections were mounted in the darkroom directly onto precooled coverslips coated with Kodak AR 10 stripping film with the emulsion upward. After exposure at temperatures of $-20°$ to $-30°C$, the sections were quickly fixed and then developed. The close contact between section and emulsion results in very good resolution. The detection of water-soluble activity was demonstrated by the autoradiograms. At 15 min after thymidine-^{3}H injection into mice grains were quite uniformly distributed over cytoplasm and nucleus of the cells with preference to some nuclei that obviously later on turn out to be labeled. After 60 min, labeling was almost completely confined to some nuclei.

Feinendegen and Bond (1962) painted bone marrow cells directly with a small paint brush onto slides covered with stripping film AR 10 with the emulsion side upward. The smears were dried and stored directly in the cold. At the end of the exposure time, the cells were fixed in methyl alcohol.

A special method for detecting water-soluble substances and a way of quantitation of soluble and insoluble radioactivity in single cells was described by Miller et al. (1964a,b). Single cells were placed within a small circle marked on the slide with a wax pencil, and extraction solvents were dropped onto the cell. The thin layer of wax formed a barrier that retained the extraction fluid, and the materials extracted were spread relatively evenly in the defined area. The dried specimen were then covered with a film layer dried in a wire loop. This way the authors were able to distinguish between the water-soluble activity extracted and the incorporated activity retained within the cell.

For a detailed description of methods for autoradiographic detection of water-soluble substances in plant cells see Lüttge and Weigl (1965).

The autoradiographic method for demonstration of water-soluble substances is still in development and partly open to some criticism. It is not quite clear whether the results represent *in vivo* conditions. It is also possible that intracellular diffusion or diffusion of the isotope from intracellular to extracellular sites may occur in some step of preparing specimens for autoradiography. On the other hand, a further improvement of this method is important because of the many water-soluble substances the distribution of which within tissues and cells is of great interest. See also "Int. Conf. on High Resolution Autoradiography of Diffusible Substances" (1969).

For a description of electron microscopic techniques in combination with autoradiography and some applications see Chapter 7.

3. Application of Different Isotopes

I. Iodine-131 and Iodine-125

Radioactive iodine has been extensively used in studies of the iodine metabolism of the thyroid gland. Furthermore, it has often been used as a suitable label for studying the behavior of various substances by means of autoradiography. Most of those studies have not yielded results at the cellular level. This is partly due to the high β-energy of the ^{131}I with a corresponding low resolution. For the future, better prospects for employing iodine in autoradiographic studies may be provided by the use of ^{125}I. Since, in the case of ^{125}I (K-capture), the low energy conversion electrons and Auger electrons with energies of about 3 and 30 keV are utilized in autoradiography, resolution should be similar to that of tritium. This would open a wide field for autoradiographic studies with ^{125}I in general and considering complementary application of ^{125}I DU in DNA studies in particular. To date only a few autoradiographic studies using ^{125}I are known. Appelgren et al. (1963a) demonstrated the significantly better resolution of ^{125}I compared to ^{131}I in autoradiographic experiments with labeled microtest charts. Andros and Wollman (1964) used ^{125}I for studies of inorganic iodide uptake by thyroid epithelial cells. Schultze and Hughes (1965) showed that ^{125}I-labeled ribonuclease injected into mice intravenously is localized in the epithelia of the proximal tubules in the kidney. Kayes et al. (1962) used ^{125}I in electron microscopic autoradiography of radioiodine in the thyroid, obtaining good pictures of ultrastructural details without removing the remaining gelatin. Similar studies are performed by Kayes et al. (1962), Stein and Gross (1963), Dohlman et al. (1964), Sheldon et al. (1964), Lupulescu et al. (1964), and Lupulescu and Petrovici (1965, 1966), Bauer and Meyer (1965) and Nunez et al. (1966). For further autoradiographic studies with ^{125}I see Nilsson and Cederlund (1966), Höbel and Lehrnbecher (1967) and Kleine (1967).

Kyogoku et al. (1964) injected ^{125}I-labeled antibody against the stroma sediments of N-2-fluorenyacetamide-induced hepatoma and normal liver into tumor bearing and normal rats and found in both cases antibody localized in the walls of sinusoids and in connective tissue parts of the tumor as well as in normal liver. After passage through normal rats, there were some differences in the localization pattern of the antibodies in the tumor.

46

The loss of radioactivity during the preparation of autoradiograms from rats injected with ^{125}I-labeled antigens was studied by Mitchell (1966).

A. IODINE METABOLISM OF THE THYROID

The iodine metabolism in the thyroid has been extensively examined with ^{131}I, mostly by Leblond and his group (Leblond, 1943a,b, 1944, 1948a,b, 1949, 1951; Leblond et al., 1946, 1948a; Leblond and Gross, 1948, 1949, 1951; Gross and Leblond, 1947a,b, 1950, 1951; Gross and Pitt-Rivers, 1952). According to their results in normal rats, most of the radioactive iodine was found in the cells which appeared as rings up to 30 min after intravenous injection of radioactive iodide. At that time, only a smaller amount of radioactivity was localized in the colloid. After 24 hours, however, the autoradiograms showed only round spots corresponding to the deposition of radioiodine in the colloid. Up to 15 min after injection, Nandi et al. (1956) found half of the ^{131}I activity in the cells and half in the colloid (rat). After 3 hours most of the ^{131}I was shown to be in the colloid. The iodine was obviously present in an organically bound form since it had not been removed from the tissue by fixation and dehydration in alcohol. Quantitative chemical studies by Bogoroch et al. (1951) showed that 30 min after injection of ^{131}I and after 24 hours of fixation in Bouin, 75% of the radioiodine in cells and 77% in the colloid is bound to thyroglobulin. After longer experimental intervals more iodine should be protein bound. These results suggested that circulating iodide is continuously bound to thyroglobulin in the cytoplasm of the cells, preferably in the apical region corresponding to the Golgi area (Leblond, 1951). It is then released into the colloid, this sequence being most rapid in active thyroids and slow in resting thyroid tissue. This process can be accelerated by iodine depletion in the animals prior to application of radioiodine or by activation of the thyroid with thyrotropic hormones. In those cases deposition of radioiodine is exclusively found in the colloid even at 1 hour after injection. On the other hand the deposition of radioiodine can be inhibited by hypophysectomy or thyroxine application. After thyroxine treatment of rats, Doniach and Pelc (1949) found radioactive iodine deposition only into cells, not into colloid. The subsequent administration of thyrotropic hormone over several days did not reestablish a normal deposition into colloid, but only intensified the ring effect of cellular incorporation. Since protein-bound radioiodine is found very early in the colloid, in some cases 2 min after injection, the possibility of thyroxine formation inside the colloid has also been discussed (Leblond, 1948a; Doniach and Pelc, 1949). Recent autoradiographic studies with labeled amino acid precursors—partly in combination with an electron microscope—have shown that the protein component of the thyroglobulin is formed in the ergastoplasm of the follicle cells. It is only after secretion of the colloid to the lumen of the follicle that the glycoprotein compound is combined with iodine, thus forming the final thyroglobulin (Nadler et al., 1960, 1964; Nadler, 1965).

All the experiments showed that all follicles in the gland are active at all times in fixing iodine. However, the rate of iodine fixation by the various follicles is variable. The most rapid iodine uptake and its corresponding rapid disappearance was found in the smaller, more centrally located follicles in which the epithelium was relatively high and staining was basophilic, i.e., which resemble the activated follicles. Less uptake was observed in the larger, more peripherally situated follicles with relatively low acidophilicly stained epithelium that resemble the resting follicles and are still radioactive after 48 hours (Leblond, 1948a; Doniach and Pelc, 1949; Bourne, 1948). More detailed examinations of the relationship between iodine uptake and size of follicles confirmed that the iodine turnover in the smaller follicles seemed to be higher; but if the iodine turnover is related to the follicle surface, all follicles have the same iodine turnover. Since there is a proportionality between follicle surface and number of epithelial cells in the follicle, it was concluded that all follicular cells have the same iodine turnover (Nadler, 1951, 1953a; Nadler and Bogoroch, 1951; Nadler et al., 1954).

Recently the iodine uptake in the thyroid gland was studied with electron microscopic autoradiography using ^{125}I and ^{131}I (Kayes et al., 1962; Stein and Gross, 1963; Dohlman et al., 1964; Sheldon et al., 1964; Lupulescu et al., 1964; Lupulescu and Petrovici, 1965, 1966). Labeling was mainly found over the colloid, and only to a much smaller extent over the large cytoplasmic granules or vesicles, respectively.

1. Factors Influencing Iodine Uptake in the Thyroid

Application of thiouracil prior to or together with radioactive iodine resulted in a complete failure of the autoradiographic demonstration of the thyroid in fixed sections (Couceiro and Vieira, 1944; Doniach and Pelc, 1949). On the other hand, radioactive iodide was demonstrable autoradiographically in freeze-dried sections of thyroids of rats given thiouracil, but there was no autoradiographic reaction in thyroids of untreated animals (Pitt-Rivers and Trotter, 1953; Doniach and Logothetopoulos, 1955). These results indicate that free iodide is taken up by the thyroid in spite of treatment with thiouracil. The concentration of iodide was higher in the colloid than in the epithelial cells. Rose and Nelson (1956) were able to demonstrate autoradiographically the inhibitory effect of thiouracil on the transformation of inorganic iodide into organically bound iodide in thyroids of dogs.

Bogoroch and Timiras (1951) found that stress (forced muscular exercise, subcutaneous injections of 10% formalin, and transsection of the spinal cord) led to 6–8 times less radioiodine uptake by the thyroid and more rapid excretion of iodine in the urine than in normal animals. The mechanism is thought to lie in a decrease or suppression of the thyrotropic stimulation by the stress.

Harris *et al.* (1955) studied the influence of acute and chronic exposure to sodium fluoride on the thyroid iodine metabolism of rats and did not find any inhibitory effect on the iodine uptake by the thyroid gland or its transport through the acinar cell stage into the colloidal phase.

2. Iodine Uptake by the Fetal Thyroid

Several autoradiographic investigations concerning the beginning of radioiodine uptake by the fetal thyroid resulted in the conclusion that the accumulation of radioactive iodine is coincident with the first appearance of discrete follicles and that the quantity of iodine containing colloid increases with the number of follicles present and with the age of the embryo. In hamster embryos the first iodine uptake was found between day 12 and day 13 of development (Hansborough and Seay, 1951). In rats the functional ability to store iodine begins in 18- to 19-day-old rat embryos (Gorbman and Evans, 1943). In chick embryos the first incorporation of radioiodine into colloid-containing follicles was observed on day 11 of incubation (Hansborough and Khan, 1951) when microscopic observations showed that discrete follicles appeared for the first time. Carpenter *et al.* (1954) were able to show that on day 16 of chick embryo development the radioiodine uptake was the same *in vivo* and in explanted glands grown for 8 days *in vitro*. That the capacity of concentrating radioactive iodine is maintained up to 2 months in cultivated infantile thyroid tissue of rats could be confirmed by Pavlovic (1955). Carpenter *et al.* (1954) also found higher activity in the apical parts of the follicular cells. The human fetal thyroid has the ability to accumulate demonstrable amounts of ^{131}I by week 12 of gestation (Hodges *et al.*, 1955). In near-term bovine fetuses, the thyroids contained about twice as much ^{131}I as the maternal thyroid. The concentration of ^{131}I was 6–7 times greater in the fetal thyroids, and the fetal thyroglobulin was 27 times more radioactive than that of the mother (Gorbman *et al.*, 1952). In frogs the first faint autoradiograms were produced in 10.0 mm larvae (Gorbman and Evans, 1941).

3. Uptake by Tumors

Autoradiographic studies concerning the radioiodine uptake by thyroid tumors and the correlation with the different histological cell types were performed by Fitzgerald and his group (Fitzgerald, 1952a,b, 1955; Fitzgerald and Foote, 1949; Fitzgerald et al., 1950; Duffy and Fitzgerald, 1950a,b), Hamilton et al. (1940), Marinelli et al. (1947), Dobyns and Lennon (1948), Dobyns and Maloof (1951), Godwin et al. (1951), Salter and Johnston (1948), Black et al. (1953), Kreutzer et al. (1950), Forbes (1954), Stuart (1955), and Philipp (1955). No distinct correlation between cell type and iodine uptake was found. In adenomas, cellular hypertrophy and hyperplasia was often associated with hyperfunction, but there were also adenomas with cellular hypertrophy and hyperplasia with scarcely any iodine uptake. The latter group showed increased variability in the cell height and resembled the class of tumors known as papillary adeno-carcinoma (Dobyns and Lennon, 1948). Fitzgerald (1952a) found the adenomas to be mostly microfollicular with a decreased iodine uptake as compared to normal thyroid tissue.

In thyroid cancer a certain relation was found between the tumor type and the iodine uptake. Little or no uptake was found in the papillary type, whereas the follicular type stored iodine to a variable degree. For iodine accumulation, the presence of colloid seems to be prerequisite, although not all tumors with colloid necessarily store iodine. In general, the iodine uptake by thyroid cancer tissue was found to be less than in normal thyroid tissue (Fitzgerald, 1955). This is of importance for the therapeutic use of [131]I.

B. ^{131}I-LABELED SUBSTANCES

1. Hormones

[131]I has been widely used as a tag for autoradiographic localization of different substances. Ford et al. (1957) examined the localization of ^{131}I-labeled thyroid hormones in the tissues of guinea pigs. After injection of labeled triiodothyronine, radioiodine was found in the cortex of the kidney, the liver parenchyma, the alveolar tissue of the lung, the red pulp of the spleen, and cardiac, skeletal, and smooth muscle fibers. After thyroxine injection, a similar but considerably less intense and more diffuse localization was demonstrable (Gross and Leblond, 1947b; Leblond, 1949; Leblond and Cameron, 1952). Eränkö (1957) was able to demonstrate autoradiographically the presence of labeled norepinephrine and epinephrine in the adrenal medulla of hamster, mouse, and rat after incubation with ^{131}I-labeled iodate and iodate–formalin. Narahara et al. (1958) studied the metabolism of insulin-^{131}I and glucagon-^{131}I in the kidney of the rat. At intervals of less than 2 minutes after injection, the radioactivity was prominent in the lumina of the proximal convoluted tubules. At later intervals, the radioactivity became more concentrated in

the cells of the proximal convoluted tubules. The authors concluded that this observation supports the hypothesis that proteins may be filtered through the glomerular membrane and be reabsorbed in the tubules. Sonenberg *et al.* (1951a) studied the behavior of ^{131}I-labeled anterior pituitary preparations with adrenocorticotropic hormonal activity. They found a rapid entrance and disappearance of radioactivity in the adrenal with concentration in the inner layers of the adrenal cortex. ^{131}I-labeled anterior pituitary preparation with prolactin hormonal activity was found to be localized in the ovary (corpora lutea, follicular fluid), adrenal, liver, spleen, kidney, and thyroid, while there was no significant concentration of radioactivity in the mammary tissue of the rat (Sonenberg *et al.*, 1951b).

2. Antigens and Antibodies

Warren and Dixon (1948) and Dixon and Warren (1950) studied the uptake of ^{131}I-labeled antigen in anaphylactic shock in the guinea pig. Significant amounts of labeled antigen were picked up only by liver and lung, whereby the uptake and distribution in liver was the same for sensitized and nonsensitized animals, while the uptake by the lung of sensitized animals was twice that of controls. A concentration of antigen was found in the bronchial fibrous tissue which seems to be a binding of specific antigen at the site of one of the sensitivity reactions, the bronchial wall.

On autoradiograms of brain tumors and adjacent brain tissue after infusion of ^{125}I-labeled anti-glioma-antibodies, antibody localization was found to be distinct from nonspecific localization confined to the pattern of tumor cell distribution (Mahaley *et al.*, 1965).

C. [131]I STUDIES IN ANIMALS

Larvae and adults of *Drosophila gibberosa* accumulated ^{131}I, which was added to the food, only in the chitin containing exoskeleton. The iodine is probably in association with a protein complex. The capacity to link iodine to a protein complex in the exoskeleton is characteristic not only of *D. gibberosa*, but of other arthropods as well (Wheeler, 1947).

Gorbman (1941) and Gorbman and Creaser (1942) studied the accumulation of radioactive iodine by the endostyle of larval lampreys, which is assumed to be an organ with the function of the thyroid. A special cell type (type III) was found to be the principal loci of iodine accumulation, less uptake was found in cell type V, and in the other cell types iodine uptake was negligible or absent. The adult elasmobranch fishes can concentrate iodine in their thyroids, as shown by Lin and Goldberg (1951).

Chavin (1956) demonstrated with ^{131}I that the functional thyroid in goldfish (*Carassius auratus* L.) occurred in the throat and in the lymphoidal pronephric remnants, the head kidneys. The throat kidney revealed a more rapid rate of iodine uptake than the head kidney. Iodine accumulation was inhibited by hypophysectomy, application of thyroxine, cortisone, and thiouracil as well as by stress, and it was increased by the administration of thyrotropin.

D. ^{131}I Studies in Plants

Roche and Yagi (1952) studied ^{131}I uptake in algae and found that most of the accumulated iodine remains in the state of inorganic iodide, and only a very small part is contained in the protein.

II. Sulfur-35

The application of ^{35}S for autoradiographic studies of metabolic processes in the cell is confined to two main problems: One group of investigations employs ^{35}S-labeled amino acids for studying protein metabolism, while the other group employs sulfate-^{35}S in order to examine ^{35}S incorporation into sulfomucopolysaccharides. Since the results of the first group agree with those obtained using tritiated amino acids, and in addition better resolution of the latter label provides more details, these studies will be described in Chapter 6 (dealing with the protein metabolism) together with those made with tritiated amino acids.

A. Sulfomucopolysaccharide Metabolism in the Animal

Most of the applied sulfate-^{35}S is quickly excreted by the mammalian organism. Only a small part is incorporated into sulfomucopolysaccharides, and none into proteins. Plants and microorganism, however, are capable of synthesizing amino acids from inorganic sulfate, thus allowing protein metabolism to be followed by application of sulfate-^{35}S (Howard and Pelc, 1951a,b; Pelc and Howard, 1952). Mammalian cartilage, connective tissue, vessel walls, basal membranes, and mucous substances contain chondroitin sulfate or mucoitin sulfate as sulfopolysaccharide fraction of muco- or glucoproteins. Autoradiographic studies of sulfate-^{35}S incorporation into different cells of the mammalian organism provide a method for investigating the turnover of the sulfomucopolysaccharides. Boström (1953) compared the turnover of sulfomucopolysaccharides by autoradiography and quantitative chemistry. The results of both methods were in good agreement.

1. Cartilage

Sulfate-^{35}S is incorporated into the different types of cartilage, which remain radioactive when the ^{35}S activity has disappeared from all other tissues of the organism (Amprino, 1954b, 1955a,b,c; Bélanger, 1954a; Boström, 1953; Boström *et al.*, 1952; Campbell, 1951; Campbell and Persson, 1951; Cohen and Delassue, 1959; Davies and Young, 1954a; Dziewiatkowski, 1951b, 1952a,b, 1953, 1954a,b, 1958; Kutzim, 1962; Pellerin, 1961; Pelc and Glücksmann, 1955; Odeblad and Boström, 1952). By chemical analysis it could be shown that most of the sulfate-^{35}S is incorporated into chondroitinsulfuric acid (Dziewiatkowski, 1951a; Boström, 1952, 1953; Larsson, 1960). Furthermore, the intensity of sulfate-^{35}S incorporation corresponds to the localization of stainable sulfomucopolysaccharides (Amprino, 1954b).

The *epiphyseal cartilage* of the long bones shows the most intensive sulfate-^{35}S incorporation (Bélanger, 1954a; Dziewiatkowski, 1951b,c, 1952a,b, 1953; Davies and Young, 1954a; Pellerin, 1961; Kutzim, 1962). Short-term experiments demonstrated that labeling of chondroitinsulfuric acid occurs most actively in the hypertrophic proliferating columnar cells whereas the vacuolized columnar cartilage cells incorporate it to a much smaller degree (Bélanger, 1954a; Dziewiatkowski, 1951b; [Engfeldt and Westerborn, 1960). With increasing time, the sulfomucopolysaccharides are passed on to the intercellular substance, and the ^{35}S activity shifts more and more to the zone of ossification. In mouse, rat, and rabbit ^{35}S activity is found within the cartilage islands surrounded with bone trabeculas 7 days after injection of sulfate-^{35}S, and after 15 days it is localized in the bone trabeculas of the metaphysis (Engfeldt and Westerborn, 1960).

Sulfate-^{35}S incorporation into *hyaline cartilage* is less intensive than into epiphyseal cartilage, but the former shows higher incorporation than the fibrous joint cartilage. The mature chondrocytes of the periphery of hyaline cartilage synthesize sulfomucopolysaccharides more actively than the immature chondrocytes of the perichondrium and the subperichondral region. With increasing time the labeled substance is passed on to the intercellular substance (Pelc and Glücksmann, 1955).

In vitro experiments with human cartilage tissue also showed intracellular ^{35}S incorporation into chondroitinsulfuric acid of the chondrocytes (Collins and Meachim, 1961; Meachim and Collins, 1962; Wolfe and Vickery, 1964). Comparison of turnover rates of sulfomucopolysaccharides in cartilage from young and old animals showed decreasing turnover rates with increasing age (Dziewiatkowski, 1954b; Hauss *et al.*, 1960). No ^{35}S incorporation could be found in degenerating cartilage (Bélanger, 1954a).

Larsson (1960, 1962a,b) studied the localization and metabolism of sulfomucopolysaccharides in connection with the development of the secondary palate in mice autoradiographically. He found very active metabolism of sulfomucopolysaccarides in the fibroblast zone and concluded that the sulfomucopolysaccharides give the ground substance of the palatine shelves the ability to undergo changes in shape, a prerequisite for closure of the secondary palate.

The synthesis of sulfomucopolysaccharides is not influenced by X-rays (Odeblad and Ziliotto, 1955) but is considerably inhibited by high doses of vitamin A (McElligott, 1962; Fell *et al.*, 1956) and cortisone (Boström and Odeblad, 1953b; Layton, 1951b; Kowalewski, 1958; Larsson, 1962c). Liver extracts, on the other hand, have a distinct stimulating effect on ^{35}S incorporation. Detailed studies concerning the influence of hormones on the turnover of polysaccharides in connective tissue were performed by Dziewiatkowski (1964).

2. Bones

Tonna and Cronkite (1959) found considerable incorporation of ^{35}S into osteoblasts, although these cells do not show a metachromatic staining reaction. The authors assume that the chondroitinsulfuric acid is quickly passed on to the preosseal substance, where it reacts as a binding agent between the collagen and the apatite crystals. There is a proportionality between incorporation of sulfate-^{35}S and growth (Dziewiatkowski, 1954b); with increasing age sulfate-^{35}S incorporation decreases (Tonna and Cronkite, 1960). A similar effect is caused by growth-inhibiting substances. Autoradiographic studies showed that thiouracil, thyroidectomy, or treatment with ^{131}I as well as Mg depletion result in an inhibition of sulfate-^{35}S incorporation (Boström, 1953; Boström and Jorpes, 1954; Boström and Mansson, 1953; Dziewiatkowski, 1957; Bélanger, 1958). Inversely, sodium fluoride leads to increased synthesis of chondroitinsulfuric acid in cartilage and bones of growing animals (Bélanger *et al.*, 1957). It could be shown by autoradiography that there was no increased sulfate-^{35}S incorporation into callous tissue in bone fractures within the first week. The incorporation was double that of the normal after 3 weeks and back to normal again after 8 weeks (Duthie and Barker, 1955). Also, in the case of fracture, the ^{35}S incorporation occurs intracellularly in osteoblasts and osteoclasts (Tonna, 1960b).

3. Connective Tissue

According to the content of chondroitinsulfuric acid and hyaluronic acid in connective tissue, relatively intensive sulfate-^{35}S incorporation into connective tissue of the different locations was found (Bélanger, 1954b; Boström, 1953; Layton, 1951a; Boström and Odeblad, 1953a; Boström and Jorpes, 1954; Odeblad and Boström, 1952, 1953a,b). In the cutis, the ^{35}S activity was relatively equally distributed (Boström *et al.*,

1953). Incorporation into the media predominated in the walls of large vessels, contrasting to the less intensive ^{35}S activity in the intima and adventitia (Boström, 1953; Boström and Odeblad, 1953a; Duthie and Barker, 1955; Odeblad and Boström, 1952, 1953b). In general there was a proportionality between the intensity of sulfate-^{35}S uptake and the size of the vessel (Bélanger, 1954b). Kunz and Braselmann (1965) found a significantly higher incorporation rate of [35]SO_4 into the aorta thoracica ascendens than into the aorta thoracica descendens and the aorta abdominalis of rats. In all segments of the aorta, the highest sulfate-^{35}S incorporation occurred in the inner third of the media, the lowest in the outer third. Whole-body irradiation with 500 R caused an initial increase and a subsequent decrease of sulfomucopolysaccharide synthesis as well as an accelerated catabolism.

Corresponding to the conditions in the cartilage, the incorporation into connective tissue occurs intracellularly into fibroblasts and also into fibrocytes with a later transfer to the intercellular substance. The incorporation rate was higher in young animals and decreased with increasing age (Mancini and de Lustig, 1954; Mancini et al., 1961).

The incorporation of sulfate-^{35}S in atherosclerotic processes was studied by Buck (1955) and Hauss and Junge-Hülsing (1961). Increased incorporation into media and intima plaques was found; and since the ^{35}S activity was highest in fibroblasts, synthesis of chondroitinsulfuric acid was assumed to occur in fibroblasts.

Increased sulfate-^{35}S incorporation was found in the course of inflammatory processes (Drenckhahn and Meissner, 1956), in granulation tissue (Oppenheimer et al., 1960), in the environment of tumor transplants (Harwood et al., 1961), and also after administration of vitamin C (Dziewiatkowski, 1958), while in scurvy the uptake of ^{35}S into sulfomucopolysaccharides was disturbed (Kodicek and Loewi, 1955). Similar to the results in cartilage, cortisone leads to an inhibition of sulfate-^{35}S incorporation (Boström, 1953; Dziewiatkowski, 1964).

Synthesis of chondroitin sulfate B., heparitin sulfate, and keratosulfate in cirrhotic septa was ascertained by combined methods of staining, differential enzyme digestion, and autoradiography in experimental liver cirrhosis of rats (Rubin, 1966).

4. Other Tissues

Sulfate-^{35}S is incorporated into the epidermis epithelium of adult animals (Boström et al., 1953), into the outer layer of the hair root sheets (Montagna and Hill, 1957), and into the epithelium of tongue and prestomach (Oehlert, 1968).

High sulfate-^{35}S uptake was found in mast cells of the connective tissue in the whole organism (Boström *et al.*, 1953; Bélanger, 1954b; Duthie and Barker, 1955; Jorpes *et al.*, 1953; Roth *et al.*, 1963; Sacerdote and Pennisi, 1965). An activity maximum in the mast cells was observed 6–48 hours after sulfate-^{35}S injection, depending on the age of the animal.

Some bone marrow cells like megacaryocytes of hamster (Bélanger, 1954b) incorporate sulfate-^{35}S *in vivo* and *in vitro* (Dziewiatkowski, 1958). Concentration of ^{35}S was observed in megacaryocytes and platelets of guinea pigs as well as in fibroblasts of healing wounds (Upton and Odell, 1956). Lajtha *et al.* (1953) found ^{35}S-uptake in myeloic cells of human bone marrow cultures; but the chemical status of the ^{35}S-labeled substance which was found not to be sulfomucopolysaccharides remained unknown.

In general ^{35}S-uptake by liver, kidney, pancreas, and the central nervous system is insignificant. Also, tumor cells of connective tissue tumors did not show any considerable ^{35}S-uptake.

Dziewiatkowski (1958) has summarized the investigations concerning sulfate-^{35}S incorporation into *embryonic tissues*. ^{35}S-uptake into embryos depends on the development of the fetus. In the beginning of the fetal life ^{35}S-uptake is small. With increasing time and differentiation ^{35}S-incorporation increases and becomes related to special tissues, whereby mesenchymal tissues are preferred (neural tube, heart valves) (Friberg and Ringertz, 1954, 1956). Later on ^{35}S-uptake into cartilage predominates and exceeds that of the mother, while ^{35}S-uptake in the gut is higher in the mother than in the fetus (Boström and Odeblad, 1953a; Dziewiatkowski, 1953). At the end of fetal life sulfate-^{35}S uptake is highest in the columnar cells of the epiphyseal cartilage.

5. Mucus Secreting Cells

Intensive sulfate-^{35}S incorporation occurs in the different mucus-secreting cells of the gastrointestinal tract, which produce sulfur-containing mucous substances (Boström, 1953; Bélanger, 1954b; Davies and Young, 1954b; Jennings and Florey, 1956; Dziewiatkowski, 1958; Odeblad and Boström, 1952; Oehlert, 1968; Roth *et al.*, 1963; Holland and Nimitz, 1964). High uptake of sulfate-^{35}S was found in the mucous epithelia of the salivary glands, while the epithelia of the serous parts showed only insignificant ^{35}S-uptake. A few hours after sulfate-^{35}S is injected, the foveolae of the gastric mucous membrane showed intensive ^{35}S incorporation, while the superficial epithelia and the basal regions of the glands incorporated much less activity. Within the goblet cells, ^{35}S was first localized in the supranuclear or Golgi region before it was distributed throughout the intracellular mucin. Later the mucus on the surface contained considerable ^{35}S activity. This shifting of the ^{35}S activity was explained by the movement of the cells from the foveolae to the surface.

Also, goblet cells of the intestine and colon had high sulfate-^{35}S uptake, Here, also, shifting of the ^{35}S activity to the surface occurred within 12 hours by movement of the cells to the surface (Dziewiatkowski, 1958; Jennings and Florey, 1956; Oehlert, 1968).

Within single cells sulfate-^{35}S incorporation occurred first in the basal region of the cells and then extended over the entire cytoplasm.

B. [35]S Studies in Plants

Since plant tissues are able to synthesize sulfur-containing amino acids from sulfate-^{35}S, ^{35}S-activity uptake is at least a partial measure for amino acid synthesis, i.e., protein synthesis.

Harrison *et al.* (1944) studied ^{35}S uptake in wheat. They found relatively equal distribution within leaves and the most intensive accumulation in the grains. Hofmann and Süss (1954) followed the ^{35}S uptake in the different growth phases of potatoes, beans, and corn. In young plants all tissues were active after 5 hours, and the ^{35}S activity was mainly found in the intercostal regions. Penetration of the ^{35}S activity in older plants took 12 hours. Chromatographic examination showed that the ^{35}S label was bound to methionine. For a microautoradiographic study of ^{35}S activity distribution in the intact bean root, see Biddulph (1967).

Howard and Pelc (1951a,b) and Pelc and Howard (1952) studied the ^{35}S sulfate incorporation into the root tips of *Vicia faba*. Cells in mitosis showed ^{35}S labeled proteins in their chromosomes. From similar experiments in anthers of *Tradescantia* and *Lilium longiflorum*, Taylor and Taylor (1953) concluded that there is continuous protein synthesis in the cell nucleus which is increased during the DNA synthesis phase. Scheuermann (1964) found that under comparable conditions methionine-^{35}S was incorporated into the root tip cells of *Vicia faba* 8 times as fast as sulfate-[35]S.

III. Phosphorus-32

A summary of the use of ^{32}P in studies of *nucleic acid metabolism* is given in Chapter 4, which treats in detail studies of the DNA metabolism using tritiated nucleic acid precursors.

A. Formation and Mineralization of Bones and Teeth

Except those ^{32}P studies concerning incorporation into DNA, ^{32}P has been used as a label for investigating the formation and mineralization of bones and teeth.

Percival and Leblond (1948), Leblond *et al.* (1950), and Leblond and Bélanger (1946) studied the ^{32}P uptake in bones and teeth and found a rapid entry and deposition at the ossification points of the bones of newborn rats and mice, an observation suggesting that the bony structures are constantly being renewed at a rapid rate. Tracing the fate of the new bone, the diaphysis of tibia and humerus revealed a triple origin: periostal in its midportion, endosteal nearer to the epiphyseal plates, and endochondral immediately below the epiphyseal plates. Exchange behavior of young bones and teeth *in vitro* was comparable to *in vivo* conditions. Young normal tissue exchanged ^{32}P at a greater rate than older tissues, growing bone more than normal bone, and in adult human teeth cementum exchanged more than dentine, and dentine more than enamel (Bélanger, 1953). These findings were confirmed by Engfeldt et al. (1952) and Engfeldt (1953), who found that young Haversian systems of the bones of young dogs have the highest ^{32}P uptake, while with increasing age the amount of mineral salts approaches a maximum, and ^{32}P uptake becomes very low. Furthermore, ^{32}P uptake in the different bone structures was the same under *in vivo* and *in vitro* conditions. In weanling pigs Comar et al. (1952) distinguished bone regions of periosteal origin by sharp autoradiographic images with relatively slow deposition and slow removal from the regions of endochondral origin with diffuse images and rapid deposition and removal. Amprino (1952a) studied the *in vitro* uptake of ^{32}P into bones of young dogs and reported high ^{32}P uptake into the less calcified intercellular substances. High ^{32}P concentration in the callus of healing bones was observed by Ruf and Philipp (1950, 1951) and Ruf (1955). Also, Wilkinson and Leblond (1953) observed high ^{32}P uptake in the trabeculae of the new bone 2–4 days after fracture.

In birds Smith et al. (1957) found the ^{32}P uptake in marrow-containing bones to be higher than in pneumatized bones and concluded that the presence of bone marrow has an influence on the phosphate exchange. Vitamin D intensified the phosphate-^{32}P metabolism of the bones (Shimotori and Morgan, 1943), while parathyroid hormone was found to decrease the renewal rate of bone phosphate in young animals and to increase that of old animals (Engfeldt and Zetterström, 1954).

Uptake of ^{32}P into the different dental structures of rats, hamsters, and monkeys has been studied by Bélanger and Leblond (1950), Bélanger (1951, 1952a,b, 1953), and Sognnaes and Shaw (1952). In the dentine a thin band first appeared near the pulp in autoradiograms and ascended to the area of the dentinoenamel junction while slowly decreasing. The ability of the enamel tissue to deposit ^{32}P increased to a maximum with age and maturation and then decreased rapidly. Ameloblasts and odontoblasts showed a slight concentration of ^{32}P.

B. ^{32}P AS A LABEL FOR PARTICULATE CHROMIUM COMPOUNDS

Injection of particulate chromic phosphate containing ^{32}P has been used for studying uptake by cells of the reticuloendothelial system of mice,

I. General Aspects of the Use of Thymidine

A. THYMIDINE AS A SPECIFIC PRECURSOR FOR DNA SYNTHESIS

A very useful tool was found for the study of DNA synthesis when Reichard and Estborn injected ^{15}N-labeled thymidine into rats in 1951 and discovered thymidine to be a specific precursor of DNA. Friedkin et al. (1956) and McQuade et al. (1956a) administered ^{14}C-labeled thymidine to chick embryos and onion root tips, respectively, and showed that the labeled thymidine was a specific precursor of the DNA-thymidine with negligible diversion of radioactivity to any other component of DNA and with practically no incorporation into RNA. On the other hand, thymine-2-^{14}C was not incorporated into DNA. This corresponded to the findings of Plentl and Schoenheimer (1944), who used thymine-^{15}N, and was confirmed in more recent studies by Crathorn and Shooter (1960), Rubini et al. (1962), and Zajicek et al. (1963) using thymidine-^{3}H.

1. Incorporation of Labeled Thymidine into the Nucleus

Great progress was made in the use of thymidine in autoradiography when tymidine labeling with tritium was accomplished by Hughes (1957), Taylor et al. (1957), Verly and Hunebelle (1957), and Verly et al. (1958a,b). The specificity of thymidine and the high autoradiographic resolution of tritium (see Chapter 1, Section IV, B, 2), has made this compound a very frequently used tool in the investigation of DNA metabolism and all related problems of cell proliferation. Autoradiographic pictures of cells labeled with thymidine-^{3}H show a very distinct labeling of the cell nucleus or even of single chromosomes, with almost no scattering of the grains over the border of these cell structures. With regard to autoradiographic studies the possibility was considered that minute amounts of radioactivity in RNA of the fixed tissue or in the form of mono-, di-, and triphosphate or other substances may simulate DNA labeling. However, Ficq and Pavan (1947) and Amano et al. (1959) were able to show that removal of DNA by deoxyribonuclease treatment of the sections completely eliminated the autoradiographic reaction over nuclei after injection of thymidine-^{3}H, but ribonuclease had no effect.

2. Incorporation of Labeled Thymidine into the Cytoplasm

Because of the known specificity of labeled thymidine as a precursor of DNA and the limitation of the label to the nucleus observed in most autoradiograms, incorporation of labeled thymidine into the cytoplasm reported by several investigators at first was accepted with hesitation and scepticism and was regarded to be due to faulty techniques.

However, cytoplasmic incorporation of thymidine-^{3}H was definitely shown in *Lilium longiflorum*, where transfer of labeled DNA from the nucleus to the cytoplasm could be excluded since cytoplasmic labeling occurred in cells whose nuclei were not labeled (Takats, 1960). Paper chromatographic analysis of the extract of this labeled cytoplasmic substance showed that some of the activity was due to degradation products like BAIBA (β-amino-iso-butyric acid) and BUIBA (β-ureido-iso-butyric acid), but this did not account for all the cytoplasmic label (Takats and Smellie, 1963).

Cytoplasmic incorporation of thymidine-³H has been observed also in several unrelated strains of *Amoeba proteus*, although there was no information on the chemical nature of the labeled substance beyond its sensitivity to deoxyribonuclease. Incorporation occurs in the presence as well as in the absence of the nucleus (Plaut and Sagan, 1958; Plaut, 1960). A correlation between the location of microscopically detectable nucleic acid-containing granules and the acid-insoluble and deoxyribonuclease-sensitive labeled molecules suggests that cytoplasmic DNA synthesis in *Amoeba proteus* occurs in association with these particles which obviously multiply intracellularly (Rabinovitch and Plaut, 1962a,b). By application of electron microscopic autoradiography, these particles in the cytoplasm were identified as sites of incorporated DNA precursors; this supports the conclusion that these particles are self-duplicating in the cytoplasm (Wolstenholme and Plaut, 1964).

In the cytoplasm of chick embryo fibroblasts cultivated *in vitro*, thymidine-³H incorporation was observed close to certain modified mitochondria in which DNA was detected by the Feulgen reaction and deoxyribonuclease treatment. It is believed that the cytoplasmic DNA does not originate in the nucleus, but is synthesized by these modified mitochondria and may enter the nucleus later on (Chèvremont *et al.*, 1959, 1960; Chèvremont and Baeckeland, 1960; Chèvremont, 1961, 1962; Meyer and Ris, 1967; Meyer, 1967).

Biochemical investigations showed too that there is incorporation of ¹⁴C- or ³H-labeled thymidine into DNA of a mitochondrial fraction in liver, kidney, heart, and brain of the rat (Neubert *et al.*, 1965).

Incorporation of thymidine-³H into the cytoplasm of *Tetrahymena pyriformis* was found by several investigators (Scherbaum, 1960; Parsons, 1964, 1965; Stone *et al.*, 1964; Stone and Miller, 1964, 1965; Cameron, 1966). In the meantime it was shown that most of this cytoplasmic DNA is localized in mitochondria (Gibor and Granick, 1964). Furthermore, it could be demonstrated that this cytoplasmic DNA is stable and conserved during the growth and proliferation of the cells (Stone and Miller, 1965; Parsons, 1964). Thymidine-³H is incorporated continuously into mitochondria of *Tetrahymena pyriformis*, i.e., also at periods in the cell cycle, when nuclei are not synthesizing DNA (Parsons, 1965). These findings were confirmed by Cameron (1966) and Guttes et al. (1967). However, Cameron (1966) concluded from his experiments that there is some relationship between the synthesis of nuclear DNA and that of cytoplasmic DNA, since there is an increase in cytoplasmic DNA synthesis during the initial stage of DNA synthesis in the macronucleus and during DNA synthesis in the micronucleus. On the other hand the author admits that the increased thymidine-³H incorporation into cytoplasmic DNA may be caused by a change in the precursor pool. General occurrence of mitochondrial DNA in plant and animal cells was described by Nass el al. (1965).

Thymidine-³H labeling of chloroplasts in the cytoplasm of *Acetabularia* and *Euplotes* as well as *Spyrogyra*, young leaves of *Nicotiana rustica*, marine algae, and meristem cells of *Sinapis* and maize has also been reported (Brachet, 1958; Stocking and Gifford, 1959; Wollgiehn and Mothes, 1963, 1964; Lima-de-Faria and Moses, 1964; Steffensen and Sheridan, 1965; Bernier and Jensen, 1966; see also Meyer, 1966). The latter observation was brought into connection with the increasing evidence that chloroplasts contain DNA. In recent studies in synchronized *Euglena gracilis* using ³H-labeled adenine (thymidine is not incorporated into DNA of *Euglena gracilis*), Cook (1966) showed that incorporation of adenine-³H occurs during all phases of the cell cycle. Increased synthesis of cytoplasmic, preferably chloroplastic, DNA was observed shortly after the division of chloroplasts and immediately before the beginning of chloroplast division. The latter coincides with the S phase of the nuclear DNA. The author correlates both S phases of the cytoplasmic DNA with two different kinds of chloroplastic DNA: one that controls the morphogenesis of the chloroplastic DNA including the synthesis of chlorophyll, and another that initiates the replication of the chloroplasts.

Whether all cytoplasmic labeling with thymidine-³H can be defined as labeling of cytoplasmic DNA structures, which are diluted too much to be Feulgen positive, cannot yet be decided. From recent experiments Bryant (1966) concluded that tritium from thymidine-methyl-³H is incorporated into the protein of the cell (mouse). Transfer by tritiated water was excluded; however, transmethylation was assumed to be the transfer mechanism by which the tritium of degradation products of thymidine is bound to certain amino acids. Apart from a diffuse labeling of the cytoplasm—in the exocrine pancreas preferably of the zymogen granules—nuclear protein was labeled too, especially in those nuclei that contained labeled DNA. Labeling of nuclear protein amounts to less than 2.5% of the whole tritium in the nucleus. Lima-de-Faria (1965) also reported that thymidine-^{3}H is incorporated into cytoplasmic proteins of *Agapanthus*.

Summarizing all those observations mentioned, it can be said that the cytoplasmic labeling observed in some instances does not impair the value of thymidine as a specific precursor in DNA synthesis studies.

B. METABOLISM OF THYMIDINE AND THYMIDINE POOL

1. Metabolism of Thymidine

Thymidine did not seem to be a naturally occurring intermediate metabolic substance in the synthesis of DNA in the cell. Schneider (1956) did not find any free thymidine in rat tissue. On the other hand, experiments by Reichard and Estborn (1951) indicated that the rat seems to have an enzyme system which irreversibly transforms deoxycytidine into thymidine. This corresponds to the findings that an increased amount of deoxyribonucleosides is found in rapidly proliferating tissue, e.g., regenerating liver, tumor tissue (Schneider, 1957; Schneider and Brownell, 1957; Rotherham and Schneider, 1958). In the cell, thymidylate is synthesized by phosphorylation of deoxyuridine and by further methylation of uridylic acid. Biosynthesis of DNA via thymidine triphosphate, including the step where thymidine enters synthesis, is shown in the accompanying scheme (modified from Kara and Weil, 1967).

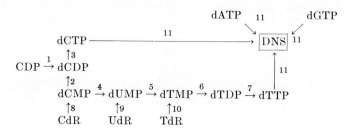

Key to abbreviation and reactions in scheme

CDP	= cytidine diphosphate	1, CDP reductase
dCMP	= deoxycytidine monophosphate	2, dCMP kinase
dCDP	= deoxycytidine diphosphate	3, dCDP kinase
dCTP	= deoxycytidine triphosphate	4, dCMP deaminase
dUMP	= deoxyuridine monophosphate	5, dTMP synthetase
dTMP	= thymidine monophosphate	6, dTMP kinase
dTDP	= thymidine diphosphate	7, dTDP kinase
dTTP	= thymidine triphosphate	8, Cytidine kinase
dATP	= deoxyadenosine triphosphate	9, Uridine kinase
dGTP	= deoxyguanosine triphosphate	10, Thymidine kinase
CdR	= deoxycytidine	11, DNA polymerase
UdR	= deoxyuridine	
TdR	= thymidine	

The enzymes necessary for the different synthetic steps have been discovered and partly isolated during recent years. Weissman *et al.* (1960) were able to isolate from extracts of Ehrlich ascites tumor cells the kinases responsible for the formation of thymidine 5-monophosphate, -diphosphate, and -triphosphate from thymidine. Those enzymes were also found in high concentration in rabbit tissue, especially in thymus and bone marrow. Thymidine 5-monophosphate and diphosphate kinases appear in this sequence in regenerating rat liver after hepatectomy, at a time prior to the onset of DNA synthesis (Weissman *et al.*, 1960). In fibroblast cultures from mouse strain NCTC those kinases were observed during the early growth phase. Before growth stops, the activity of the enzymes declines (Weissman *et al.*, 1960). Similar results were obtained in LM mouse fibroblasts by Kit *et al.* (1965). Littlefield (1966) interprets the step-by-step increase of thymidine kinase activity in synchronized mouse fibroblast cultures as synthesis of further enzymes. The first increase in enzyme synthesis precedes and accompanies the first wave of DNA synthesis. The second increase is correlated with the second DNA synthesis period, i.e., it occurs after one cell cycle. On the other hand, no difference in the enzymatic activity in *Tetrahymena* was found, no matter whether the cultures were in the growth phase or in the resting phase (Shoup *et al.*, 1966). Ives *et al.* (1963) studied these thymidine and thymidylate kinases and their properties biochemically (see also Reichard *et al.*, 1961; Bresnick and Karjala, 1964; Green *et al.*, 1964; Okazaki and Kornberg, 1964).

Thymidine is rapidly catabolized to thymine in the cell. The cell is able to reduce thymine to dihydrothymine which is further degraded to BUIBA (β-ureido-isobutyric acid). A rough scheme of the single steps in this thymidine degradation follows.

thymidine → thymine → dihydrothymine → β-ureidoisobutyric acid

$\downarrow$

β-aminoisobutyric acid

Phosphorylase is necessary for the transformation of thymidine to thymine. Marsh and Perry (1964a) found that normal human leukocytes have a higher concentration of thymidine phosphorylase than do cells of chronic myeloid leukemia, and they assume that the lesser thymidine phosphorylase activity is more a function of the cellular immaturity than a property of the leukemic cell. The same authors (Marsh and Perry, 1964b) found that both cell types are able to catabolize thymine to dihydrothymine and further to BUIBA, but that no further degradation to BAIBA occurs. Comparing the incorporation of thymidine and deoxycytidine monophosphate into DNA of human leukocytes, an inhibition of thymidine incorporation was found after 1 hour of incubation

(Cooper and Milton, 1964). This is due to the fact that the degradation products of thymidine, namely, thymine and dihydrothymine, cannot be incorporated into DNA, whereas of the degradation products of dCMP (deoxycytidine, deoxyuridine, and uracil), only uracil cannot serve as a DNA precursor.

That thymidine is catabolized without delay and very rapidly is shown by the appearance of thymidine degradation products in the culture medium as soon as 5 min after addition of thymidine. This also suggests that thymidine and its metabolic substrates pass through the cell membrane very quickly. The transformation of thymidine to thymine is a much more rapid process than the incorporation into DNA, as was shown in Landschütz ascites cells by Zajicek et al. (1963). By incubation in increasing concentrations of cold thymine the conversion of thymidine to thymine was suppressed so that an increased incorporation of thymidine-^{3}H into DNA of the ascites cells was achieved. Lang et al. (1966a) also reported that after incubation of HeLa cells for more than 48 hours the thymidine-^{3}H in the incubation medium sharply decreased while there was a correspondingly sharp increase of thymine-^{3}H; this thymine is later degraded to BUIBA. Only traces of dihydrothymine, and no thymidylic acid or other phosphorylated products or BAIBA or tritium water, were found. Only 13–15% of the thymidine-^{3}H activity originally present in the medium was incorporated into the DNA of the cells. These experiments suggest that—as in the animal organism—only a small part of the applied thymidine-^{3}H is incorporated into DNA while most of it is catabolized. See also Rubini et al. (1966).

For more details of thymidine degradation see Fink et al. (1956a,b), Hughes et al. (1958), Potter (1959), Rubini et al. (1960, 1961), Steel (1962), Lark (1963), Michelson (1963), Chang and Looney (1965), and Stewart et al. (1965).

2. Thymidine Pool

Closely related to the use of thymidine-^{3}H as a DNA precursor is the question of the thymidine pool in the cell nuclei. In recent years several authors have studied the size of the thymidine pool in certain animal organs or in cultured cells, either by application of different amounts of thymidine-^{3}H (or dilution of thymidine-^{3}H with cold thymidine, respectively) or by microbiological or microchemical determinations of the nucleosides or nucleotides. The results are summarized in Table IV.

In recent experiments Stone et al. (1965) have studied the relationship between the nuclear thymidine-^{3}H pool or its derivatives, respectively, and the DNA synthesis in Tetrahymena pyriformis, using a special autoradiographic method that makes it possible to demonstrate water-soluble

TABLE IV

Concentration of Thymidine and Thymine Nucleotides in Different Organs of Several Animal Species

I Animal	II Organ	III[c] Original	IV μMoles/g (wet wt.)	V μMoles/mg DNA	VI Method	VII References
Mouse, 34 g	Ileum, crypts	10^6–10^7 molecules per cell	1.6×10^{-3} – 1.6×10^{-2}	2×10^{-4} – 2×10^{-3}	Appl. ³H-TDR	Steward et al. (1965)
Mouse 5–10 weeks old	—	0.04 – 0.05 μmoles[a] per mouse	2.5×10^{-3}	—	Appl. ³H-TDR and IDU	Hughes et al. (1964)
Mouse, 23 g	Ileum	6.5×10^{-3} μmoles[a] per gram	6.5×10^{-3}	8.3×10^{-4}	Appl. ³H-TDR	Lang et al. (1968)
Rat, 175 g	Spleen	5.74 mμmoles TDR/g 0.62 mμmoles TMP/g 2.50 mμmoles TDP/g 1.45 mμmoles TTP/g	1.03×10^{-2}	$8.8 \times 10^{-4\,b}$	Microbiological and microchemical, respectively	Potter and Nygaard (1963)
Rat, 200 g	Spleen	3.1 μg Thymidylate/g	9.7×10^{-3}	1.0×10^{-3}	Microbiological	Benes et al. (1965)
Rat, 175 g	Thymus	15.63 mμmoles TDR/g 4.29 mμmoles TMP/g 25.4 mμmoles TDP/g 32.3 mμmoles TTP/g	7.76×10^{-2}	$2.9 \times 10^{-3\,b}$	Microbiological and microchemical, respectively	Potter and Nygaard (1963)
Rat, 200 g	Thymus	79 μg thymidylate/g	2.5×10^{-1}	1.1×10^{-2}	Microbiological	Benes et al. (1965)
Rat, 80–120 g	Thymus	0.10 μmoles TMP/g 0.18 μmoles TDP/g 0.39 μmoles TTP/g	6.7×10^{-1}	$2.5 \times 10^{-2\,b}$	Microchemical	Bettendorf et al. (1960)

TABLE IV (*Continued*)

I	II	III[c]	IV	V	VI	VII
Animal	Organ	Original	μMoles/g (wet wt.)	μMoles/mg DNA	Method	References
Rat, 200 g	Liver	0.011 μg thymidylate/g	3.5×10^{-5}	1.6×10^{-5}	Microbio-logical	Benes *et al.* (1965)
Rat, 200 g	Reg. Liver	0.057 μg thymidy-late/g	1.8×10^{-4}	7.2×10^{-5}	Microbio-logical	Benes *et al.* (1965)
Rat	Novikoff-Hepatoma	18.6 μg TDR/100 g	7.7×10^{-4}	1.3×10^{-4} [b]	Microbio-logical and micro-chemical	Schneider (1957)
Dog	Bone marrow *in vitro*	4.5×10^{-3} μmoles per 10^8 cells	—	8.0×10^{-3}	Appl. ^{3}H-TDR	Rubini *et al.* (1962)
Chicken embryo, 0.5 g	—	0.3 μg TDR per embryo	2.5×10^{-3}	1.0×10^{-3} [b]	Appl. ^{3}H-TDR	Friedkin *et al.* (1956)

[a] Sum of thymidine and thymine nucleotides.
[b] Conversion into μmoles/mg DNA, using DNA values by Leslie (1955).
[c] Column III contains the quotations of the original paper. For the purpose of better comparison, the sums of thymidine and thymine nucleotides are recalculated as micromoles per gram wet weight and per milligram of DNA, respectively, in columns IV and V. IDU = 5-iodo-2-deoxyuridine; TDR = thymidine; TMP, TDP, TTP = thymidinemono-, -di- and triphosphate. (Courtesy of Dr. Lang.)

substances within the cell. The authors found that the uptake of thymidine in the cell is confined to the S phase. However, a "soluble" pool of thymidine-³H derivatives exists in those cells from the end of one S phase until the next S phase. This soluble pool does not turn over completely during one S phase. From these findings the authors conclude that the DNA synthesis is initiated and maintained for a short time at the expense of this pool, which was formed during the preceding S phase and that the turnover of this pool stimulates the synthesis of additional phosphorylated precursors. As a consequence of these findings, it may be assumed that the S phase actually starts at an earlier moment than indicated by the uptake of thymidine-³H. An excellent review of thymidine metabolism and cell kinetics was given by Cleaver (1967). See also Feinendegen (1967).

C. Fate of Labeled Thymidine in the Organism; Availability Time

1. Fate of Labeled Thymidine in the Organism

After injection of thymidine-³H, the labeled thymidine is rapidly distributed throughout the whole organism of the animal and is available to the nucleus and cytoplasm of all cells, as was shown by Pelc and Appleton (1965) with autoradiography of water-soluble substances. With this method it could be demonstrated that 15 min after injection of thymidine-³H the nucleus and the cytoplasm of practically all cells in the tissues of the mouse were labeled; after 30 min the autoradiograms were much weaker, and after 24 hours they showed only background effect with the exception of those nuclei that had incorporated thymidine-³H into their DNA.

Rubini et al. (1960) studied the plasma clearance of injected thymidine-³H in man and found the maximum of the plasma ³H activity within 1 min after injection. It accounted for only 10% of the injected ³H activity; i.e., 90% was lost from the blood within the first minute. Further $\frac{9}{10}$ of the initial maximal plasma ³H activity was cleared within the next 4 minutes. From the amount of radioactivity detected in the body excreta, the authors concluded that 1 hour after injection about one-half of the injected thymidine-³H is catabolized to tritiated water, while the rest is incorporated into DNA or converted into other compounds. Steel (1962) pointed out that the nonvolatile activity in the excreta of rats after injection of thymidine-³H accounts for only a few percent of the injected dose, while 40% of the injected dose is converted to tritiated water. Rapid plasma clearance of injected thymidine-³H was also found in hepatectomized rats (Chang and Looney, 1965). There was a sharp decrease in the labeled thymidine during the first 10 min, and after 1 hour practically all the labeled thymidine had disappeared from the blood stream.

In the normal animal organism the liver is responsible for the rapid degradation of thymidine (Potter, 1960). Gerber (1963) studied the degradation of thymidine-^{3}H by the liver in the perfused liver of normal animals and after hepatectomy. Within 30 min after addition of thymidine-^{3}H, half of the radioactivity is converted into tritiated water. The labeled thymidine disappears even faster: 30% of the thymidine present is catabolized during one passage through the liver. Even with a 2000-fold increase of the thymidine concentration, the amount of thymidine catabolized per unit time corresponds approximately to this increased concentration. The ability of the liver to catabolize thymidine is not influenced distinctly by partial hepatectomy. Steel (1962) also reported that thymidine catabolism is not influenced by a 100-fold increase of the thymidine level and that the degree of thymidine degradation is quite well reproducible from animal to animal. Furthermore, perfusion experiments with intestine and kidney as well as the carcass have shown that there is only negligible degradation of thymidine in those organs (Gerber, 1963).

Chang and Looney (1965) also considered the rapid degradation of thymidine to be the dominant biological action of the liver after application of thymidine. Within 2 min after injection two-thirds of the injected labeled thymidine catabolized to thymine and BAIBA appears in the acid-soluble fraction of the liver cells. Comparison of the incorporation of ^{125}I labeled iododeoxyuridine (IDU) into tissues of the mouse after injection into the vena cava on the one hand and into the vena porta on the other has shown that the incorporation into skeleton and intestine of IDU injected via the portal vein was decreased to less than half that of IDU injected via the vena cava. This suggests that over half of the IDU passing through the liver is catabolized there. On the other hand, the uptake of IDU by the liver is only slightly increased after intraportal injection. (Hughes et al. 1964).

Because of the rapid degradation of injected labeled thymidine, the portion of thymidine incorporated into DNA in the organism is very small. There are differing reports about the absolute percentage of labeled thymidine incorporated into DNA. Experiments by Hinrichs et al. (1964) have shown that at doses between 10 and 100/μCi of thymidine-^{3}H (specific activity 6.7 Ci/mmole) per mouse only 8–9% of the injected dose is incorporated into the DNA of the organism. More than 90% is recovered in the acid-soluble fraction, two-thirds as tritiated water and the rest as thymine-^{3}H. Half of the thymidine-^{3}H which is incorporated into DNA, namely about 4%, is used for DNA synthesis in the intestine. Contrary to these findings, Lang et al. (1968) and Hempel (1966a) reported that under the same experimental conditions ~8–10% of the injected thymidine-³H is incorporated into the DNA of the intestine. These authors found that the amount of thymidine incorporated into the DNA of other organs also was 2–3 times greater than reported by Hinrichs et al. (1964), i.e., the entire thymidine-³H activity incorporated into the DNA of the organism is about 20% of the injected thymidine-³H.

The method of injection should presumably have practically no influence on the utilization of thymidine. However, Petersen and Baserga (1964) found that the thymidine-³H activity incorporated into DNA is definitely increased after subcutaneous injection, namely about 30% compared to intravenous and intraperitoneal injection. There was no distinct difference between intravenous and intraperitoneal injection. On the other hand, the different distribution of the water-soluble thymidine in the smooth muscle of the intestine after intravenous and intraperitoneal injection, as shown by Pelc and Appleton (1965), suggests that the method of injection influences the total amount of incorporated thymidine-³H activity at least in some organs. Skougaard and Stewart (1966) compared the effect of intraperitoneal and intramuscular injection of thymidine-³H into mice by counting grains over tongue and crypt epithelia. They found the same grain counts over tongue epithelia after intramuscular and intraperitoneal injection as well as over crypt epithelia after intramuscular injection. On the other hand, crypt epithelia had almost twice the number of grains after intraperitoneal injection. The authors therefore concluded that the uptake of thymidine-³H from the peritoneal cavity into the intestine leads to a higher dose of thymidine-³H in the intestine. Similar conditions were found in Ehrlich ascites tumor-bearing mice by Lang (1967). The DNA of the Ehrlich ascites tumor cells was about 5 times more radioactive after intraperitoneal injection than after subcutaneous injection. The percentage of labeled cells was equal in both cases; however, the intensity of labeling was much stronger after intraperitoneal than after subcutaneous injection. In the case of intraperitoneal injection 20–25% of the injected ³H activity was incorporated into the DNA of the tumor cells, but only 1% into the DNA of the intestine.

Lang et al. (1966a) determined the utilization of thymidine-³H added to the medium in cultured cells. HeLa cells incorporate 7.5% of the added thymidine-³H activity into their DNA during 2 hours' incubation and about 15% after 48 hours.

2. Availability Time

The injected labeled thymidine not only is catabolized very quickly, but also is incorporated into DNA very rapidly. Rubini et al. (1960) found positive autoradiograms of human bone marrow cells as early as

1 min after injection. Estimation of the availability time of thymidine-^{3}H by measuring the curve of increasing average grain counts over cells includes the time from injection of thymidine-^{3}H until water-insoluble and stable DNA is synthesized which is retained by the histological procedure. That means it includes the rapid uptake by the cell—possibly via phosphorylation of thymidine to thymidylic acid (Hughes *et al.*, 1958)—and the state of water-soluble and exchangeable intermediates. The integral availability time determined this way is about 40–60 min with the usually applied amounts of thymidine-^{3}H whereas most of the thymidine-^{3}H is incorporated after 20 min (Hughes *et al.*, 1958; Rubini *et al.*, 1960, 1962; Kisieleski *et al.*, 1961a; Koburg and Maurer, 1962; Cronkite *et al.*, 1962; Potter and Nygaard, 1963; Wegener *et al.*, 1964; Lennartz and Maurer, 1964). Quastler and Sherman (1959) observed a somewhat shorter availability time. According to these authors, half of the maximum values of the grain counts were reached in crypt cells 5 min after intraperitoneal injection, and saturation was reached after 10–20 min.

Recently, Staroscik *et al.* (1964) approached this problem experimentally from another side. They isolated "spontaneous" mammary tumors in mice from circulation by clamping at the time of thymidine-^{3}H injection and measured the uptake of thymidine in the tumor cells as a function of elapsed time before the circulation was reestablished. In contrast to removal of tissue samples and counting average grain numbers over cells, which provide more reliable data for the period immediately after injection, the clamping experiments tend to give better resolution for the later period. The similarity of the results between clamping and removal experiments suggests that, in labeling experiments, *in vivo* conversion time of tritiated thymidine into DNA is relatively short and local storage of thymidine-^{3}H is relatively minor. The only difference between the two kinds of experiments was that after clamping the uptake of thymidine-^{3}H was still significant 40 min after injection.

Also in cell cultures an "availability time" of about 20–40 min was reported. In *in vitro* studies with Landschütz ascites cells, Zajicek *et al.* (1963) found that thymidine-^{3}H incorporation into DNA (retained in the cells after fixation) reached its maximum within the first 20 min. Maximal labeling of human leukemic blood and dog marrow cells *in vitro* was achieved after 40 min; during the first 20 min thymidine-^{3}H seemed to remain as a nucleoside or nucleotide, as shown by exchangeability (Rubini *et al.*, 1962). The rate of incorporation of the precursor into ascites tumor cells decreases with increasing incubation time. After 15 min, half of the precursor is incorporated into DNA, and after 2 hours saturation is achieved, i.e., thymidine uptake into the cells is finished after 1–2 hours of incubation (Crathorn and Shooter, 1960). In contrast to these results and others in HeLa cells, experiments with L-strain cells have shown that a pool of thymidine-³H phosphates with a long biological half-life is formed within these cells during the period of labeling. If cells are allowed to continue growth in a cold medium after they have been labeled, the content of this pool is used as a source of precursors for DNA synthesis. The amount of thymidine-³H activity in precipitable DNA continues to increase up to 3 hours after removal of the label (Cleaver and Holford, 1965). Similar results were obtained by Evans (1964) in *in vitro* experiments with root tips of *Vicia faba*; in these cells, labeled thymidine was found to be still available for incorporation into DNA 40 min after removal of the roots from the thymidine-³H solution. The soluble precursor pool in *Tetrahymena pyriformis*, which is preserved even from one S phase to the next, was already mentioned (Stone et al., 1965).

As shown by these differing results from *in vitro* experiments, availability time may depend entirely on the behavior of the corresponding cell type, i.e., on whether a precursor pool exists or whether thymidine is immediately degraded by the cell.

The short availability time of injected labeled thymidine is another advantage in using this nucleotide as a DNA precursor. It permits a sort of "pulse" labeling even in animal cells *in vivo*. Since the availability time is only a small fraction of the DNA synthesis time, the labeling index (percentage of labeled cells in the whole cell population) can be used for estimating DNA synthesis time or generation time.

D. Relationship between Grain Number per Nucleus and DNA Synthetic Rate

1. Grain Number per Nucleus

In studies of DNA synthesis with thymidine-³H grain numbers per nucleus are often interpreted as the DNA synthetic rate (mass per time unit). Some experimental results supported the assumption that the grain number per nucleus could be a measure of the DNA synthetic rate. Thus, Koburg and Maurer (1962) and Koburg (1963b) found approximately equal grain numbers per nucleus in different mouse tissues after injection of thymidine-³H and assumed that the DNA synthetic rate of these nuclei and, therefore, also the duration of the S phase are very similar. Pilgrim and Maurer (1965) confirmed this assumption by direct measurements. They found concurrent values for the S phase of about 7.5 hours for 27 different cell types of the mouse. On the other hand, a three times longer S phase was found for spermatogonia with corresponding grain counts three times smaller (Hilscher and Maurer, 1962). Similar correlations were reported for the ear epidermis epithelia of the mouse with an S phase lasting about 18 hours and a correspondingly lower grain count (Pilgrim et al., 1966).

Different results were obtained by Wegener et al., (1964) in fetal cells of the rat (day 20 of gestation). While the durations of the S phases were also very similar for 13 different cell types measured with two independent methods, the grain number per nucleus varied by a factor of 2 among the various cell types. In this case, the number of grains per nucleus obviously does not represent the DNA synthetic rate.

2. Percentage of Participation of Labeled Thymidine in DNA Synthesis

The number of grains per nucleus is a measure of the DNA synthesis rate only if the entire physiological DNA synthesis, or the same proportion in all cell types always is replaced by the injected labeled thymidine. Despite the frequent use of thymidine-^{3}H for studies of DNA synthesis no definite knowledge was obtained for a long time about how far the exogenous labeled thymidine replaces the endogenously synthesized thymidine or thymidine phosphate, respectively, in DNA synthesis. Some references in the literature suggested, however, that the participation of the exogenous thymidine in DNA synthesis is minute. According to Rubini et al. (1962), only about 1% of the endogenous thymidine or thymidine phosphate, respectively, is replaced by labeled thymidine during DNA synthesis. Similar values were reported by Stewart et al. (1965). These authors found that less than 1% of the injected labeled thymidine is incorporated into the DNA of the mouse. However, corresponding experimental results were not quoted.

Lang et al. (1966b, 1968) have determined experimentally the percentage of participation of thymidine-^{3}H in the DNA-thymine synthesis in the ileum of the mouse over a limited time period. In biochemical experiments these authors measured the radioactivity of the thymidine-^{3}H incorporated into DNA as a function of different amounts of injected thymidine. As shown in Fig. 8, the activity of thymidine-^{3}H incorporated into DNA increases linearly with the injected activity within the limits of the usually injected doses (0.0156–ca. 1.56 μg of thymidine-^{3}H per gram of mouse). With higher thymidine-^{3}H activities the curve becomes flatter. As shown in Fig. 8, the proportion of the entire DNA-thymidylic acid synthesis replaced by the injected exogenous thymidine-^{3}H reaches only from 0.1% up to a few percent (for thymidine-^{3}H activities usually applied in studies of DNA synthesis). In this region the rise in the curve under 45 degrees shows that these doses lie within the tracer region, i.e., they are small compared to the pool present in the cell.

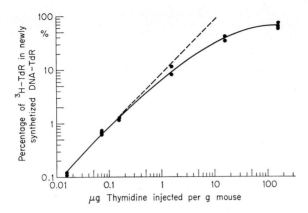

FIG. 8. Percentage of participation of [3]H- or ^{14}C-labeled thymidine in DNA-thymine synthesized during the experimental period (30 min) as a function of the amount of thymidine applied. (From Lang *et al.*, 1968.)

In the same experiments mean grain counts over nuclei of various tissues were determined on autoradiograms as a function of different amounts of labeled thymidine injected. The results show that the mean grain counts in the tissues examined (liver, kidney, epidermis, salivary gland, and ileum) are very similar (variations of about a factor of 2 only) and that the grain number curves have the same shape as the biochemically measured one in Fig. 8. This means that the proportion of participation of the exogenous thymidine-^{3}H should be of the same order of magnitude in these tissues as that measured biochemically for the ileum (Fig. 8).

Since the endogenous thymidylate is replaced only to such a small degree by the exogenous thymidine, the number of grains per nucleus can only be considered as a measure of the DNA synthesis rate, if the same proportion is replaced in the different cell types. In other words, the same proportion must be replaced in the different nuclei and also within one and the same nucleus during the course of the entire DNA synthesis phase in normal and treated or irradiated animals, respectively. As shown by the experiments mentioned above, this seems to be true for a number of cell types in the normal animal.

Differences in the relative participation of the injected labeled thymidine in DNA synthesis can be caused by different processes; utilization of the applied thymidine can be changed on the one hand; and on the other, the percentage of participation of the exogenous thymidine in DNA synthesis can vary. This latter proportion depends on two competing processes: (1) blocking of the enzymes for the endogenous thymidylate synthesis, and (2) effectiveness of the phosphorylation of the injected thymidine. Considering this situation, one has to be aware that patho-

TABLE V
IN VIVO INCORPORATION OF TRITIATED THYMIDINE INTO THE DNA OF GUT AND SPLEEN[a,b]

	Specific activity of DNA	
Species	Intestine	Spleen
Mus (C57 mouse)	374	139
Mesocricetus (golden hamster)	487	178
Glis (common dormouse)	392	262
Eliomys (garden dormouse)	415	206
Sciurus (2 μCi/g) (gray squirrel)	96	23
Tamiasciurus (red squirrel)	13	28
Tamias (chipmunk)	44	7.5
Marmota (2 μCi/g) (woodchuck)	1.8	0.3
Citellus tridecemlineatus (ground squirrel)	1.0	0.7
C. lateralis (ground squirrel)	1.6	0.2

[a] From Adelstein et al. (1964).
[b] Intraperitoneal injection of 4 μCi/g unless otherwise noted. The tissues were taken 4 hours after injection. Results are given in counts per minute per microgram of DNA.

logical or experimental conditions such as irradiation may lead to differences in the proportion of thymidine-^{3}H taking part in DNA synthesis, without the rate of DNA synthesis being changed. Therefore, only with great reservations may grain counts per nucleus be considered as representative of the rate of DNA synthesis. Furthermore, it should be mentioned here that the effectiveness of DNA labeling by labeled thymidine is very different in various animal species, as shown in Table V (from Adelstein et al., 1964). This effect too must be due to the relative activity of both the competing processes mentioned above.

E. STABILITY OF DNA

It is generally assumed that DNA as the genetic material is stable, i.e., does not undergo any metabolic processes (Furst et al., 1950; Hershey, 1954; Fresco et al., 1955; Hecht and Potter, 1956; Kihara et al., 1956; Siminovitch and Graham, 1956; Healy et al., 1956; Revesz et al., 1956; Scott and Taft, 1958; Bennett et al., 1960a,b; Bond et al., 1962a; Maruyama, 1964). Furthermore, it is generally accepted that only those cells synthesize DNA that are preparing for cell division or that become polyploid or polytene without succeeding cell division. However, recently some evidence has been obtained by several investigators indicating that there may be synthesis of DNA unrelated to cell division and that DNA is renewed at a slow rate. Pelc (1958, 1959, 1962, 1963a,b, 1964, 1968c) concluded from his experimental results that the incorporation of labeled thymidine exceeds the requirements for cell division by a factor of approximately 8–12 in seminal vesicles, heart muscle, and smooth muscle of the mouse. Histiograms of seminal vesicle cells showed a group of weakly labeled cells well separated from the heavily labeled ones that incorporate thymidine at a full rate. Pelc concluded that there may be a periodic renewal of DNA in the cell at a low rate. Thus, he could estimate biological half-lives for the DNA of the different cell types including nondividing ones. Gall and Johnson (1960) examined the validity of Pelc's conclusion in special experiments but did not find any reason to postulate a special "metabolic" DNA.

In *Vicia faba* seedlings La Cour and Pelc (1959a) and Pelc and La Cour (1959) found intensive thymidine-^{3}H incorporation into nuclei of cells in the elongation zone which do not synthesize DNA. They considered it to be metabolic exchange of thymidine. On the other hand, good agreement between the number of labeled nuclei and the number of interclass nuclei was found (Woodard *et al.*, 1961). Tschermak-Woess (1960) considered this heavier labeling to be due to DNA replication in the course of endomitosis occurring in the elongation zone, not to metabolism of DNA.

Ficq and Pavan (1957) concluded from the thymidine-^{3}H incorporation in the course of chromosome puffing in larvae of *Rhynchosciara angelae* that there is local DNA synthesis during certain periods of larval development. Gabrusewycz-Garcia (1964) in *Sciara coprophila* salivary gland chromosomes found similar differences in the relative rates of uptake of thymidine-^{3}H in a number of bands in a certain proportion of chromosomes.

Intensive labeling of a Feulgen-positive body, which is present in the oogonia and oocyte nuclei in larvae of *Tipula oleracea* and suddenly disintegrates at diplotene, was found by Lima-de-Faria (1962a,b, 1964) and interpreted as metabolic DNA. In the house cricket *Acheta domesticus* Heinonen and Halkka (1967) described a spherical Feulgen-positive body that is first seen in premeiotic interphase and begins to disintegrate in diplotene. Features of its metabolism and especially its mode of disintegration suggest that this Feulgen-positive body contains metabolic DNA.

A number of biochemical investigations on the stability of DNA measuring the incorporation of thymidine-^{3}H and its subsequent loss support the view to some degree that there is metabolic DNA. For a number of dividing tissues, Gerber *et al.* (1960) found different DNA fractions with different biological half-lives, one with a faster and one with a slower rate.

Similarly, Sampson et al. (1963) extracted two DNA fractions from growing plant tissue: one with high molecular weight for which no evidence of turnover was obtained, and one of lower molecular weight which is characterized by a relatively rapid turnover rate and obviously differs in composition from its high molecular weight counterpart. In recent experiments Sampson and Davies (1966) found that the DNA fraction with the low molecular weight is more heavily labeled than the fraction with the high molecular weight, after labeling with ^{32}P for 4 hours. After 48 hours "chasing" with unlabeled phosphorus, most of the activity is lost from the fraction of the light molecular weight.

Devik and Halvorsen (1963) found a considerable decrease in DNA activity in the liver of normal mice which could not be explained by cell replacement. On the other hand, Fresco and Bendich (1960) reported a very small decrease in the specific activity with time in the liver of nongrowing rats labeled with adenine-^{15}N and glycine-^{14}C which could be accounted for by cell death and replacement.

Turnover studies of tritium from thymidine-^{3}H performed by Steel and Lamerton (1965) in tissues of the rat do not support the view that metabolic DNA exists. Furthermore, strong support for the assumption that DNA is stable was provided by the experiments of Bennett et al. (1960a), who labeled dividing fetal tissue with adenine-^{14}C by administering the labeled precursor to pregnant mice. The radioactivity in the DNA of brain and liver, which become mitotically inactive in the adult animal, was determined at periods from 9 days to 1 year after birth. During this period, half the life span of the animal, no loss of ^{14}C-activity from the DNA of brain and liver was found. That means that radioactive precursors incorporated into the DNA of liver and brain of embryos may remain fixed for the whole life of the animal.

In a very recent paper, Pelc (1968a,b) reviewed all the different findings suggesting the existence of metabolically labile DNA and interpreted the turnover of DNA found in the experiments as (a) using up of DNA during the normal function of differentiated cells, (b) replacement of metabolic DNA, (c) repair, and (d) appearance of new DNA in some cells. Furthermore, he presented some evidence that metabolic DNA is different from genetic DNA. According to Pelc (1967) differentiated cells in higher organisms contain, in addition to stable, genetic DNA, at least one other species of DNA which is functional and is sometimes replaced.

F. REUTILIZATION OF LABELED THYMIDINE

Reutilization of labeled DNA or DNA metabolites has been observed by a number of investigators. However, most of the experiments performed in the course of these studies did not answer the question whether reutilization occurs at the level of whole DNA molecules, of DNA fragments, or of nucleosides or nucleotides.

Hill (Hill and Drasil, 1960; M. Hill, 1961a,b, 1962) found labeling of bone marrow cells after injection of ^{32}P-labeled donor lymphocytes into X-irradiated mice. The label was resistant to deoxyribonuclease treatment. He concluded that the recipient bone marrow cells take up the ^{32}P-DNA of dead donor lymphocytes for the transfer of which he assumed phagocytosis by granulocytes. Repetition of his experiments with thymidine-^{3}H *in vivo* and *in vitro* showed that there was no label in the dialyzate of dead labeled cells and that the intensity of the label of the bone marrow cells was of the same order of magnitude as the donor lymphocytes, suggesting that only nondialyzable DNA or DNA fragments were being utilized. That labeled exogenous thymic DNA, when injected into mature mice, was recovered in the endogenous DNA of the recipient cells was shown by Yoon and Sabo (1964). Similar results were obtained by Adams *et al.* (1965) in HeLa cells, by Kay (1966) in Lettré-Ehrlich ascites tumor cells, and by Ledoux *et al.* (1967) in perfused rat livers. Ledoux *et al.* pointed out that the uptake of DNA is not simply a diffusion from the blood stream to the cells, but involves binding of DNA at specific metabolically active sites in the cell. Obviously it is not a resynthesis of DNA which had been catabolized. Furthermore, incorporation of low molecular weight precursor follows a quite different scheme concerning the time sequence of incorporation as well as the chromatographic pattern of the newly synthesized DNA. Uptake of DNA originating from damaged cells into cultured cells was reported by Hill (1967). See also the review about uptake of DNA by Ledoux (1965).

Experiments by Rieke (Rieke, 1962; Schwarz and Rieke, 1963), who transplanted ascites tumor cells into mice previously labeled with thymidine-^{3}H are contradictory. In the earlier published experiments no labeling of tumor cells occurred if cells were implanted subcutaneously or in a Millipore diffusion chamber intraperitioneally; the later report stated that labeling of the tumor cells occurred regardless of whether they were implanted intraperitoneally, subcutaneously, in Millipore diffusion chambers, or in dialysis bags. Therefore Rieke eventually concluded that labeling must have come from a circulating dialyzable substance. Similar results were obtained by Dumont *et al.* (1962) in sarcoma cells implanted into previously labeled mice. The authors concluded that DNA components, presumably bigger fragments, were released from dead leukocytes and incorporated into proliferating tumor cells and fibroblasts. Diderholm *et al.* (1962) and Fichtelius and Groth (1963) observed labeling of skin grafts transplanted into mice previously labeled with thymidine-^{3}H as well as labeling of host cells after implantation of previously labeled mouse tissue. They also concluded that labeling occurred locally by degradat on of labeled leukocytes.

From labeling of liver and RES cells in partially hepatectomized mice after injection of labeled lymphocytes or thymidine-^{3}H either several hours after, or 1 to 2 days prior to, hepatectomy, Bryant (1962, 1963a) concluded that reutilization occurred more locally and at a higher molecular level. In later experiments (Bryant, 1963b) he introduced label by administering thymidine-^{3}H 36 hours after partial hepatectomy and 5 months later injected carbon tetrachloride which caused extensive necrosis of liver parenchyma. In animals sacrificed 2 days later, he found labeling of 15–25% of the spermatogonia, 82–86% of the crypt cells, and 84–96% of the epithelium of the villi. These results supported the assumption that an effective DNA precursor (thymidine or thymidylic acid) is released from the necrotic liver cells to the plasma. From recent experiments with Ehrlich ascites tumor cells which became labeled after implantation into previously labeled mice, Bryant (1965) concluded that the delayed utilization of thymidine-^{3}H by these cells is a result of reutilization of DNA thymidine from dead cells and not of incorporation of thymidine catabolites or long-lived intracellular thymidine pools.

Somewhat similar results were reported by Milyutina (1967), who injected thymidine-^{3}H into mice 1 day prior to partial hepatectomy. 10–80% of the hepatocytes were labeled 3 days after the operation. The author concluded that the hepatocytes were labeled by thymidine-^{3}H entering from other tissues. According to his results, thymidine-^{3}H reutilization replaces about 2–2.5% of its de novo synthesis.

Strong support for reutilization of low molecular DNA precursors at the level of nucleosides derived from degradation of DNA or a long-lived intracellular pool was provided by the experiments of Robinson and Brecher (1963) and Robinson et al. (1965). Reutilization of thymidine-^{3}H by regenerating mouse liver was almost completely suppressed by continuous infusion of nonradioactive thymidine. It was assumed that the reutilized label probably originates in all tissues with a high rate of cell turnover.

Maruyama (1964) observed a slight uniform labeling of growing LSA ascites tumor cells and bone marrow cells in mice which were injected intravenously with thymidine-^{3}H labeled tumor cells previously killed by X-ray; this suggests that DNA components released by dead cells are preserved and reutilized. Since application of unlabeled thymidine (simultaneous or started 1 day previously) suppressed the labeling at least partly, the author concluded that the transfer of the label occurs as thymine, thymidine, or more complex compounds, or as combinations of these. The incomplete suppression of the reutilization process suggests that the latter assumption is correct. Reutilization of thymidine-^{3}H by various tumors was reported by Steel (1966).

Incorporation of thymidine-^{3}H originating from labeled chromosomes into the chromosomes of fresh Chinese hamster cells and of human leukocytes cultures was observed by Whang-Peng et al. (1967). The uptake of label was inhibited by the presence of added carrier thymidine in the medium, in an amount insufficient to inhibit DNA synthesis. Therefore, the authors concluded that most of the incorporation seemed to have involved previous degradation of the DNA at least up to the level of free nucleotides.

Kotani et al. (1967) injected lymphocytes labeled with thymidine-^{3}H into the intestine of recipient rats. The appearance of ^{3}H activity in the blood and thoracic duct lymph plasma showed that DNA breakdown products from the lymphocytes in the gut were absorbed and transferred by way of both the portal vein and the thoracic duct. The authors provided autoradiographic evidence that the activity was actually incorporated into the DNA of proliferating cells of the recipients.

Even 7 days after injection of thymidine-^{3}H, Brière and Isler (1966) still found radioactivity (10^{-6} μCi/ml) in the serum of young rats. Cells that were incubated in this serum (removed at different times after thymidine-^{3}H injection) showed nuclear labeling on autoradiograms even if the serum was removed 30 hours after injection. The presense of DNA precursors in the serum such a long time after injection of thymidine-^{3}H suggests that DNA from other cells is reutilized.

Feinendegen et al. (1966a) found slower exponential decay of the specific activity of DNA in bone marrow cells (rat), if these cells were labeled with thymidine-^{14}C or -^{3}H compared to those labeled with 5-^{131}IDU. The authors conclude that there is reutilization of thymidine, the extent of which was reported to be 35–40% of the thymidine released by DNA catabolism. Thymidine seems to be the main way of transfer. However, reutilization of higher molecular components cannot be excluded. In further experiments (Feinendegen et al., 1966b) the influence of reutilization of thymidine on studies of cell proliferation and DNA synthesis was measured autoradiographically using ^{125}IDU; reutilization of thymidine seemed most probably responsible for the almost 100% labeling of megacaryocytes 3 days after injection of the thymidine-^{3}H.

The various experiments described above demonstrate that there is reutilization of thymidine. The recent experimental results have shown that reutilization of catabolized DNA mainly occurs at the level of low molecular substances. However, additional means of transfer, i.e., transfer of higher molecular fragments, cannot be excluded. That reutilization of DNA at a low molecular level was not recognized in earlier experiments may have been due to faulty techniques, i.e., to the use of specific activities of the injected thymidine-^{3}H (or of the labeled cells) too small to cause labeling sufficiently intensive to reveal this process.

G. TOXICITY AND RADIOTOXICITY OF LABELED THYMIDINE

When the application of thymidine-^{3}H as a DNA precursor increased, the warnings of the influence of the toxicity and radiation damage produced by this labeled compound on the experimental results became more frequent. Because of the incorporation of thymidine-^{3}H into the genetic substance of the nuclear material and the very weak β-energy of tritium which is absorbed within the nuclear material, radiation effects are to be expected and should be considered thoroughly. In a recent paper, dosimetry of the ^{3}H activity in the cell nucleus and related radiobiological problems were discussed by Bond and Feinendegen (1966). On the other hand, a possibly toxic effect of thymidine has to be considered, since unlabeled thymidine seems to have some cytological effect on the cell too.

Thus, Greulich et al. (1961) observed an increase in mitotic activity by unlabeled thymidine in the duodenal epithelia of the mouse after injection of 10 μg of cold thymidine per mouse. During a 6-hour period of observation the number of metaphases was increased by about 30% compared to normal. The authors considered the increase in number of mitoses as due to the fact that these amounts of thymidine led to considerable shortening of the DNA synthesis phase and that, therefore, the number of cells entering mitosis was increased. Barr (1963), however, concluded from his experiments with HeLa cells that the increased mitotic index is entirely due to a prolonged metaphase, i.e., a cytological effect rather similar to that of colchicine. The same conclusion was drawn by Ames and Mitra (1967), who also found an increased mitotic index in root meristem cells of Haplopappus gracilis.

For more details on an inhibitory effect of thymidine on ^{32}P incorporation into DNA of rat thymus cells, see Whittle (1966).

Painter et al. (1964) observed strong inhibition of growth in HeLa S3 cultures after addition of 20 μg of unlabeled thymidine per milliliter to the culture medium. The same amount of thymidine suppressed the colony formation by about 40%. Growth inhibition depends on the concentration of the "inactive" thymidine and leads to a growth inhibition of more than 70% at 200 μg/ml.

It should be mentioned here that those amounts of thymidine which inhibit growth also synchronize growing cell populations. Drew and Commerford (1967) studied the incorporation of thymidine-^{3}H and

[125]IDU as well as of deoxycytidine-^{3}H into HeLa S3 cells after releasing the thymidine block and found that deoxycytidine-^{3}H was incorporated without delay, a finding which suggests that 90–97% of the cells were arrested in the S phase. The thymidine-^{3}H and [125]IDU incorporation was inhibited, suggesting the formation of an extensive intracellular thymidine pool during the treatment with thymidine.

Yang et al. (1966) reported chromosome aberration in different cell lines of Chinese hamster cells if they are grown in higher concentrations (1 mmole and more) of thymidine. Constrictions, chromatid exchanges, and breaks as well as chromosome exchanges were most frequently observed. This chromosome damage seems to be connected with an interruption of DNA synthesis or with DNA synthesis in the presence of a pool which is not in the nucleotide equilibrium.

1. Growth Inhibition and Cytological Anomalies

Growth inhibition and cytological anomalies are the most frequently observed effects after application of tritium-labeled thymidine which were reported very early in thymidine-^{3}H studies. In HeLa cells Painter et al. (1958) found distinct growth inhibition at levels of 1.25 to 5.0 μCi per milliliter of culture medium during 24 hours of incubation. From incubation experiments lasting 24–48 hours, Painter and Drew (1959) and Drew and Painter (1959, 1962) reported that as little as 0.02 μCi thymidine-^{3}H per milliliter has a growth inhibitory effect and that there are only a few cells that survive a concentration of 0.1 μCi/ml and continue to divide and form colonies. This suppressing effect is a function of dose, specific activity and period of treatment and varies with the age of the culture. Extension of the incubation time to 48 hours suppresses the colony development completely, leads to vacuolization, size increase of nuclei and giant cell formation and has a lethal effect even at a concentration of 0.02 μCi/ml. Similar results were obtained by Berry et al. (1966) in HeLa cells with a concentration of 0.05 μCi/ml (specific activity 2 mCi/mmole). Thirty-minute incubation at concentrations from 0.02 to 2.5 μCi/ml did not affect the production of colonies (Painter et al., 1964). This means that in short-term experiments thymidine-^{3}H showed no disturbing effects within certain dose limits.

Lisco et al. (1961a) also found a significant decrease in the number of Ehrlich ascites tumor cells growing in the peritoneal cavity of mice 5–12 days after several injections of thymidine-^{3}H each 4 hours apart, at dose levels of 1.0 and 10.0 μCi/g; but even at the highest dose level the percentage of decrease did not exceed 43%.

The survival rate of lymphocytes grown for 72 hours in a culture medium containing 1 μCi of thymidine-^{3}H per milliliter was equal to that of controls. However, after 190 hours the survival rate of the experimental cells was only 25% of the controls (Osgood, 1959).

Marin and Bender (1963a,b) studied the survival kinetics of mammalian tissue culture cells (HeLa S3) containing ³H-labeled nucleosides and determined the relative importance of nuclear and cytoplasmic damage in radiation-induced cell death. From their experiments using various amounts of ³H-thymidine or ³H-uridine for incorporation they concluded that all the cell killing observed can be accounted for by the β-radiation to which the cell is exposed and that the contribution of cytoplasmic damage to radiation-induced reproductive death of mammalian cells is very small.

In the intact mammal, Johnson and Cronkite (1959) were the first to report a decrease in the number of spermatocytes compared to Sertoli cells as well as an increasing number of necrotic cells 4 days after injection of thymidine-³H. The decrease in cellularity occurred at dose levels of only 0.5 μCi/g and was more than 50% at 20 μCi/g. These findings were fully confirmed by Samuels and Kisieleski (1963) and Samuels et al. (1964), who found a linear correlation between the uptake and retention of thymidine-³H in mouse testis and the average number of surviving resting spermatocytes. An apparent decrease in cell population was observed 1 week after injection of 1.0 μCi/g and a significant decrease at a dose level of 10.0 μCi/g.

Studies on the effect of increasing doses (0.1–50.0 μCi/g) of thymidine-³H on spermatogenesis in mice and the comparable effect of 50 μCi/g between 2 and 4 days to that of 10 μCi/g between 4 and 6 days led to the conclusion that there is a threshold value for demonstrable effects at about 125 disintegrations per nucleus and that the number of spermatocytes is reduced to one-half at about 400 disintegrations per nucleus (Kisieleski et al., 1964).

Thymidine-³H administered to young rats after partial hepatectomy at doses above 1 μCi/g leads within 72 hours after injection to a transient inhibition of regeneration as demonstrated by (1) the depressed rate of increase in residual liver mass, (2) delayed and afterward prolonged, elevated mitotic activity, and (3) an increased number of mitotic abnormalities indicated by anaphase bridges (Grisham, 1960).

Cell death a few days to several weeks after a single injection of only 1 μCi/g mouse of thymidine-³H was also found by Garder and Devik (1963).

Post and Hoffman (1961) reported that in 3-week-old rats 2.0 μCi of thymidine-³H per gram leads to a shift to higher ploidy classes; within 24 hours the ploidy distribution resembled that of 8-week-old controls 5 days after injection and that of 2-year-old controls 14 days after injection. According to the interpretation of the authors the ploidy changes appear to be an early stage in the spectrum of alterations after irradiation and may indicate radiation-induced aging. In recent experiments the same authors (Post and Hoffman, 1967) studied the effect of thymidine-^{3}H (2 μCi/g and 10 μCi/g) on the replication of liver cells in growing rats. At 3–5 weeks after injection, the length of the generation cycle of the diploid hepatocytes was double that of controls without change in the duration of S, G_2, and mitosis—the change being due to a prolongation of G_1. However, no histological anomalies were found at the doses used.

Cronkite et al. (1962) found up to 10% pycnotic nuclei in labeled lymphocytes of the rat after administration of 5–25 μCi of thymidine-^{3}H per gram. Dose levels of 0.05–0.1 μCi/g are considered to cause no damaging effect.

In plant tissue, McQuade et al. (1956b) reported chromosomal aberration in onion root tips after application of thymidine-^{14}C; the frequency of aberrant cells increased with exposure to thymidine-^{14}C for more than 12 hours. McQuade and Friedkin (1960) observed radiation damage in 99.5% of the cells of onion seedling root tips if the incubation medium contained 20.0 μCi per milliliter of thymidine-^{3}H; at a level of 1.0 μCi/ml only 6.9% of the cells showed radiation effects; 10.0 μCi/ml depressed the formation of lateral roots in *Vicia faba* (Stein and Quastler, 1964). Furthermore, Natarajan (1961) found chromosome breakage and mitotic inhibition in *Vicia faba* incubated with thymidine-^{3}H at dose levels routinely used for labeling experiments.

2. Tumor Induction with Labeled Thymidine

Injected thymidine labeled with tritium or with ^{14}C was found to shorten the life span of animals and to produce tumors in mice (Lisco et al., 1961b; Baserga et al., 1962b, 1966). The incidence of tumors is greater in animals injected as young adults or labeled as embryos *in utero* than in ammals injected later in life. The shortening of the life span and the incidence of tumors further increases with the dose applied and is distinctly increased at high doses like 10 μCi of thymidine-^{3}H per gram animal weight. On the other hand, Johnson and Cronkite (1967) did not find an influence on the average life span or tumor induction at doses of 1–5 μCi per gram animal weight in the mouse.

3. Mutation Caused by Tritiated Thymidine

Bateman and Chandley (1962) studied the mutagenic effect of 7.5 μCi of thymidine-^{3}H per gram (in divided doses) on male mice. Up to 100% dominant lethal mutations were found in the implants of females bred to males which had received the first injection of thymidine-^{3}H 5–6 weeks earlier.

The deleterious influence of orally administered thymidine-^{3}H on the reproductive capacity was investigated by Greulich (1961). Female mice received drinking water containing per milliliter 2.0 μCi of thymidine-^{3}H before and during the course of gestation, the uptake totaling between 245 and 300 μCi per animal. Male mice also consumed the same tritiated water during contact with the females; the uptake totaled between 8 and 167 μCi per animal. No radiation damage was observed in the litters of the first mating experiment. In subsequent breeding experiments an increasing incidence of stillbirth, fetal resorption, and male sterility was found. Also, breeding between the animals from the first successful litter showed a markedly reduced reproductive capacity with an incidence of stillbirth and neonatal death of about 70%.

In plants phenotypic alterations in flower color, which are assumed to be somatic mutations, have been produced by incorporated thymidine-^{3}H (Wimber, 1959). In the male larvae of *Drosophila melanogaster* an increase in frequency of mutations due to thymidine-^{3}H application was found by Kaplan and Sisken (1960).

Dewey *et al.* (1965) compared thymidine-^{3}H, ^{3}H$_2$O, and Co^{60} γ^2-rays as factors inducing chromosomal aberrations in hamster cells growing *in vitro*. They concluded that on the basis of energy absorbed in the nucleus or chromosomes the β-particles from TdR-^{3}H were less effective in producing chromosomal aberrations than the β-particles emitted either from ^{3}H$_2$O distributed in the nucleus or from γ-rays absorbed in the cell.

4. Concluding Remarks

All investigations on radiotoxicity and radiation damage mentioned not only are concerned with the effect of the β-particles of the corresponding isotope, but in the case of tritium labeling also include the unknown effect of transmutation of tritium to helium within the molecule and the recoil energy effect of the emitted β-particle. The investigations of radiation damage caused by labeled thymidine which are summarized under Sections 1–3 above show that the results obtained by the use of labeled thymidine have to be interpreted with adequate caution and that, in any case, the doses applied should be kept as small as possible.

II. Autoradiographic Studies of the Cellular DNA Synthesis with Labeled Thymidine

A. CELL PROLIFERATION IN THE NORMAL ANIMAL

Earlier studies applying thymidine-^{3}H determined more qualitatively the proliferative activity of different cell types. In those studies the labeling index (number of labeled cells per total number of cells) was considered a measure of proliferative activity. However, even as early as that it was realized that the labeling index gives only a rough estimate of the rate of proliferation, since it is influenced by the length of the DNA synthesis period and, thus, does not depend solely on the generation time (Hughes *et al.*, 1958; Leblond *et al.*, 1959b; Schultze and Oehlert, 1960; Messier and Leblond, 1960; Edwards and Klein, 1961; Baserga and Kisieleski, 1962b).

Chief sites of cell production within the animal organism were found to be the epithelia of the gut, other surface epithelia, the germinal centers of the lymphatic tissue, cells of the recticuloendothelial system, etc. Similar results had already been obtained by Walker and Leblond (1958) using ^{14}C-labeled thymidine. On the basis of the different thymidine-^{3}H incorporation into the various cell types and in accordance with a scheme that Cowdry (1952) had postulated based on the mitotic activity of the tissues, the cell types were classified into 3 groups: (1) fixed postmitotic cells, static or stable cell populations that no longer divide and in which no labeled cells were found; (2) reversible postmitotic cells, expanding or growing cell populations with only a small number of labeled cells; and (3) vegetative intermitotic cells, renewing cell populations with a relatively large number of labeled cells.

Even thus early it was shown that a close relationship exists between the labeling and mitotic indexes in rats and mice, the labeling index being 8–15 times higher than the mitotic index in all tissues investigated (Schultze and Oehlert, 1960; Noltenius *et al.*, 1964; Stöcker and Altmann, 1964; Dhom and Stöcker, 1964a,b). Because of the fairly constant duration of mitosis, as determined by colchicine experiments, the rather constant correlation between mitotic and labeling indices led to the conclusion that the time required for DNA synthesis would also have to be very similar for the different cell types. Later experimental results have confirmed this conclusion and have shown that the duration of DNA synthesis is generally approximately 7–8 hours, although in some cases it is 18–26 hours for most of the various cell types of the adult animal (see Section II, D, 2, this chapter).

Since labeling with thymidine-^{3}H by autoradiography has come into use as a method to estimate the generation cycle and its phases, emphasis has shifted to such measurements. Because of the special methods and the innumerable results, investigation of the generation cycle will be reported on in a special section (II, D, 2, this chapter).

Cell proliferation studies on the tissues in the normal animal were performed by a great number of investigators. Oehlert and Büchner (1961) as well as Leblond *et al.* (1964) and Oehlert *et al.* (1966) studied intensively the physiological regeneration of the squamous epithelia, especially of the skin. For a review on this subject see Oehlert (1966). The physiological cell proliferation in the adrenal of the rat was studied by Diderholm and Hellman (1960) and by Reiter and Pizzarello (1966). Investigation of the kinetics of the proliferation is of special importance for the hemopoietic system. Cell proliferation in the hemopoietic and lymphatic systems of different animals was studied by various authors (Cronkite *et al.*, 1959a,b,c, 1961b; Lajtha, 1959; Schooley *et al.*, 1959; Patt and Maloney, 1959; Little *et al.*, 1962; Cronkite and Fliedner, 1964; Keiser *et al.*, 1964, 1966; Fliedner *et al.*, 1964b, 1965; Ebbe and Stohlman, 1965; Craddock, 1965; Stryckmans *et al.*, 1966; Blenkinsopp, 1967a,b; Lipchina, 1967; see also Bond *et al.*, 1965).

The influence of growth on the labeling index was investigated by Stöcker *et al.* (1964a), who determined the labeling index in liver and kidney of rats as a function of increasing age. A very steep decrease of the index up to the age of 2–4 months was observed. The authors concluded that up to the age of 4 months some of the cells grow exponentially, and that subsequently all cells are in a steady state of cellular proliferation. Similar results were obtained for kidney parenchymal cells of mice by Litvak and Baserga (1964), for the pituitary gland of the rat by Crane *et al.* (1965), for the thymus of the rat by Berman *et al.* (1966), and for the smooth muscle of the rat intestine by Dubinko (1966).

B. CELL PROLIFERATION UNDER DIFFERENT PATHOLOGICAL AND EXPERIMENTAL CONDITIONS

Cell proliferation studies were performed under numerous pathological and experimental conditions, like regeneration processes, influence of drugs, hormones, carcinogenic substances, cytostatica, intoxication, or changed environmental conditions as well as X-ray irradiation and other conditions. In these studies a change in proliferative activity was mainly deduced from the changed labeling index. Later on such somewhat qualitative studies were partly supplemented by determinations of generation cycles. Results of this type are reported in Chapter 4, Section II, D, 2, and the influence of irradiation on proliferation is described separately in Chapter 4, Section II, D, 2.

1. Regenerating Tissue.

Autoradiographic studies of regenerating processes with thymidine-^{3}H have revealed that tissues consisting of resting, nonproliferating cells, when stimulated, react with an increase in DNA synthesizing cells and sometimes with a shortening of the generation cycle.

Liver regeneration after partial hepatectomy in rat and mouse has been studied extensively by means of thymidine-^{3}H incorporation. In the rat liver hepatocytes begin to synthesize DNA about 12–18 hours after $\frac{2}{3}$

hepatectomy. DNA synthesizing cells reach a maximum of 30% labeling between 24 and 36 hours, i.e., the labeling index increases by a factor of up to about 200 compared to normal (ca. 0.16%). The peak incidence of hepatocytes synthesizing DNA precedes the peak incidence of cells in mitosis by about 6 hours (Lesher et al., 1960; Grisham, 1962; Oehlert et al., 1962a; Klinman and Erslev, 1963). Similar results were obtained for the mouse by Bade et al. (1966). It is interesting to note that these authors found diurnal fluctuations of the labeling index.

Edwards and Koch (1964) reported that the average time required for DNA synthesis, G_2, and mitosis is unaffected by partial hepatectomy, but Stöcker and co-workers (Stöcker and Bach, 1965; Stöcker and Heine, 1965b; Stöcker and Pfeifer, 1965, 1967; Stöcker, 1966b) found considerable changes in the duration of DNA synthesis under these experimental conditions. The usual duration of DNA synthesis in adult normal rats of 18 hours was found to be reduced to about one half, i.e., 9 hours, by 18–20 hours after hepatectomy. Simultaneously the mean grain number per nucleus increases by a factor of 2. Also G_2 and mitosis were drastically reduced.

In dogs DNA synthesis after partial hepatectomy starts about 1 day later than in rats and continues at an increased rate for a longer period, from day 2 to day 5 after hepatectomy (Sigel et al., 1965).

Autolyzing liver tissue injected into the peritoneal cavity of mice after partial hepatectomy stimulates DNA synthesis of hepatocytes. The labeling index is increased distinctly compared to that of hepatectomized controls, but there is no such effect on the mesenchymal cells of the liver (Lahtiharju and Teir, 1964).

Inhibition of liver regeneration after hypophysectomy was found in rats and was represented by a marked decrease in labeled cells (Wrba et al., 1964). Application of thioacetamide prior to hepatectomy leads to a much lesser increase in the number of DNA synthesizing cells than in control animals which were only hepatectomized. Neither an increase in the DNA synthesis rate nor a corresponding shortening of the S phase was found (Stöcker et al., 1966b).

Biochemical experiments showed that pretreatment with cortisone (5 mg daily for 5 days prior to partial hepatectomy) greatly retards the increase in the DNA synthesis that would usually occur during the course of liver regeneration. Epinephrine was also found to be an effective inhibitor of DNA synthesis (Sakuma and Terayama, 1967).

Increased thymidine-^{3}H incorporation into the pituitary and thyroid gland was observed following the active phase of liver regeneration after partial hepatectomy (Nakamura et al., 1963).

CCl_4 intoxication leads to an increased DNA synthesis in rat liver cells. The regenerative response following the hepatotoxic injury can be correlated with the presence of necrosis and inflammation and seems to be influenced by a circulating humoral factor. In the same experiments the influence of different drugs on this effect was tested (Leevy et al., 1962; Leevy, 1963).

Repair processes in *healing wounds* and *bone fractures* were studied with thymidine-³H in different animal species. Injury of the transitional epithelium of the bladder in the mouse with a scalpel leads to an increase in the number of labeled cells (Walker, 1959). Injury of the skin and tongue epithelium by cutting or electrocauterization results in a quick rise of the number of labeled cells at a distance of about 200–300 cells away from the edge of the wound. Very few cells immediately adjacent to the wound were labeled at the onset of the healing process. At 96 hours the maximum in the number of labeled cells was observed not farther than 100 cells away from the border of the wound. Response of the connective tissue was slower than the epithelial response (Block et al., 1963). Hell and Cruickshank (1963) studied thymidine-³H incorporation during epidermal healing in guinea pigs. Microinjuries of the epidermis cause an increase in DNA-synthesizing cells as well as a temporary synchronization and a shortening of the cell cycle. After mechanical lesions of the lens surface in rabbit eyes, an increased number of labeled epithelial cells was observed by Harding and Srinivasan (1961).

Regeneration during bone fracture repair is essentially due to the proliferative capacity of the periosteum and diminishes with age, explaining the slow rate of repair in older animals (Tonna, 1960a; Tonna and Cronkite, 1962b).

Participation of connective tissue in healing and regeneration after gingivectomy was studied by Ramfjord et al. (1966). They observed that labeled cells in the connective tissue appear later than in labeled epithelia. Although the number of labeled epithelia reaches a maximum 1 day after gingivectomy, the connective tissue cells are only starting their DNA synthesis at about that time, and it is interesting that they are localized a considerable distance under the wound surface. The maximum of proliferation in the connective tissue is reached on day 3 to 4 after operation.

In the *neuroglia*, which does not show any labeling under normal conditions, labeled cells were found following electrolytic lesions of the corpus geniculatum laterale in rats (Altman, 1962), injury of the spinal cord (Adrian and Walker, 1962), and also experimentally produced brain edema (Schultze and Kleihues, 1967). Crushing of the nervus hypoglossus in rabbits leads to the appearance of labeled glial cells in the immediate surroundings of the regenerating motor nerve cells of the N. hypoglossus (Sjöstrand, 1965a,b, 1966).

Unilateral *nephrectomy* results in an increased labeling index in all tubular epithelia of the rat kidney; however, the increase is greatest in the middle region (Noltenius *et al.*, 1964). When the proliferative activities of the tubulus cells of very young and of adult rats were compared after unilateral nephrectomy, it was found that, apart from the decreased relative proliferative activity in the adult animals, the reaction is qualitatively very similar in both animal groups, namely, a 5- to 10-fold increase of the labeling index after 36 hours (Phillips and Leong, 1967). Differences between young and adult mice in the proliferative activity of the kidney cells during compensatory hypertrophy were described by Antipova (1966). An increased labeling index in glomeruli, tubuli, and intertubular capillaries in rabbits after an experimental glomerulo-nephritis was observed by Noltenius *et al.* (1962). Stöcker *et al.* (1964b), Stöcker and Heine (1965a,b), and Stöcker (1966b) found a shortening of the S phase from 18 to 9 hours in the tubular cells of the rat after unilateral ischemia. This reduction in the S phase was observed in the ischemic as well as in the contralateral kidney. Simultaneously, the rate of DNA synthesis was doubled compared to that in untreated controls. G_2 and M were also reduced in the ligated kidney.

Resection of half of the small intestine in rats did not lead to differences in the labeling index compared to normal or sham-operated animals (Knudtson *et al.*, 1963). On the other hand, *starvation* in mice caused a reduction in cell renewal and rate of migration of the epithelial cells to the villus tips. The labeling index was reduced to half the normal value (Brown *et al.*, 1963).

Segmental excision in the pancreas does not cause an increase in the labeling index, whereas ligation of the artery as well as of the duct to the splenic segment leads to a significantly increased labeling of the acinar cells (Fitzgerald, 1963).

In the forelimb regeneration of the adult newt *Triturus*, regenerating processes and migration of labeled cells were studied by Riddiford (1960) and Hay and Fischman (1961). Epidermal and mesenchymal cells as well as muscle, nerve sheaths, and connective tissue of the stump were labeled. However, in transplantation experiments there was no movement of labeled epidermal cells into the unlabeled blastema, showing that the blastema does not arise from the epidermis.

2. Various Experimental Conditions

ACTH stimulation leads to an increase in DNA synthesizing cells in the adrenal gland and also to a change in distribution of labeled cells within the various zones of the cortex (Machemer and Oehlert, 1964). A marked adrenal enlargement and a significant increase in the labeling index in the outer zona fasciculata after application of ACTH to rats was also observed by Bury and Crane (1965). On the other hand, hydrocortisone significantly depressed the labeling index in this outer cortical layer. In pancreas, treatment with hydrocortisone or ACTH results in a decrease of the labeling index in the exocrine pancreatic epithelia, but to an increase in the islet cells (Crane and Dutta, 1964).

Stöcker et al. (1965a) found that 2 weeks after castration of rats there was an increase in the number of DNA synthesizing cells in the parenchymal and mesenchymal cells of the adrenal cortex. The opposite effect was observed 2 weeks after thyroidectomy. Application of CCl_4 to mice causes a centripetal migration of thymidine-^{3}H labeled cells from the outer fascicular zone (Brenner, 1963).

Under the conditions of deoxycorticosterone-induced hypertension, considerable increase in the uptake of thymidine-^{3}H was seen in the smooth muscle of arteries and arterioles of rats. Furthermore, thymidine-^{3}H uptake was found in the nuclei of endothelium and of fibroblasts proliferating in the adventitia as well as in glomeruli, tubular epithelia, basement membrane supporting cells, and hypertensive vascular lesions in the kidney (Crane and Dutta, 1963; Crane and Ingle, 1964, 1965).

In the endocrine pancreas the number of thymidine-^{3}H labeled A-cell nuclei increases after application of insulin, while glucagon treatment leads to a decrease in the number of labeled A- and B-cells (Stöcker et al., 1966a).

At 20 hours after application of colchicine, the number of thymidine-^{3}H labeled liver parenchymal cells and Kupffer cells increases (Klinge and Stöcker, 1965). It is not quite clear whether this increase is reactive and due to the preceding necroses, to a temporary insufficiency of the liver parenchyma, or to a specific effect of colchicine. The appearance of labeled mitoses even 1 hour after injection of thymidine-^{3}H suggests that the physiological course of the generation cycle has changed. The authors have concluded that the application of colchicine in order to determine relative cell turnover rates by counting mitoses seems to be problematic.

Actinomycin D in small doses inhibits the start of DNA synthesis, but not its continuation in Ehrlich ascites tumor cells. This suggests that there is an actinomycin D-sensitive metabolic process, the inhibition of which prevents the cells from entering the S phase (Baserga et al., 1965; see also Rothstein et al., 1966).

Starvation, and to a greater extent poisoning with ethionine, was found to cause a decrease in the number of DNA-synthesizing cells in proliferating tissues of the rat (Kramsch et al., 1963). Starvation also prevents compensatory proliferation in the remaining kidney after nephrectomy in mice (Reiter, 1965). If feeding is resumed, the number of cells entering S and mitosis is increased in the duodenal epithelia of chickens (Cameron and Cleffmann, 1964).

Hibernation causes a reduction in the percentage of labeled cells in cultured hamster lymphoid tissue (Manasek *et al.*, 1965).

Oxygen deficiency leads to an inhibition of DNA synthesis in all organ anlages of the various larval developmental stages in *Triturus helveticus*. After the normal oxygen content is restored, DNA synthesis starts slowly, then approaches, and later overshoots, normal synthesis (Hara, 1966; Büchner and Hara, 1966).

A single injection of *isoproterenol* stimulates DNA synthesis and cell proliferation in salivary gland cells of the mouse. This stimulation is inhibited by minute doses of actinomycin D (Baserga and Heffler, 1967).

Pathogenesis of *tuberculous granulation tissue* was studied in guinea pigs with thymidine-³H by Wolfart (1964). The tubercle bacteria activate reticulohistiocytic cells, which show an increase in DNA synthesis, multiply and differentiate into epithelioid cells that are labeled and therefore, capable of further division. On the other hand, Langhans' giant cells were not labeled and were, therefore, assumed to originate by confluence of cells.

After heavy *bleeding* metamyelocytes seem to be able to synthesize DNA and divide (Harris and Kugler, 1966).

3. Carcinogenesis

Carcinogenic hydrocarbon-7,12-dimethylbenz[α]anthracene applied to plucked skin of mice was found to inhibit the incorporation of thymidine-³H into DNA in the growing hair follicle by about 50% within 24 hours. The number of grains per nucleus was reduced to half, the labeling index was slightly increased, and the generation time was prolonged (14–26 hours) (McCarter and Quastler, 1962a,b). Oehlert and Coté (1961) and Dörmer *et al.* (1964) found an increase in the number of labeled cells in the epidermis of the mouse after treatment with methylcholanthrene. The authors interpreted their findings as due to a shortening of the generation cycle. Application of diethylnitrosamine to rats leads to an increased labeling index in the hyperplastic nodules and the carcinoma of the liver (Rubin *et al.*, 1964). In mice, induction of tumors in the uterus can be caused by depositing threads soaked with methylcholanthrene into the cervical canal. At the onset of the malignant changes autoradiograms showed incorporation of thymidine-³H not only into the basal layer of the epithelium, but also into the internal region of the epithelial alveolar structures (Nagata *et al.*, 1965). Using the colchicine method and simultaneous measurement of the loss of radioactivity, Elgjo and Skjaeggestad (1965) found that hyperplasia after repeated treatment with methylcholanthrene is due to more rapid proliferation without a corresponding increase in cell loss.

A detailed description of DNA synthesis during carcinogenesis using thymidine-^{3}H was given for the respiratory tract of the hamster after treatment with diethylnitrosamine by Dontenwill and Wiebecke (1964) and for the prestomach of the rat after application of N-methyl-N-nitroso-urethan by Toledo (1965).

4. Tumors

Thymidine-^{3}H incorporation into tumor cells has been studied by many investigators (Baserga et al., 1960, 1962a; Baserga and Kisieleski, 1962a; Mendelsohn et al., 1960; Mendelsohn, 1960b, 1962a,b; Kisieleski et al., 1961a; Johnson et al., 1960a,b; Cronkite et al., 1961a; Bertalanffy and Lau, 1962; Clarkson et al., 1962; Goldfeder and Miller, 1962; Killmann et al., 1962a,b; Reiskin and Mendelsohn, 1962; Choné and Frischbier, 1962, 1963; Choné, 1963; Vesely, 1963; Kury and Carter, 1965). Labeling indexes have been compared to those in corresponding normal tissue, and generation times and lengths of other parts of the cell cycle have been calculated. As Mendelsohn (1963) emphasized in his review, parameters such as the duration of DNA synthesis varied from tumor to tumor much less than from one normal tissue to another. On the other hand, it was found that the uptake of thymidine-^{3}H varied from one metastatic nodule to another in the same animal, and in the same metastatic nodule from one area to the other. Furthermore, Mendelsohn pointed to a fact that had been disregarded, namely, that not all tumor cells necessarily take part in proliferation. Determination of the "growth fraction" of a tumor can be achieved only by determining the distribution of grain counts, the relation of labeling index to the index of labeled mitoses, or by saturation labeling during continuous infusion (Baserga et al., 1960; Edwards et al., 1960; Mendelsohn, 1960a, 1962a,b, 1964a,b). Dose survival curves of normal hemopoietic and transplanted lymphoma cells of mice after repeated thymidine-^{3}H injections (6 mCi per mouse) for 24 hours decreased in the case of normal cells to a value of about 20% and in the case of lymphoma cells, to less than 1% (Bruce and Meeker, 1965). These results indicate that most normal cells do not pass through S in 24 hours, while most lymphoma cells do take up thymidine-^{3}H and are probably killed. It was generally found that tumor cells do not necessarily proliferate faster than normal cells. See also Baserga (1965) and Hoffman and Post (1967).

5. In Vitro Incubation of Tissue Samples

During recent years more and more excised specimens of proliferating human or animal tissue, mainly tumors, have been incubated in vitro with thymidine-[3]H (Johnson and Bond, 1961; Rubini et al., 1961; Wolberg and Brown, 1962; Sky-Peck and Hendrickson, 1962; Choné and Frischbier, 1962, 1963; Choné, 1963; Veenema et al., 1963; Oehlert et al., 1963a,b; Lesch et al., 1964; Fettig and Oehlert, 1964; Fettig and Sievers, 1966; Oehlert and Lesch, 1965; Kury and Carter, 1965; Steel and Bensted, 1965; Rajewsky, 1965, 1966; Titus and Shorter, 1965; Trepel et al., 1966; Lieb and Lisco, 1966).

In short-term experiments with thymidine-^{3}H the excised tissue samples were incubated either directly without time delay or after storing at 4°C in Ringer solution or a corresponding culture medium. The average dose of activity used in the experiments has been 1 μCi of thymidine-^{3}H per milliliter of medium. In some cases the incubation medium has been suffused with oxygen, hyaluronidase has been added, or incubation was performed under elevated oxygen pressure.

These incubation experiments had the purpose of investigating the proliferative activity of the tissue or the growth rate of the tumor, both of which are of great interest for diagnostic reasons. The incubation performed immediately following excision is supposed to reveal in vivo conditions that cannot be studied by application of thymidine-^{3}H to human beings because of the danger of radiation damage. When interpreting the autoradiographic results of those incubation experiments, it has been assumed that cells in the DNA synthesis phase in vivo continue to incorporate labeled thymidine after excision in vitro. This important and by no means self-evident presumption should be stressed.

Incubation experiments are complicated by the fact that the labeled thymidine penetrates only a marginal zone of about 100 μ. Therefore, labeling is confined to a very small marginal region. This makes a quantitative evaluation very difficult. By increasing the oxygen partial pressure (incubation under 2 atmospheres of oxygen) the zone of penetration for thymidine can be widened up to 500 μ, which facilitates the determination of more reliable labeling indexes (Steel and Bensted, 1965; Rajewsky, 1965, 1966). Because of the quickly starting autolytic changes, most authors recommend short incubation times of 30–60 min. However, see also Rajewsky (1965, 1966) and Wolberg and Brown (1962).

The presumption mentioned above, that the incubation experiments represent in vivo conditions, seemed to be justified by the fact that in some cases about the same labeling indexes were obtained in vivo and in vitro. However, the question arises: is it actually the same cells that incorporate thymidine-^{3}H in both circumstances. For a long time only the work by Lala et al. (1965) answered this question. Investigating cells of the myeloid and erythropoietic system in bone marrow of dogs, of a hematologically normal human being, and of a case of acute myeloid leukemia, these authors found by double labeling with thymidine-^{3}H and -^{14}C that the same cells incorporate labeled thymidine *in vivo* and *in vitro*. Recently, Helpap and Maurer (1967a,b) studied by the same method the liver epithelia of the rat, 3 ascites tumors with different ploidy of the mouse, 3 sarcomas of the mouse and rat, and 1 melanoma. One hour after injection of thymidine-^{3}H, tissue samples or ascites tumor were removed and incubated for 1 hour in a culture medium with thymidine-^{14}C at 37°C and 2.2 atm O_2. It was found that most of the labeled cells were doubly labeled with ^{3}H and ^{14}C, as was expected, if the same cells incorporate labeled thymidine *in vivo* and *in vitro*. In parallel experiments thymidine-^{3}H was injected into animals, and after 1 hour a second injection of thymidine-^{14}C followed. After a further 60 min tissue samples were removed. A comparison of the in vivo-in vivo experiments with the in vivo-in vitro experiments showed that the injection of thymidine-^{14}C and incubation with thymidine-^{14}C leads to the same percentage of doubly labeled, of ^{3}H-labeled, and of ^{14}C-labeled nuclei. The proportion of singly labeled nuclei is understandable considering the time between the application of the two labels and the duration of the corresponding S phase. For the tissues investigated, the incubation experiments obviously reproduce *in vivo* conditions. Similar results were recently reported by Frindel *et al.* (1967b) for an experimental tumor (fibrosarcoma) in C3H mice.

Provided the labeling index determined *in vitro* generally corresponds to *in vivo* conditions, *"in vivo"* generation times of cells in human tissue samples can be estimated. However, in experiments with human tissue the duration of S must be estimated based on values measured in animals. Estimates of generation cycles of excised tumor material from incubation experiments are problematic also for another reason. It is known that the labeling index in tumors varies very much in the different tumor regions and even in one and the same tumor or metastatic nodule (Mendelsohn, 1964a,b; Baserga *et al.*, 1962a). Thus, the labeling indexes obtained may differ very much according to the method of selection of areas for study. Furthermore, the estimation of the length of the generation cycle is very difficult, since little is known about the growth rate of the corresponding tumors. Estimation of generation times from the labeling index and the duration of S under the assumption of a steady state system as done by some investigators are incorrect in any case. Not much is known to what extent tumor cells grow exponentially. It is only with short generation times that these growth conditions have little influence on calculated values, shown by Wegener *et al.* (1964) and Lieb and Lisco (1966). Much more important for the estimation of generation cycles is the lack of knowledge about the growth fraction, i.e., the number of cells that participate in proliferation of the tumor under investigation (see also Chapter 4, Section II, D, 4). Also the loss of cells, especially in tumors of the intestinal tract, influences the estimation of generation times considerably (Steel and Bensted, 1965).

All the problems mentioned show that the diagnostic use of autoradiographic incubation studies on tissue samples with thymidine-³H, and much more so the conclusions drawn on generation cycles, have to be considered with due caution.

C. MIGRATION OF LABELED CELLS

The permanent labeling of cells by labeling their DNA enables the investigator to follow the fate of these cells, especially if they migrate from the place where labeling occurred.

It has long been known that active proliferation of the intestinal epithelium occurs in the crypts, and it has been assumed that daughter cells migrate along the villus to the extrusion zone, where histological findings made their ejection from the epithelium into the lumen probable. Labeling with thymidine-³H has fully confirmed these assumptions. Even timing the progress of labeled cells along the villi was possible (Quastler and Sherman, 1959). For the jejunum of the mouse a transit time of about 27 hours between base and tip of the villi was found by Hughes et al. (1958). Later experiments have shown that there may be significant differences between experimental results. A transit time for the cells of the villi in the mouse of about 46 hours was found by Quastler and Sherman (1959), and of about 3 days by Baserga and Kisieleski (1962a).

Furthermore, labeling with thymidine-³H is an excellent means of studying the influence of irradiation on the migration of mature cells along the villi. Irradiation of mice with 800–2500 rads leads to a sharp decrease in cell movement during the second day after irradiation, preceded and followed by movement at about the normal rate (Sherman and Quastler, 1960).

Migration processes are of great importance in the study of hemopoietic processes and other hematological problems. Origin and fate as well as transit of the different cells through the various proliferating and functional compartments can be followed. For a review of this special field see Bond et al. (1965). By the method of permanent labeling, pathways of migration and recycling of lymphocytes were studied. Thus, lymphocytes were found to be migrating from lymph nodes to blood or marrow and back to lymph nodes (Gowans, 1959; Keiser et al., 1964). Labeled thymic lymphocytes intravenously injected into homologous rats and isologous mice were found to disappear rapidly from the blood and to accumulate later on in spleen, lymph nodes, and bone marrow (Murray and Murray, 1964). Thymic lymphocytes labeled *in situ* by local application of thymidine-^{3}H were found to be located preferentially in mesenteric lymph nodes and spleen in guinea pigs; also, transformation into other cell types was observed (Murray and Woods, 1964).

In studies of embryonic development the tracing of those labeled migrating cells has given some valuable information. In the embryonic development of the nervous system, for instance, study of postmitotic labeled cells clearly showed the complex pathway of migration array from proliferative centers to form the brain, retina, and spinal cord (Hicks *et al.*, 1961). Combination of ^{3}H-labeling and irradiation in these studies showed that cells proliferate in the periventricular zone, delay 24 hours before they start migration through the subcortical white matter, and do not arrive in the cortex until 48 hours have elapsed. Soon these cells differentiate into young nerve cells which lose their radiosensitivity.

D. DETERMINATION OF THE CELL CYCLE AND ITS PHASES

Most of the knowledge of the generation cycle and its phases for the different cell types is due to autoradiographic studies with labeled thymidine. Determination of the duration of DNA synthesis, the so-called S phase, was of main interest in such studies.

Howard and Pelc (1951a,b,c, 1953) first concluded from experiments with root meristem cells, using ^{32}P, that the process of DNA doubling is confined to a certain portion of the interphase. Introducing the nomenclature usually applied up to now, they divided the cell cycle into: postmitotic presynthetic resting stage G_1, DNA synthesis phase S, postsynthetic premitotic resting stage G_2, and mitosis M. The designation "gap" for G_1 and G_2 is only supposed to express that there was no knowledge about those phases or about their metabolic processes at that time. To Lajtha (in Ris *et al.*, 1963) the definition of S for the whole cell does not make much sense. He would prefer the S phase to be defined only for chromosomes, or even better for parts of chromosomes.

According to the scheme of the cell cycle accepted generally today, the cell leaves mitosis, enters G_1, the duration of which varies considerably, then passes through S, during which it doubles its DNA, passes through G_2, and enters the next mitosis. Some of the cells lose their ability to divide and differentiate during G_1. Gelfant (1963) concluded from his specially devised experiments that cells can also be arrested in G_2 and—after a period of variable length—as a result of a stimulating irritation, enter mitosis without going through S at all. A summarizing review of the pertinent experiments was given by Gelfant (1966). Some investigators introduced a further definition G_0 into nomenclature. G_0 cells are understood by some authors to be cells that normally no longer divide, but upon stimulation (like hepatectomy) can reenter the proliferative pool, resume DNA synthesis, and divide. G_0 cells are assumed either to have a very long G_1 phase, like liver cells (Lajtha, in Ris *et al.*, 1963), or to belong to the nongrowth fraction of the cell population (Wolfsberg, 1964).

1. Methods

Applying autoradiography and labeled thymidine, several methods are available for determining the length of the different phases of the cell cycle, of which the duration of the S phase is of special interest. Mainly two methods are used in the studies measuring the S phase: (1) the method of counting the percentage of labeled mitoses as a function of time after labeling with thymidine-^{3}H; and (2) the method of double labeling with thymidine-^{3}H and -^{14}C. Furthermore, the generation cycle can be estimated from the halving time of grains per nucleus, or by continuous labeling with thymidine-^{3}H which leads to the generation time and S.

a. Determination of S with the percentage of labeled mitoses method. The method of counting the percentage of labeled mitoses at different time intervals after application of labeled thymidine was first applied by Quastler and Sherman (1959) and Painter and Drew (1959) for the determination of S phases in intestinal epithelia of the mouse or in HeLa cells. Figure 9 depicts the time course of the percentage of labeled mitoses for the cells of the tail tip of the embryonic mouse.

After a single injection of labeled thymidine, all cells are labeled that are in the S phase at the time of injection. With increasing time more and more of those labeled cells pass S and mitosis. If the time between injection of labeled thymidine and sacrifice of the animal is shorter than G_2, no labeled mitoses are observed. If the time interval between labeling and sacrifice exceeds G_2, the first labeled mitoses appear. After a time interval greater than $G_2 + M$ all mitoses are labeled, and this continues until the experimental time exceeds $G_2 + M + S$, when the first unlabeled mitoses reappear. The time interval from the appearance of labeled mitoses to the reappearance of unlabeled mitoses corresponds to the duration of S. Generally the duration of S is derived from the 50% values for labeled mitoses on the increasing and decreasing slopes of the curve. This intersection of the 50% value with the increasing and decreasing slopes of the curve can be defined more easily on the one hand and corresponds more to the mean duration of S on the other.

This curve of percentage of labeled mitoses not only reveals the values for S, but also those for G_2 and M. The time interval between O and the

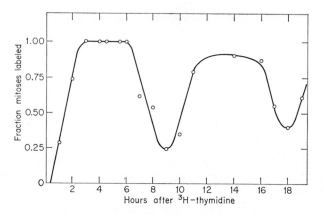

FIG. 9. Percentage of labeled mitoses as a function of time after injection of tritiated thymidine for cells of the tail tip of the embryonic mouse at 12–13 days' gestation. $G_2 + \frac{1}{2}M = 1.5$ hour (distance on the abscissa from 0 hour to 0.5 point on first ascending curve). $S = 6.25$ hours (distance on the abscissa from 0.5 intersect on ascending curve to 0.5 intersect on descending curve). T (generation time) = 9 hours (distance from mid-point on first curve to mid-point on second curve). (From Wimber, 1963.)

first appearance of labeled mitoses corresponds to the minimal value for the duration of G_2. The time interval between O and the point when 100% labeling is reached gives the maximal value for $G_2 + M$. If the rising slope of the curve is linear, a value for the duration of M can be deduced. As shown in Fig. 9, the first labeled mitoses appear after about 30 min. Thus, for this cell type the G_2 phase lasts about 30 min, $G_2 + M$ about 2 hours, and the duration of S about 6–7 hours.

The relatively slow decrease in most of the curves is due to biological variations in G_2, M, and S (see also Quastler, 1963). The duration of S can be determined by this method only if the biological variation of the single phases is not too great. In some instances this method is not applicable at all, namely, if the variations in G_2 are so extensive that the curve is very flat and does not reach 100% labeling (Koburg and Schultze, 1961; Koburg and Maurer, 1962). Generally this method is very suitable for rapidly proliferating cell types, like intestinal epithelia of the adult animal, fetal cell types, rapidly growing tumors, cell cultures, and spermatogonia. Applying this method to tissues with a low rate of proliferation is very time consuming because of the small numbers of mitoses. For those tissues the determination of the duration of S by the double-labeling method is more advantageous, since with this method 10 times as many S phase nuclei are scored.

b. *Method of double labeling with thymidine-³H and -¹⁴C.* The method of double labeling with thymidine-³H and -¹⁴C was first applied by Hilscher and Maurer (1962), Pilgrim and Maurer (1962), Wimber (1963), Wimber and Quastler (1963), Baserga (1963), Wegener *et al.* (1964), Lennartz and Maurer (1964), and Pilgrim and Maurer (1965). In double-labeling experiments a first pulse-labeling with thymidine-³H is followed by a second pulse-labeling with thymidine -¹⁴C after a defined time inter-val (Δt) or vice versa. After a short time (about 0.5 hour), the animals are sacrificed or specimens incubated *in vitro* are fixed and autoradio-grams are prepared. The time interval Δt should not exceed $G_2 + M$, since labeled cells will divide after longer periods and will be counted doubly. With the first application of thymidine-³H all nuclei in the S period at the time of this first injection are labeled. During the time interval (Δt) between the two injections some of the nuclei move out of S and enter G_2. Meanwhile, new G_1 nuclei have entered S. With the second administration of thymidine-¹⁴C, all those nuclei are labeled with ¹⁴C which are in S at the time of the second thymidine application. Conse-quently, in autoradiograms nuclei with three different kinds of label can be distinguished: (1) nuclei labeled only with thymidine-³H—they have left S before thymidine -¹⁴C was injected; (2) nuclei labeled with ¹⁴C only—these are the cells that have entered S in the meantime; and (3) nuclei that are double labeled with ³H and ¹⁴C—these were in S at the time of both injections and form the majority of the labeled cells (Fig. 10 and 10A). If the frequency distribution of the cells throughout the whole generation cycle is constant, as it is assumed to be in a steady-state system, the following relationship exists:

$$\frac{S}{\substack{\text{time interval} \\ \text{between injections}}} = \frac{\text{¹⁴C-labeled cells (with + without ³H label)}}{\text{only ³H-labeled cells}}$$

As pointed out, this simple relationship is true only in a steady-state system with constant frequency distribution of the cells throughout the entire generation cycle. In exponentially growing cell types—for instance,

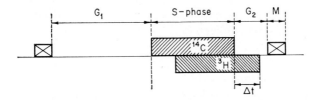

FIG. 10. Schematic depiction of the determination of S by double labeling with thymidine-³H and -¹⁴C (first injection of thymidine-¹⁴C; after Δt, second injection of thymidine-³H).

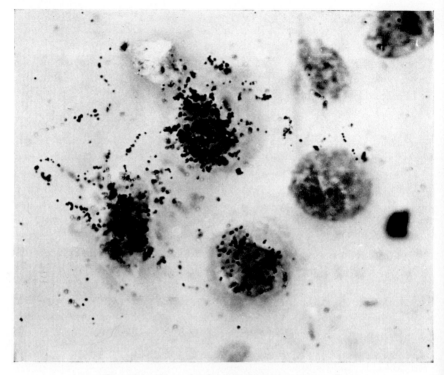

FIG. 10A. ³H- and ¹⁴C-labeled ascites tumor cells.

in cell cultures or tumors—the frequency distribution of the cells within the cell cycle is not constant. It decreases from the beginning of the cycle to the end of mitosis exponentially by a factor of 2. The determination of S from the number of doubly labeled cells and those labeled only with ³H or ¹⁴C is more complicated. In this calculation the values for S and T (generation time) are obtained simultaneously. The only value that has to be known for the calculation is the approximate duration of $G_2 + M$. For details of this calculation, see Lennartz and Maurer (1964) and Lennartz et al. (1964, 1968a,b,c).

Since it is sometimes difficult to recognize closely adjacent ¹⁴C-labeled cells as labeled, because of the scattering of the β-tracks, a variation of this technique has proved to be of advantage (Pilgrim and Maurer, 1962; Wegener et al., 1964): The first injection of a small amount of thymidine-³H is followed by a second injection of ten times the thymidine-³H activity. In autoradiograms weakly and heavily labeled cells can easily be distinguished. The number of ¹⁴C-labeled cells is here replaced by the number of heavily ^{3}H-labeled cells. S is calculated as follows:

$$\frac{S}{\Delta t} = \frac{\text{number of heavily labeled cells}}{\text{number of weakly labeled cells}}$$

Determination of the duration of S with both methods (double labeling method and percent labeled mitoses method) resulted in equal values (Wegener et al., 1964).

c. *Determination of the generation cycle.* Up to the application of the autoradiographic method for determination of generation times, the duration of cell cycles was predominantly measured with the colchicine method. Alternatively, cell cycles have been determined cinematographically by direct measurement of the time interval between two anaphases of a single cell. The latter method is very time consuming and provides values for only a limited number of cells.

Applying autoradiography after labeling with thymidine-^{3}H, generation times can be determined by three independent methods:

1. Determination of the generation time from the labeling index and the duration of S; this is the most frequently applied method. In a population of cells with constant frequency distribution of the cells throughout the whole cell cycle, the number of labeled cells to the number of all cells (labeling index) is proportional to the duration of S to the generation time (T):

$$\frac{\text{Number of labeled cells}}{\text{Total number of cells}} = \frac{S}{T}$$

Of course, those calculations lead to correct values only if all cells of the population participate in proliferation, and if the generation times of all cells in the population do not vary too much. If only part of the cells participate in proliferation, the determination of the labeling index leads to values that are too small, since the labeled cells are related to a number of unlabeled cells that is much too large, including all cells that are no longer dividing. The labeling index counted is too small, and the generation time calculated from it is too long.

2. Another method, independent of the first, permits a direct measurement of the generation time. It is possible to follow the curve of labeled mitoses after a single injection of labeled thymidine through a second rise which is caused by labeled, divided daughter cells in mitosis for the second time (Fig. 9). The time interval between two corresponding points in the two successive waves of labeled mitoses then gives the direct value for the generation time. This method deals only with those cells actually participating in proliferation (growth fraction).

3. Finally, it is possible to determine the generation time from the dilution of grains per nucleus counted at different times after injection

of labeled thymidine. The grain number per nucleus is reduced to half by each division. This method has been applied but rarely, since it provides less exact values.

For an analysis of the cell cycle and the different methods of determining the generation time and its phases, see Dondua and Dondua (1964).

2. Results

a. *Tabular survey of generation cycles and their phases for different cell types (up to 1967)*. Tables VI–XI summarize the values for the different phases and for the whole generation cycles of various cell types in the adult animal (Table VI), in embryos and newborn animals (Table VII), in blood and bone marrow (Table VIII), in tumors (Table IX), in cell cultures (Table X), and in plants (Table XI). The tables give a review of all data in the literature up to the spring of 1967, which is as complete as possible. This material which is continuously increasing permits some general conclusions that will be discussed in the following sections.

b. *S phase*. As demonstrated in the tables, there is a surprising constancy of the duration of S for a great number of cell types within one and the same animal and even for the cell types in different animal species. For adult animals the duration of S is about 6–8 hours; for fetal cell types it is somewhat shorter, about 5–6 hours. Figure 11 illustrates graphically the combined statistics of all S phases listed in all the tables. The graph shows the number of cell types that have a certain S phase length and depicts a relative constancy of S considering the many different cell types. For more details on the relative constant duration of S see Pilgrim and Maurer (1965), Cameron (1964), and Wegener *et al.* (1964).

During the past years quite a number of exceptions to the overall constancy of S have been found. Cells with a longer S phase known up to now are the spermatogonia of rat and mouse, the epithelia of the ear epidermis, and the alveolar cells of the mammary gland in mice as well as the liver and tubular epithelia in rats. For the different spermatogonia of the rat, a value of 23–26 hours for S was found (Hilscher and Maurer, 1962; Hilscher, 1964; Hilscher *et al.*, 1966, Hilscher and Makoski, 1968), for those of the mouse a value of 7 to 14.5 hours was reported (Monesi, 1962). For the S phase of the epidermal epithelium of the mouse ear Sherman *et al.* (1961) found a value of 30 hours with the percentage of labeled mitoses method, and Pilgrim *et al.* (1966) found the length of S to be 18 hours for the same cell type, regardless of whether they used the percentage of labeled mitoses method or the double-labeling method. Bresciani (1965a,b) using the double-labeling method reported the duration of S to be 20 hours (varying between 14.8 and 27.6) in the alveolar cells of the mammary gland in mice. Stöcker and Heine (1965a,b) and Stöcker (1966b) obtained from their experiments a value for S of 18 hours

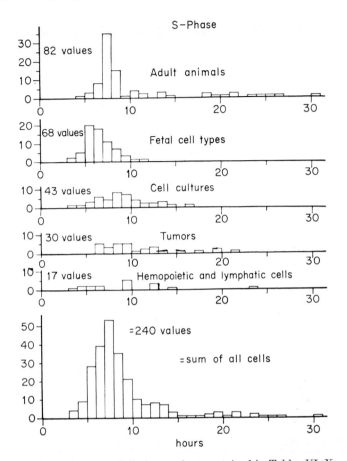

Fig. 11. Statistics of all S-phase values contained in Tables VI–X.

for the liver epithelium and the tubular epithelia of the kidney in adult rats. Wolfsberg (1964) estimated from her curves of percent labeled mitoses a value of 13.5 hours for the S phase of the prestomach epithelium of the mouse.

The influence of ploidy on the duration of S is of great interest and can be seen in Table IX. The question arises whether in higher ploidy stages the DNA synthesis rate has increased or the duration of S is prolonged. In some cases of tetraploid Ehrlich ascites tumor cells, the S phase was found to be about twice as long as in diploid Ehrlich ascites tumor cells (Table IX) (Lennartz et al., 1966, 1967). It is not yet certain how far this finding can be generally applied to tetraploid tumors. Further experiments should clarify this problem.

c. Mitosis. As demonstrated in the tables, the autoradiographic values

TABLE VI

DURATION OF THE GENERATION CYCLE AND ITS PHASES FOR VARIOUS CELL TYPES OF THE ADULT ANIMAL

Cell type	Age	Phases of cell cycle (in hours)					References
		G_2; M; G_2 + M	S	S + G_2 + M	Generation time T	G_1	
MOUSE							
Duodenum, crypt epithelial cells	93 days	G_2 = <1; G_2 + M = <2	6.9 (5)	—	11.5[b]/16.1	4.5–5.5	Lesher et al. (1961a)
	372 days	G_2 = <1; G_2 + M = <2	7.9 (5)	—	11.5[b]/18.4	4.5–5.5	
	940 days	G_2 = <1; G_2 + M = <2	11.1	—	<15.5[b]/25.8	—	
	Adult	M = 1.38	—	—	11.2–11.5	—	Fry et al. (1961a,b)
	Adult	—	7.4	—	18.5	—	Cameron and Greulich (1963)
Duodenum, stem cells	Adult	G_2 = 1; M = 0.5	4.5 ± 1	—	11	~4.8	Choumak (1963b)
	Adult	G_2 + M = ~2.0	7.0	—	12.0	~3	Maisin and Lambiet-Collier (1967)
Jejunum, crypt epithelial cells	Adult	G_2 = 40 min	7–8	—	~15	~6	Koburg and Maurer (1962)
	Adult	G_2 + M = <100 min; M = 0.8	7.5[a]	9	18	9	Pilgrim and Maurer (1965)
Ileum, crypt epithelial cells	Adult	G_2 = 0.5–1	7.5	~9.3	18.8	~9.5	Quastler and Sherman (1959)
	6–8 weeks	—	7.0	—	—	—	Sherman et al. (1961)
	Adult	—	7–8	—	—	—	Koburg and Maurer (1962)
	Adult	—	7.9[a]	—	—	—	Pilgrim and Maurer (1965)
	Adult	—	7.1	—	16.7	—	Cameron and Greulich (1963)
	Adult	—	6.4 ± 0.4	—	—	—	Wimber and Lamerton (1966)

Tissue	Age	Cell cycle phases					Reference
Colon, epithelium	Adult	$G_2 \geqq 1$; $M = {\sim}1.5$	~6.5	~8	16	~8	Lipkin and Quastler (1962)
	Adult	—	7.5	—	32.6	—	Cameron and Greulich (1963)
	Adult	—	7–8	—	—	—	Koburg and Maurer (1962)
	Adult	—	6.5–8.5[a]	—	—	—	Pilgrim and Maurer (1965)
	Infant	$G_2 + P = 1$–2	7.3	—	15[b]/32	—	Thrasher (1967)
	Adult (young)	$G_2 + P = 1$–2	8.0	—	19[b]/35	—	
	Adult	$G_2 + P = 1$–2	8.0	—	19[b]/39	—	
	Senescen	$G_2 + P = 1$–2	7.7	—	21[b]/49	—	
Skin							
Epidermis (back) basal layer	Adult	$G_2 \geqq 40$–80; $M = {\sim}1$; $G_2 + M = 1.5$–2.3	~6	—	—	—	Devik (1962)
Epidermis (stomach) basal layer	Adult	$M = 0.5$	6.2	~12	151	139	Pilgrim and Maurer (1965)
Hair follicle in growth	Adult	$G_2 = 1.5$	7.5 ± 1	—	13	—	McCarter and Quastler (1962b)
	Adult	$G_2 + M = \text{mean } 1.5$	7 ± 0.9	9	~12	3	Cattaneo et al. (1961)
Epidermis of the ear, basal layer	60–70 days old	$G_2 = 4.8$; $M = \text{ca. } 1.3$; $G_2 + M = \text{mean } 6.5$	~30	—	~528–586	~483–549	Sherman et al. (1961)
Buccal mucosa, basal layer	Adult	—	7.2	—	85	—	Cameron and Greulich (1963)
	Adult	$G_2 = 0.3$; $M = 0.7$	8	—	80	—	Toto and Dhawan (1966)
Incisors, preameloblasts	Adult	$G_2 = 0.82$; $M = 0.5$	5.5	—	14.2–24	7.4	Hwang et al. (1966)
Tongue, epithelium	Adult	—	7.0	—	40	—	Cameron and Greulich (1963)
	Adult	$G_2 = 20$ min; $M = 40$ min	10	—	—	89	Toto and Ojha (1962)
	Adult	$G_2 = 0.3$; $M = 0.7$	8	—	80	—	Toto and Dhawan (1966)

TABLE VI (Continued)

Cell type	Age	Phases of cell cycle (in hours)					References
		G_2; M; $G_2 + M$	S	$S + G_2 + M$	Generation time T	G_1	
Esophagus, epithelium	Adult	M = 0.4	7.3[a]	—	61	—	Pilgrim and Maurer (1965)
	Adult	G_2 = <1; $G_2 + M$ = <4	6.9	—	181	—	Cameron and Greulich (1963)
	Adult	M = 0.7	7.2[a]	~12	87	75	Pilgrim and Maurer (1965)
	Adult	G_2 = 40 min–10 hrs	—	—	—	—	Koburg and Maurer (1962)
Prestomach, epithelium	Adult	M = 1.0	6.9[a]	~12	168	156	Pilgrim and Maurer (1965)
	Adult	G_2 = 40 min–8 hrs	—	—	—	—	Koburg and Maurer (1962)
Cornea, epithelium	Adult	—	7	—	55	—	Frankfurt (1967a)
	Adult	G_2 = 1–2; M = 1–2	13.5	—	—	—	Wolfsberg (1964)
	Adult	G_2 = ~4; M = 0.75	8.5 ± 1	—	~72	~59	Choumak (1963a)
	Adult	—	8.7[a]	—	—	—	Pilgrim and Maurer (1965)
	Adult	G_2 = 3.5–9	—	—	—	—	Koburg and Maurer (1962)
Uterus, epithelium	Adult	M = 1.0; $G_2 + M$ = 2	8.5 ± 2	—	42	32.5	Epifanova (1963)
Mammary gland, alveoli	Adult	G_2 = 1; M = 1	8.5	—	42	31.5	Epifanova (1966)
	Adult	G_2 = ~3; M = ~1.6	21.7	—	71	45.7	Bresciani (1965a)
Mammary gland alveolar cells (C3H/He mouse) Day 8 of pregnancy	Adult	—	14.1	—	—	—	Banerjee and Walker (1967a)
Day 15 of pregnancy Ductus seminiferus			8.2				

							Reference
Spermatogonia							
Type AI	Adult	$G_2 = 14$	7–7.5	—	27–30.5	7.5–10.5	Monesi (1962)
Type AII	Adult	$G_2 = 14$	7–7.5	—	27–30.5	7.5–10.5	
Type AIII	Adult	$G_2 = 11$	8	—	27–30.5	7.5–10.5	
Type AIV	Adult	$G_2 = 8$	13	—	27–30.5	7.5–10.5	
Intermed. type	Adult	$G_2 = 6$	12.5	—	27–30.5	7.5–10.5	
Type B	Adult	$G_2 = 4.5$	14.5	—	27–30.5	7.5–10.5	
Liver, mesenchyme cells	Adult	—	7.8[a]	—	—	—	Pilgrim and Maurer (1965)
parenchyma cells	Adult	—	7.0[a]	—	—	—	
Kidney	Adult	—	7.3[a]	—	—	—	
Adrenal gland	Adult	—	7.5[a]	—	~29	8–10	Khrushchov (1963)
Fibroblasts	Adult	$G_2 = 2\text{–}3; M = {\sim}3.5$	11–12	—	21–22	$M + G_1\ 9\text{–}11$	
Macrophages	—	$G_2 = 2\text{–}3$	8–9	—	—	—	
RAT							
Duodenum crypt	Adult	—	7.2[a]	—	—	—	Pilgrim and Maurer (1965)
Jejunum crypt	Adult	—	7.6[a]	—	—	—	
Ileum crypt	Adult	—	7.6[a]	—	—	—	
Colon crypt	Adult	—	7.8–8.1[a]	—	—	—	
Epidermis, epithelium	Adult	—	4.8–8.0[a]	—	—	—	
Tongue, epithelium	Adult	—	7.7[a]	—	—	—	
Salivary gland	Adult	—	8.0[a]	—	—	—	
Esophagus	Adult	—	4.8–5.5[a]	—	—	—	
Prestomach, epithelium	Adult	—	7.2–9.6[a]	—	—	—	
Stomach, epithelium	Adult	—	7.8[a]	—	—	—	
Cornea, epithelium	Adult	—	7.7[a]	—	—	—	
Uterus (gland), epithelium	Adult	—	8.2[a]	—	—	—	
Ovary, follicle cells	Adult	—	8.0[a]	—	—	—	
Theca cells	Adult	—	8.1[a]	—	—	—	
Kidney tubule, epithelium	Adult	—	7.0[a]	—	—	—	
Lung (alveolar cells)	Adult	—	7.2[a]	—	—	—	
Jejunum, crypt epithelium	~56 days	$G_2 = 1; M = 1$	6.5	—	10.5	2	Cairnie et al. (1965a,b)

TABLE VI (Continued)

Cell type	Age	Phases of cell cycle (in hours)					References
		G_2; M; $G_2 + M$	S	$S + G_2 + M$	Generation time T	G_1	
Germinal-center cells	—	G_2 = 30 min	~5	—	13.4	—	Fliedner et al. (1964a)
Liver, parenchyma cells	Adult	G_2 min = ~2.5; M max = ~5.5	~18	—	—	—	Stöcker and Heine (1965b)
Kidney tubule, epithelium	Adult	G_2 min = ~1.8; M max = ~5.8	~18	—	—	—	
Lens epithelium	Adult (young)	G_2 = >5; M = 1.2	~10	—	—	—	Scullica et al. (1963)
Hair bulbs	10 days	$G_2 + M$ = 2.0	7	—	13	4	Smoliar (1966)
Resting spermatocytes	Adult	—	26.2[a]	—	—	—	Hilscher and Maurer (1962)
Ductus seminiferus Spermatogonia	Adult						
Type AI	Adult	G_2 = 11.0	19.5	31	~144	~114	Hilscher et al. (1966)
Type AII	Adult	G_2 = 9.0	20.5	31	39	9.5	
Type AIII	Adult	G_2 = 8.0	21.0	31	42	13.0	
Type AIV	Adult	G_2 = 7.0	23.0	31	42	12.0	
Intermed. type	Adult	G_2 = 6.0	24.0	31	42	12.0	
Type B	Adult	G_2 = 5.5	25.5	31	42	11.0	
HAMSTER							
Basal epithelium of pouch	Adult	G_2 = 2-3	8-12	—	—	—	Reiskin and Mendelsohn (1962)
Seminiferus, epithelium		G_2 = 1.6; M = 2.6	10.2	—	142	—	Reiskin and Mendelsohn (1964)
			—	—	216	—	de Rooij (1968)
Bone marrow cells	Adult	G_2 = <2	>8	—	10-12	—	Utakoji and Hsu (1965)

RABBIT						
Lens, epithelium (germinative zone)	Adult	$G_2 = 1\text{-}4$	9-13	—	—	—	Thomson et al. (1962)
Spermatogonia	Adult	$G_2 = <4$	~8	—	—	—	Srinivasan (1964)
Type A	Adult	—	—	—	82	—	Swierstra and Foote (1965)
Intermed. type I	Adult	—	—	—	14	—	
Intermed. type II	Adult	—	—	—	67	—	
Intermedia. type B	Adult	—	—	—	26	—	
SHEEP						
Wool follicle cells	Adult	$G_2 + P = 1.6$	9.5 ± 2.7	11.6	21	9.4	Downes et al. (1966)
HUMAN						
Colon and rectum	Adult	$G_2 = 1\text{-}2$	11-15	—	10-30	—	Lipkin et al. (1963b)
		$M = <1$	—	—	—	—	Lipkin (1965)
Stomach						
Ileum						
Colon	Adult	$G_2 = 2$	9-14	—	—	—	Lipkin et al. (1963c)
Rectum						
Triturus veridescens						
Lens regeneration	15 days	$G_2 = {\sim}2$	~19.0	—	65	~40.0	Zalik and Yamada (1967)

[a] Double-labeling method.
[b] Percentage of labeled mitoses method.

TABLE VII
DURATION OF THE GENERATION CYCLE AND ITS PHASES FOR VARIOUS CELL TYPES OF EMBRYOS AND NEWBORN ANIMALS

Cell types	Age	Phases of cell cycle (in hours)					References
		G_2; M; G_2 + M	S	S + G_2 + M	Generation time T	G_1	
MOUSE							
Placenta							
Trophoblast cells	8-day (grav.)	—	7.0	—	9.4	—	Cameron (1964)
Trophoblast cells	12-day (grav.)	—	6.5	—	15.0	—	
Yolk sac epithelium	12-day (grav.)	—	7.1	—	—	—	
Embryos							
Tail epithelia	13-day (grav.)	G_2 + ½M 1.5	6.25	—	—	1.25 (G_1 + ½M)	Wimber (1963)
Ependymal and mesenchymal cells	11-day (grav.)	G_2 = 1; M = ~1	5.5	—	~11	3.5	Atlas and Bond (1965)
Erythroblasts neural tube	10-day (grav.)	—	4	—	~11 8.5	—	Kauffman (1966)
neural tube	10-day (grav.)	G_2 + ½ M 1.25, G_2 = 0.59, M = 1.32	4.62	—	8.5	1.97	Kauffman (1968)
	11-day (grav.)	G_2 = 1.15, M = 1.23	5.38	—	10.5	2.74	
Embryonic cells	4–10 day (grav.)	—	4–6	—	6–12	—	Zavarzin et al. (1966)
Newborn, cerebellum external granular layer	10–11 days	G_2 = 2; M = 0.5	8	—	19	8.5	Fujita (1967)
RAT							
Embryos							
Intestinal epithelia		G_2 = 1.8; M = 0.6	5.6	7.9	13.5	5.6	Wegener et al. (1964)

						Reference
Salivary gland	$G_2 = 1.2$; $M = 0.8$	5.7	7.7	15.8	8.1	Zavarzin (1964)
Skin, basal layer	$G_2 = 1.7$; $M = 0.7$	5.5	7.9	18.9	11.0	
Tongue, epithelium	$G_2 = 1.6$; $M = 0.5$	5.6	7.7	23.3	15.6	
Tongue, muscle	$G_2 = 1.9$; $M = 0.3$	6.8	9.0	32.5	23.5	
Hibernation gland	$G_2 = 1.4$; $M = 0.4$	5.6	7.5	34.7	27.2	
Cartilage, parenchyma	$G_2 = 1.8$; $M = 0.7$	7.3	9.8	40.5	30.7	
Pancreas, exocrine	$G_2 = 1.5$; $M = 1.2$	6.2	8.8	40.4	31.6	
Nose, epithelium	$G_2 = 1.8$	6.1	—	—	—	
Kidney, epithelium	$G_2 = 1.7$	5.8	—	—	—	
Retina	$G_2 = 1.9$	~6.5	—	—	—	
Ependyma	$G_2 = 1.7$	~8.5	—	—	—	
Embryos Duodenal epithelium 15-day (grav.)	$G_2 = 1.0$	7.0	—	17.0	$G_1 + M = 9.0$	Zavarzin et al. (1964)
18-day (grav.)	$G_2 = 1.0$	4.5	—	9.5	$G_1 + M = 4.0$	
20-day (grav.)	$G_2 = 1.0$	5.0	—	12.5	$G_1 + M = 6.5$	
Newborn Duodenal epithelium 1 day old	$G_2 = 1.5$	7.0	—	14.5	$G_1 + M = 6.0$	
	$G_2 = 1.5$	8.0	—	18.5	$G_1 + M = 9.0$	
Embryos Salivary gland 15-day (grav.)	$G_2 = 2.0$	6.0	—	16.0	$G_1 + M = 8.0$	Zavarzin et al. (1964)
18-day (grav.)	$G_2 = 1.5$	5.2	—	24.2	$G_1 + M = 17.5$	
Embryos Pancreas 15-day (grav.)	$G_2 = 2.0$	7.0	—	22.0	$G_1 + M = 13.0$	
18-day (grav.)	$G_2 = 2.0$	5.0	—	11.0	$G_1 + M = 4.0$	
20-day (grav.)	$G_2 = 2.0$	5.5	—	20.5	$G_1 + M = 13.0$	
Newborn (pancreas) 1 day old	$G_2 = 2.0$	7.0	—	>30.0	$G_1 + M = {>}21.0$	
Embryos Stratified flat squamous epithelium (tail) 15-day (grav.)	$G_2 = 1.0$	6.0	—	~17.0	$G_1 + M = {\sim}10$	Lebedeva and Zavarzin (1964)

TABLE VII (*Continued*)

Cell types	Age	Phases of cell cycle (in hours)					References
		G_2; M; $G_2 + M$	S	$S + G_2 + M$	Generation time T	G_1	
Embryos CNS matrix cells, ependymal layer	15–day (grav.)	$G_2 = 1.5$	6.8	—	16.3	$G_1 + M = 8.0$	Gracheva (1964d)
	18–day (grav.)	$G_2 = 2.0$	5.5	—	20.0	$G_1 + M = 12.5$	
	20–day (grav.)	$G_2 = 2.0$	5.5	—	18.0	$G_1 + M = 10.5$	
Newborn, CNS matrix cells, ependymal layer	1 day old	$G_2 = 2.0$	11.7	—	26.0	$G_1 + M = 12.3$	
Embryos Spinal cord Ependymal layer	15–day (grav.)	$G_2 = 1.5$	6.8	—	13.3	$G_1 + M = 5.0$	Gracheva (1964d)
Embryos Cerebellum ependymal layer	15–day (grav.)	$G_2 = 1.0$	7.5	—	18.0	$G_1 + M = 9.5$	Nevmivaka (1964)
External granular layer	18–day (grav.)	$G_2 = 2.0$	5.0	—	21.0	$G_1 + M = 15.0$	
Ependymal layer	18–day (grav.)	$G_2 = 2.0$	4.0	—	—	—	
Newborn External granular layer	1 day old	$G_2 = 1.0$	9.5	—	26.5	$G_1 + M = 16.0$	
Internal granular layer	1 day old	$G_2 = 1.0$	8.5	—	—	—	
Embryos Eye Retina Central zone	15–day (grav.)	$G_2 = 1.5$	10.5	—	19.5	$G_1 + M = 7.5$	Zavarzin and Stroyeva (1964)
Peripheral zone, marginal zone		$G_2 = 2.0$	6.5	—	15.5	$G_1 + M = 7.0$	
Iris Central zone		$G_2 = 2.0$	6.5	—	—	—	

Cells	Age		S				Reference
Peripheral zone, marginal zone		$G_2 = 2.0$	6.5	—	—	—	Zavarzin and Lebedeva (1964)
Lens, proliferative zone	15-day (grav.)	—	5.5	—	17.0	$G_1 + M = 10.5$	
Epithelium		—	5.5	—	17.5	$G_1 + M = 11.0$	
Newborn							
Lens, proliferative zone]	1 day old	—	9	—	—	—	Andreeva (1964)
Embryos							
Placenta	12-day (grav.)	—	7.1	—	15.4	—	
Trophoblast cells (giant cells)	14-day (grav.)	—	6.3	—	23.6	—	
	15-day (grav.)	—	6.1	—	31.0	—	
Diploid	14-day (grav.)	$M = 0.5$	5.5	—	12–13	4.5–5.5	Zhinkin and Andreeva (1963)
	15-day (grav.)	$G_2 = 1.5$	5.5	—	13.0	$M + G_1 = 7.5$	
Monoploid	14-day (grav.)	$M = 0.7$	4.0	—	12.0	5.8	
	15-day (grav.)	$G_2 = 1.5$	3.7	—	10.0	—	
	17-day (grav.)	$M + G_1 + G_2 = 6.3$					
tongue muscle	6 days old	$G_2 = \sim 3$	6–7	—	18–21	8–10	Young (1962d)
Newborn, tibia cells	6 days old	G_2 min, $G_2 + M_{max}$,					
Metaphysis		1–1.5 2.5–3	8	—	36	—	
Endosteum		1–1.5 3.0–4	8	—	57	—	
Periosteum		1.5–2.0 3.0–4	8	—	114	—	
adrenal cortex parenchymal cells	6 days old						Ford and Young (1963)
Zona glomerulosa		1.0–1.5 <4.0	<8	—	80	—	
Zona fasciculata		1.5–2.0 <5.5	<8	—	~250	—	
Liver, parenchymal cells	21 days old	$G_2 = 0.5$; $M = 3.0$	9	—	21.5	9	Post et al. (1963)
Ileum	21 days old	$G_2 + M = 1$	6.0	—	—	2.0	Post and Hoffman (1968)
Prespermatogenesis	0–1 day	$G_2 = 4.8-2.9$	20.0	—	38.0	11.0–12.9	Hilscher and Makoski (1968)
Supporting cells		$M = 2.2$					
Gonocytes					192–268		

TABLE VII (Continued)

Cell type	Age	G_2; M; $G_2 + M$	S	$S + G_2 + M$	Generation time T	G_1	References
CHICKEN							
Bone marrow	7 days old	$G_2 + P = 2.5$	9.0	—	17.5	6.0	Bianchi and Molina (1967)
Liver epithelia	1.7 days old		6.0 ± 0.2	—	—	—	Mitroiu et al. (1968)
Kidney, tubulus epithelia	1.7 days old		5.0 ± 0.2	—	—	—	
Esophagus, basal epithelia	1.7 days old		5.1 ± 0.3	—	—	—	
Pectoral muscle	1.7 days old		3.9 ± 0.3	—	—	—	
Liver epithelia	20.7 days old		4.9	—	—	—	
Kidney, tubulus epithelia	20.7 days old		5.0	—	—	—	
Esophagus, basal epithelia	20.7 days old		5.8	—	—	—	
Pectoral muscle	20.7 days old		4.1	—	—	—	
Embryonic cells (neural tube)		$G_2 = 3.0$; M = 1.0	3.5	—	10.5	3.0	Dondua and Fedorova (1964)
New Hatched Duodenum crypt cells	2.5 days old		5.0				Cameron (1964)
Proventralis			6.0				
Proventralis gland			5.0				
Liver parenchyma			5.5				
Pancreas acini			5.0				
Pleurodeles walttii							
Young larvae	—	—	~30	—	42-48	—	Chibon (1968)

obtained for the duration of M are very similar. However, the accuracy of the values is small. Frequently the values are only rough estimates, because of methodological difficulties. There are no distinct differences between fetal and newborn tissues and those of adult animals. Generally there is a good agreement between these values and those evaluated by the colchicine method.

d. G_2 phase. Compared to the S phase and mitosis the duration of G_2 differs much more from one cell type to another in the adult animal. Furthermore, there are considerable individual variations of G_2 within one and the same cell type. However, considering the big differences in the generation times of the individual cell types, even the duration of G_2 is quite similar for the majority of cells. In the intestinal epithelia of the adult animal, in the rapidly growing fetal cells, and in other rapidly proliferating tissues, the duration of G_2 is relatively short and quite similar from one cell type to the other.

e. Time interval between the beginning of the S phase and the end of mitosis $(S + G_2 + M)$. As a number of authors have pointed out, the duration of $(S + G_2 + M)$ seems to be quite constant for most of the cell types investigated. This becomes especially evident for fetal cells of the rat (Table VII). $(S + G_2 + M)$ is surprisingly constant, whereas G_1 varies between 5.6 and 30 hours. In newborn rats (Table VII) $(S + G_2 + M)$ is still rather constant; however, G_1 varies much more. In the adult animal (Table VI) $(S + G_2 + M)$ is longer and shows greater variation due especially to G_2. However, compared to the great variations of the generation times, $(S + G_2 + M)$ can be considered as surprisingly constant (see also Cairnie *et al.*, 1965a). The same seems to be true for tumor cells (Table IX) and for cultured cells (Sisken and Morasca, 1965). This means that cells of widely different types, after having entered the S phase, follow a very similar time scale up to the end of mitosis.

f. Significance of the G_1 phase for the cell cycle. The great differences in the generation cycle of different cell types is obviously due mainly to the variations in G_1. Compared to these variations, the smaller differences in $(S + G_2 + M)$ are of minor importance.

During the development from the fetal to the adult organism, the duration of the S phase increases insignificantly, and mitosis changes little. The G_2 phase, about constant during fetal life, increases considerably during development to an adult animal and shows individual variations. G_1, however, shows the most important change. With increasing differentiation, G_1 increases and varies considerably (Pilgrim and Maurer, 1965; Wegener *et al.*, 1964).

g. Tumor cells. In the case of tumor cells, mainly short-lived ones have been investigated up to now, since it is much easier to study tumor cells

TABLE VIII
DURATION OF THE GENERATION CYCLE AND ITS PHASES FOR BLOOD AND BONE MARROW CELLS

Cell type	Phases of cell cycle (hours)					References
	G_2; M; $G_2 + M$	S	$S + G_2 + M$	Generation time T	G_1	
HUMAN						
Polychromatic normoblasts	$G_2 + M = 3$	9	—	15–18	3–6	Bond et al. (1959)
Pronormoblasts and basophilic normoblasts (in vitro)	—	—	—	~20	—	Lajtha and Oliver (1960)
Red cell precursors	—	~12	—	—	—	Stryckmans et al. (1964)
White cell precursors	—	~14	—	—	—	Stryckmans et al. (1966)
Red cell precursors	—	~9	—	—	—	Killmann et al. (1964)
Neutrophile precursors	—	~24	—	—	—	
Erythropoietic and granulopoietic cells	—	9–12	—	—	—	Cronkite (1964)
Leukocytes	$G_2 = 3.5$	9.6	—	17.7	4.6	Cave (1966)
	$G_2 = \sim6$	~12	—	~52	$G_1 + M$	Levina et al. (1966)
					~34	Levina and Shapiro (1967)
Leukemic myeloblasts	—	—	—	12–18	—	Monti et al. (1963)
Leukemic bone marrow cells	—	—	—	15–20	—	Mauer and Fisher (1966)
DOG						
More mature erythrocytic precursors	$G_2 = 0.5–1;$ $M = <1$	6.5–7.5	—	—	—	Bond et al. (1962b)
Myelocytes	$G_2 = 0.5–1;$ $M = 1–1.5$	4.5–5	—	10	3–4	Patt and Maloney (1963)

Myelocytes, red cell precursors	—		5–6	—	—	Lala et al. (1965)
Red cell precursors	$G_2 = 1$; $M = 1$	6	—	10	2	Lala et al. (1966)
GUINEA PIGS						
Small lymphocytes	—	—	—	21	—	Osmond and Everett (1964)
CALF						
Lymphocytes (ductus thoracicus)	$G_2 = 0.5\text{–}0.7$; $M = 0.5$	3.5	—	5.5–6	1	Wagner et al. (1967)
MOUSE						
Normal large and medium lymphocytes (thymus)	$G_2 + M = 1.3$	5.5	—	6.8–8.2	1.4	Metcalf and Wiadrowski (1966)
Lymphoma large and medium cells	$G_2 + M = 1.6\text{–}2.2$	6.0	—	7.6–20.2	12.0	Frindel et al. (1967a)
Bone marrow cells	$G_{2\,min} = 0.25$; $M = 0.17$	4.5	—	8.5	—	
Leukemia tumor L1210 cells (in vivo)	$G_2 + M + G_1 = 2.9$	8.9	—	11.8	—	Yankee et al. (1967)
Mouse in culture Leukemia L1210 cells (in vivo, in vitro)	$G_2 = 1.5$; $M = 0.5$	11.7	—	15.7	2.0	Wheeler et al. (1967)

TABLE IX
DURATION OF THE GENERATION CYCLE AND ITS PHASES FOR VARIOUS TUMOR CELLS

Type of tumor	Number of chromosomes, ploidy	Phases of cell cycle (hours)					References
		G_2; M; G_2 + M	S	S + G_2 + M	Generation time T	G_1	
Ehrlich ascites, 6 days	92 % diploid $Z = 36–46$; 8 % hypertetraploid $Z = 86–87$	M = ~1	9[b]	—	24	—	Lennartz and Maurer (1964)
M Ca l, 6 days	88 % diploid $Z = 34–44$; 12 % hypertetraploid $Z = 70–80$	M = ~0.5	8.5	—	18.5	—	Lennartz et al. (1966)
Ehrlich ascites, 4 days	Tetraploid	G_2 + M = 6	~12	—	15–18	—	Hornsey and Howard (1956)
Ehrlich ascites, 3 days	Hyperdiploid, $Z_m = 51$	$G_2 = 1.5$; M = ~5	8.5	—	18[c]	3.0	Edwards et al. (1960)
Ehrlich ascites, 4 days	Hypotetraploid	$G_2 + P^d = 6$	11	—	18	—	Baserga (1963)
Ehrlich ascites, 5 days	Hyperdiploid Z_m ~46	$G_2 = 4$	6.5–7	—	15	2.5–4.5	Defendi and Manson (1963)
Ehrlich ascites, 5 days	Hypertetraploid Z_m ~92	$G_2 = 6$	13–14	—	>38	>16	Lennartz et al. (1966)
Ehrlich ascites, 5 days	Hypertetraploid Z_m ~92	M = ~1	19.5	—	41.2	—	Lennartz et al. (1968a)
MCa1	Hypodiploid	G_2 + M = 4	9	—	42	—	
MCIM	Hypotetraploid	G_2 + M = 6; M = 0.75	12.5	—	44	—	Lennartz et al. (1968b)
MCIM ascites sarcoma	Hypertriploid	G_2 + M = 6; M = 0.83	18.2	—	44.0	—	
Ehrlich ascites, 4 and 6 days	92 % diploid $Z = 36–46$	G_2 + M = 4; M = 0.83	10	—	24.0	—	Lederer and Lennartz (1968)
	Hyperdiploid (ELD)	G_2 + M = 6; M = 0.75	11.5	—	25.0	—	
	Hypertetraploid (ELT)	G_2 + M = 6; M = 0.92	19.5	—	42.0	—	

TABLE IX (Continued)

Type of tumor	Number of chromosomes, ploidy	Phases of cell cycle (hours)					References
		G_2; M; $G_2 + M$	S	$S + G_2 + M$	Generation time T	G_1	
Ehrlich ascites, 6 days	Tetraploid	—	19	—	—	—	Helpap and Maurer (1967a,b)
Ehrlich ascites, 6 days	Hyperdiploid	—	14	—	—	—	
Ehrlich ascites, solid	Diploid	—	8	—	—	—	
Crocker sarcoma (mouse)	—	—	8	—	—	—	
Jensen sarcoma (rat)	—	—	9	—	—	—	
Guérin sarcoma (rat)	—	—	9	—	—	—	
Melanoma B16 (mouse)	—	—	7	—	—	—	
Mouse sarcoma, 180	—	$G_2 = 2.5$; $M = \sim 0.5$	7.8	—	13.5	2.7	Simpson-Herren et al. (1968)
Ehrlich ascites	Hyperdiploid	$G_2 + P = 3.5$	8.1	—	22	—	Sawicki et al. (1967a)
Ehrlich ascites	Hypertetraploid	$G_2 + P = 4.25$	9.4	—	20	—	
Ehrlich ascites, 10 days	—	$G_2 = 7$	16-25	—	46	18	Tolnai (1965)
Ehrlich ascites, 12 days "Ballon cells"	—	—	~8	—	—	—	Oehlert et al. (1962b)
NK/Ly ascites lymphoma cells	—	$G_2 + M = 3.5$	9.0	—	20-21	8.0	Varga and Varteresz (1968)
Transplantable spontaneous Breast cancer of C3H mouse	—	$G_2 = 1-4$	~10	11-16	24-84	—	Mendelsohn et al. (1960)
Mammary tumor (mouse)	—	$M = 0.9$	11.6	—	~33	16.5-19.5	Bresciani (1965b)
Mammary gland CH3/He mouse	—	—	8.5-21.5	—	—	—	Banerjee and Walker (1967a)
Mammary gland, hyperplastic, alveolar nodules, C3H/He mouse (transplanted)	—	—	13.7	—	—	—	Banerjee and Walker (1967b)
Mammary tumor (mouse)	—	$G_2 = 1$	12	—	16	3	Goldfeder (1965)
Spindel cell tumor	—	$G_2 = 2.5$	6	—	16	7.5	Reiskin and Mendelsohn (1962)
Epithelial cell tumor	—	$G_2 = 2.2$	6	—	—	—	
Pouch tumor of hamster	—	$M = 0.4-0.6$	6.1	—	17.5-20.7	—	Reiskin and Mendelsohn (1964)

TABLE IX (Continued)

Type of tumor	Number of chromosomes, ploidy	Phases of cell cycle (hours)					References
		G_2; M; G_2 + M	S	S + G_2 + M	Generation time T	G_1	
Hamster cheek pouch		G_2　　M					
DEA basal epithelium		1.14　2.15	9.3	—	—	142.4	Reiskin and Berry (1968)
Golden basal epithelium		2.6　1.6	9.9	—	—	126.4	
DEA newborn epithelium		1.56　0.27	6.7	—	—	20.6	
DEA hyperplastic epithelium		2.0　1.18	10.38	—	—	47.4	
DEA tumor		1.97　0.56	6.48	—	—	11.0	
Golden tumor		1.76　0.60	7.9	—	—	10.9	
Cream tumor		1.74　0.66	7.4	—	—	17.2	
Experimental fibrosarcoma, C3H mice		G_2 + M = 2.25	12	—	17	2.75	Frindel et al. (1967b)
Fibrosarcoma in hamster (Polyoma virus)	Aneuploid Z_m = 43	G_2 = 4	8	—	17	3–7	Defendi and Manson (1963)
Transplantable fibrosarcoma in mice (methylcholanthrene)	—	G_2 = 1–2	7	—	16	—	Johnson (1961)
Melanosarcoma (Harding-Passey) in mouse strain NMRI	—	G_2 = 1.5–4.0	8.2	11	26–36	15–25	Hempel (1966a)
Lymphoblastic leukemia of mouse (HeLa L 5178)	Aneuploid Z_m = 43	G_2 = 2(1 − 5)	6.9–7.4	—	11.5	~1.5	Defendi and Manson (1961)
Burkitt lymphoma	—	G_2 + ½M = 3.5	12	—	20	G_1 + M = 3.5	Cooper et al. (1966)
Human cancer HeLa S3	Aneuploid	G_2 = 3 M = 0.7	9.5	—	21	8	Terasima (1964)
Human basal cells epithelioma	—	G_2 + M = ~11	~19	—	72–96	—	Malaise et al. (1967)
Human epithelial adenocarcinoma	—	G_2 = 2 M = 1.5	9	—	28[a]	—	Kasten and Strasser (1966b)
Yoshida sarcoma	—	G_2 = 2.5	9–9.5	—	18.5	5.5–6	Kurita et al. (1964)

TABLE IX (Continued)

Type of tumor	Number of chromosomes, ploidy	G_2; M; G_2 + M		S	S + G_2 + M	Generation time T	G_1	References
		G_2	M					
Yoshida sarcoma (rat) Nitrogen-mustard sensitive	—	10.5	3.0	42.8	—	—	41.9	Ball et al. (1967)
	—	12.2	2.3	36.9	—	—	48.6	
	—	17.6	2.1	39.3	—	—	38.1	
	—	13.5	2.2	40.2	—	—	39.4	
	—	12.2	1.0	38.7	—	—	46.9	
	—	12.3	1.4	44.0	—	—	41.3	
Yoshida sarcoma (rat) Nitrogen-mustard resistant	—	G_2	M					
	—	6.1	2.1	44.8	—	—	47.0	
	—	13.9	1.5	43.5	—	—	40.5	
	—	7.9	2.5	39.5	—	—	49.5	
	—	7.9	1.4	42.5	—	—	48.2	
	—	9.3	2.9	45.5	—	—	42.3	
	—	4.1	3.5	39.5	—	—	53.1	
Human sarcoma HLS$_2$	—	G_2 = 4–6; M = 1–2		—	—	—	—	Bose et al. (1965a)
Human sarcoma HLS$_2$	—	G_2 = 5; M = 1		6	—	30	18	Bose et al. (1966)
Mouse fibrosarcoma MFS$_8$	—	G_2 = 2; M = <2		—	—	—	—	Bose et al. (1964)
Mouse fibrosarcoma MFS$_8$	—	G_2 = 3.5; M = 1.5		6	—	16	5	Bose et al. (1965b)
Human myxofibrosarcoma HFS$_9$	—	G_2 = 5; M = 1		7	—	19	6	Bose et al. (1966)
Hepatoma cells	—	G_2 + M = 2		17	—	31	12	Post and Hoffman (1964)

a Cinematographic values.
b Double-labeling method.
c Evaluated by cell counting.
d P = Prophase.

TABLE X
DURATION OF THE GENERATION CYCLE AND ITS PHASES FOR CULTURED CELLS

Cultured cells	Phases of cell cycle (hours)					References
	G_2; M; G_2 + M	S	S + G_2 + M	Generation time T	G_1	
HUMAN						
Fibroblasts	G_2 = 3–6	7–7.5	—	—	—	Moorhead and Defendi (1963)
	G_2 = 5	9	—	—	—	Schwarzacher and Schnedl (1965)
	G_2 = 5	7.5	—	21	8.5	Comings (1967a)
Amnion cells	G_2 + P = 2.4; M = ∼0.3	∼9.0	—	18.3–23.6	6.3–11.9[b]	Sisken and Kinosita (1961a)
	G_2 = 5–9	16	—	—	up to 24	Terskikh (1965)
Bone marrow cells	G_2 = 3–4	12–15	—	40–45	25–30	Lajtha et al. (1954a,b)
Human diploid cells (3 strains) Z_m = 46	G_2 = 4	7.5	—	18	4.5–8	Defendi and Manson (1963)
Normal early trophoblast	G_2 = 2.0	5.5	—	15	7.0	Gerbie et al. (1968)
L. 809 cells diploid	G_2 = 4.0 M = 1.0	8.0	—	19	6.0	Adolphe et al. (1968)
HeLa P_7	G_2 = 3.5 M = 0.5	7.0	—	35	24.0	Toliver and Simon (1967)
HeLa S_{3-P}	G_2 = 4.6 M = 1.1	6.0	—	20	8.4	Puck and Steffen (1963)
HeLa cells (horse serum, 10%)	G_2 = 3–10	8.5	—	∼28	∼14	Painter and Drew (1959)

TABLE X (Continued)

Cultured cells	Phases of cell cycle (hours)			Generation time T	G_1	References
	G_2; M; $G_2 + $ M	S	$S + G_2 + $ M			
HeLa cells (calf serum, 15%)	$G_2 = 2$–8	5–6	—	25	~14	
HeLa S3 cells	$G_2 = 2.3$; $M = 0.7$	9.5	—	21	8.5	Terasima and Tolmach (1963c)
HeLa S3 cells (synchronized)	$G_2 = 2.6$–2.9	10.2–10.3	—	22	8.8–9.2	
HeLa S3 cells	$G_2 = 4.4$; $M = 1.1$	5.8	$S + G_2 = >21$	20.1	8.0	Puck (1964)
	$G_2 = 3 \pm 1.5$ $M = 0.8 \pm 0.3$	—		34 ± 2.5	—	Kozuka and Moore (1966)
	$G_2 = 5$	8.5	—	28	$G_1 + M = 14$	Defendi and Manson (1963)
	$G_2 = 5.8$–8	10.5–11	—	28–32.8	8.5–14.9	Wainson and Kuzin (1965)
	$G_2 = 8$	10.5	—	28	8.5	Kuzin and Wainson (1966)
Kidney cells Type To	$G_2 = 4.5$	8.5	—	23	10	Bootsma (1965)
Type Tlv	$G_2 = 5.5$	9	—	28.5	14	
MOUSE L-strain cells	$G_2 = 3 \pm 0.7$; $M = {\sim}1$	7 ± 1.3	—	—	9 ± 3.3	Till (1961)
	$G_2 = 2$–4; $M = {\sim}1$	6–7	—	—	9–11	Whitmore et al. (1961)
	$G_2 = 4.8$	12.2	—	23.2	6.2	Cleaver (1965)
	$G_2 = 3$	14	—	20	3	Dendy and Cleaver (1964)

4. DNA SYNTHESIS

TABLE X (Continued)

Cultured cells	G_2; M; $G_2 + M$	S	$S + G_2 + M$	Generation time T	G_1	References
L cells L60	$G_2 = 3$	6–7	—	20	9–11	Stanners and Till (1960)
L strain fibro-blasts	$G_2 = 3.4$–3.8	6.2–6.4	—	—	8–8.2	Mak (1965)
Fibroblasts L-P59	$G_2 = 2.3$; M = 0.7	9.9	—	22	9.1	Dewey and Humphrey (1962)
C3H-M	$G_2 + P = 5.0$	11.5	—	25	—	Sawicki et al. (1967a)
C3H-E	$G_2 + P = 4.75$	11.5	—	25	—	
C3H-L	$G_2 + P = 4.0$	12.0	—	26	—	
L-929	$G_2 + P = 4.0$	8.5	—	23.5	—	
RAT						
Fibroblasts	$G_2 = 4$	13–14	—	25–63	7–45	Jaskowetz (1966)
Sarcoma 45	$G_2 = 4$–6	10–16	—	45–55	27–37	
CALF						
Fetal liver cells	$G_2 = 6$; M = 1	8	—	31	16	Kuyper et al. (1962a)
HAMSTER						
Fibroblast-like cells	$G_2 + P = \sim4$	8.5	—	$\sim$16–17	—	Prescott and Bender (1963a)
Connective tissue of embryos	$G_2 = 2$–3	6	—	14	5–6	Taylor (1960b, 1962a)
Ovary cells	$G_2 = 2.8$; M = 0.8	4.1	—	12.4	4.7	Puck et al. (1964); Puck (1964)
Chinese hamster cells	$G_2 = 2$–3 M = 1.0	7–8	—	16	4–5	Lomakina et al. (1967)

TABLE X (Continued)

Cultured cells	Phases of cell cycle (hours)					References
	G_2; M; G_2 + M	S	S + G_2 + M	Generation time T	G_1	
Chinese hamster cells *in vitro*	G_2 = 3.0	10.0	—	17.5	4.5	Monesi *et al.* (1967)
Chinese hamster cells	M = 0.4; G_2 + M = 2.5	5.8	—	11	2.7	Hsu *et al.* (1962)
	G_2 = 2	6–7	—	14	G_1 + M, 5–6	Taylor (1960d)
RABBIT						
Kidney cortex cells	G_2 = 4	10	—	—	32	Kishimoto and Lieberman (1964)
Blast cells of immunized animals (spleen)	G_2 = 0.7; M = 0.5	5–6.8	—	8–9	<1	Sado and Makinodan (1964)
Ocular lens (central cells)	—	—	S + G_2 = ~11–15	—	—	Wilson *et al.* (1967)
Eggs	G_2 = 10–12	3–4	—	—	—	Szollosi (1966)

P = prophase.

[a] G_1 + anaphase + telophase.

TABLE XI

DURATION OF THE GENERATION CYCLE AND ITS PHASES FOR PLANT CELLS

Plant	T	G_1	S	G_2	M	References
Allium cepa	17.4	—	10.9	—	—	Van't Hof (1965)
Allium fistulosum	18.8	—	10.3	—	—	
Allium tuberosum	20.6	—	11.8	—	—	
Belleeali	21	8	8–6	6	1	Taylor (1961)
Crepis capillaris	10.75	—	3.25	—	—	Van't Hof (1965)
Haplopappus gracilis	10.5	~3.5	4.0	1.44	1.61	Sparvoli et al. (1966)
Haplopappus gracilis	22.0	9.34	6.4	4.86	1.4	Eriksson (1967)
Helianthus annuus	9.0	—	—	—	—	Van't Hof and Sparrow (1963a)
Helianthus annuus	16	7	5.5	1.3	1.3	Van't Hof (1967)
Impatiens balsamina	8.8	—	3.9	—	—	Van't Hof (1965)
Jerusalem artichoke (culture)	—	25	14	—	2	Mitchell (1967)
Lycopersicum esculentum	10.6	—	4.3	—	—	Van't Hof (1965)
Nicotiana tabacum	12–13	—	6–8	$G_2 + P = \sim 2$	—	Collins (1968)
N. plumbaginifolia (root tips)						
Oedogenium cardiacum	—	3.5	6 ± 1	6.5 ± 1	2	Banerjee and Horsley (1968)
Pisum sativum	12	2.5	4.5	2.5	2.5	Van't Hof et al. (1960)
						Van't Hof (1963)
Pisum sativum						
Alaska	13–14	5	4.5	3.0	1.2	Van't Hof (1967)
Root meristem cells	17.9	5.2	8.9	$G_2 + M = 3.8$	—	Van't Hof (1968)
	18.0	7.3	6.9	$G_2 + M = 3.8$	—	
Weitor	14	5	4.5	3.0	1.2	Van't Hof (1967)
Witham Wonder	13	4	4.5	3.3	1.4	

TABLE XI (*Continued*)

Plant	T	G_1	S	G_2	M	References
Tradescantia occidentalis Staminal hair cells	20–21	6	10–11	1	4	Davies and Wimber (1963)
Tradescantia paludosa	20	4	10	2.7	3.3	Wimber (1960)
Tradescantia paludosa Actively growing roots	20.5	5.8	10.1	2.6	2.0	Van't Hof and Sparrow (1965)
Dormant roots	19.4	4.4	11.4	1.6	2.0	Van't Hof and Sparrow (1963a)
Trillium erectum	29	—	—	—	—	
Tulipa kaufmanniana	23	—	—	—	—	
Vicia faba	—	—	6–8	—	—	Howard and Pelc (1951b)
Vicia faba	30–18	12–2	14–4	8	4–2	Howard (1956)
						Howard and Dewey (1960)
Vicia faba	17	1	10.5	2.5	3	Wimber and Quastler (1963)
Vicia faba	13	—	—	—	—	Van't Hof and Sparrow (1963a)
Vicia faba	19.3	4.9	7.5	4.9	2	Evans and Scott (1964)
Vicia faba	18	4	9.0	3.5	1.9	Van't Hof (1967)
Vicia faba root meristem cells	16.6	3.6	8.3	2.8	1.9	MacLeod (1968)
Zea mays Cap initials	14	—	8	5	2	Clowes (1965)
Quiescent center	—	—	9	11	—	
Stele just above quiescent center	22	2	11	7	2	
Stele 200 μ from quiescent center	23	4	9	6	4	

with a high labeling index, i.e., a short generation time. The generation times of the tumors investigated vary between one and several days. If tumor cells have a longer generation time of more than one to a few days, its duration most probably will vary widely, just as the cells of the adult animal do. In the adult animal the crypt cells have the shortest generation times of all investigated cell types, including tumor cells. That means that tumor cells do not necessarily proliferate faster than normal tissues. On the contrary, the generation times in normal tissues are often shorter than those of rapidly proliferating tumors. Tumor growth, therefore, cannot be exclusively due to an acceleration of the normal proliferation process. Other factors must be of influence in this matter (Baserga et al., 1962a; Killmann et al., 1963; Mendelsohn, 1964a,b; Maurer et al., 1965; Baserga, 1965; Vasiliev, 1967).

h. *Plant cells.* Recent studies on the duration of the generation cycle and its subphases in plant cells have shown that G_1, M, and G_2 are quite constant while S varies somewhat between the different plants; however, it is of the same order of magnitude as in animal cells (Van't Hof, 1965, 1967). Results for plant cells are listed in Table XI.

i. *Change in the generation cycle or its phases by different internal and external influences.* The duration of the generation time or the different phases of the cell cycle may be influenced by various internal and external conditions. Aging, for instance, was found to lengthen the generation time of the intestinal crypt cells in mice (Lesher et al., 1961a). In mice, in the duodenal progenitor population and in colonic epithelium, lengthening of the mean duration of the cell cycle with age was reported by Thrasher and Greulich (1965) and Thrasher (1967). The prolongation of the mean duration of the cell cycle apparently results from an increase in the G_1 phase whereas S, G_2, and M remain relatively constant. Lesher et al. (1964) observed a generation time in duodenal crypt cells from germfree mice that was prolonged compared to that in conventional mice, an effect due primarily to a prolongation of S and G_1. Chronic γ-irradiation leads to a shortening of the generation time of mouse duodenal crypt cells (Lesher et al., 1961b; Fry et al., 1963; Lesher, 1966; see also Thrasher and Greulich, 1965). A similar effect, reduction of the generation cycle with a shortening of all of its phases, was found in cells of the C3H mouse mammary gland under the influence of ovarian hormones (Bresciani, 1964, 1965a). Hyperplastic, preneoplastic, and tumor cells of the mammary gland also show a shorter generation time (Bresciani, 1965b). Estrogen obviously leads to a considerable shortening of the cycle time, which is demonstrated by a reduction of 72 hours in diestrus down to 25 hours in estrus (Thrasher et al., 1966). For more details on the effect of estrogen on the length of the generation cycle in mouse uterine epithelium, see Epifanova and Smolenskaya (1963), Epifanova *et al.* (1963), and Epifanova (1964a,b, 1965a,b, 1966, 1967). Furthermore, 5-fluoro-2-deoxyuridine treatment leads to a shortening in the duration of the succeeding S phase (Till *et al.*, 1963). Microinjuries of the epidermis (guinea pig) also result in a reduction in the generation time of the epidermis cells (Hell and Cruickshank, 1963). Higher temperature (30°C) also leads to a shortening of G_1 in root tip cells of *Tradescantia paludosa* while at lower temperatures (13°C) mitosis and G_2 are approximately tripled and DNA synthesis is doubled (Wimber, 1966a). See also Sisken *et al.* (1965) and Sisken (1964). Studies on the influence of lower temperatures on proliferating cells of the smooth muscle in the rats' duodenal wall have shown that the generation cycle reacts very sensitively to lower temperatures and is distinctly prolonged (Lebedeva and Zavarzin, 1966). Lower temperatures lead to a prolongation of the S phase in kidney cells also from 1-day-old rats (Diment, 1966). Doubling of the generation time and of G_2 with the S phase remaining constant due to lower temperature (20°C) was found in *Tetrahymena pyriformis* by Cameron and Nachtway (1967). Deprivation of food, on the other hand, leads to a delayed onset of DNA synthesis and a prolongation of S. Cleffmann (1967) also reported prolongation of the generation time of *Tetrahymena pyriformis* at low temperature. However, this author found a constancy of the relative duration of all phases of the cell cycles. Vendrely *et al.* (1964) reported a shortening of S and G_1 in fibroblasts caused by virus infection. For the effect of nonspecific stress on DNA synthesis in fore and glandular stomach and in skin of mice, see Lahtiharju and Rytömaa (1967).

Quite a number of cell biologists are involved in cell kinetic studies with emphasis on different aspects of the control of cell proliferation and on the influence of different agents on the cycle (Epifanova, 1967; Dondua, 1967; Frankfurt, 1967; Lomakina *et al.*, 1967; Vasiliev, 1967; Zavarzin, 1967).

3. Diurnal Fluctuation of the Labeling Index

In all determinations of the length of the cell cycle and its phases using the labeling index—whether S is measured with the double labeling method or the generation time is calculated from the labeling index and the duration of S—precaution has to be taken, since a number of cell types in the adult animal show diurnal fluctuations of their labeling indexes similar to the known fluctuation in the mitotic index (Pilgrim *et al.*, 1963, 1965). It is interesting that diurnal fluctuations of the labeling index are observed only in those cell types that also show diurnal fluctuation in their mitotic indexes. Figure 12 depicts the conditions for some

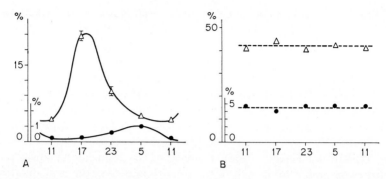

FIG. 12. Diurnal fluctuations (%) of the labeling index and the mitotic index. The abscissas indicate the time of day. (A) Great fluctuation in the epithelia of the tongue of the adult mouse and other cell types listed. (B) No fluctuation in the epithelia of the jejunal crypt cells and other cell types listed. (From Pilgrim *et al.*, 1965.)

Fluctuations occur	*No fluctuations*
Tongue, epithelium	Jejunum, crypt cells
Esophagus, epithelium	Liver, mesenchymal cells
Prestomach, epithelium	Kidney, tubular cells
Spleen, malpighian body	Adrenal gland, cortex
Ear, epidermis	
Skin, epidermis	

cell types with and without diurnal fluctuation of their labeling index. Over a 24-hour period, the labeling index may vary by a factor as great as 2–5. Principally diurnal fluctuations may have two causes: (1) variations in the duration of S; and (2) a more frequent entry of cells into the S phase depending on the time of day. From the constant grain number per nucleus over a 24-hour period, Pilgrim *et al.* (1965) concluded that the duration of S is independent of the time of day. Thus, diurnal fluctuations in the labeling index most probably are due to a more frequent entry of cells into S at different times of the day.

Determinations of the generation time, from the labeling index and the duration of S, will inevitably lead to false values if diurnal fluctuations in the labeling index are not taken into account, i.e., if the generation time is calculated from a labeling index measured irrespective of time of the day; in such a method correct values for the generation time will be obtained only if the average of the indexes measured over the whole day is used for the calculation. The same is true for the measurement of the duration of S by the double-labeling method discussed in Chapter 4, II, D, 1, b.

In literature the duration of mitosis has sometimes been derived from the relationship between the labeling and mitotic indexes. Since the waves of fluctuation in both indexes may be incongruent, incorrect values would be obtained unless the averages of both indexes over the whole day are used in the calculation.

Marked diurnal fluctuations in the uptake of thymidine-^{3}H in the percentage of labeled cells, in the grain number per nucleus, and in the mitotic index were found in the corneal epithelium of rat by Scheving and Pauly (1967). These authors consider increases in thymidine incorporation at different times of the day to be due partly to an increased DNA synthesis rate and partly to an increase in the proportion of cells that synthesize DNA.

Diurnal variations in the uptake of thymidine-^{3}H into the whole mouse were reported by Hinrichs et al. (1964), who found that maximum uptake of thymidine occurs at about midnight, while lowest uptake was found at noon. Similar results were obtained by Frenkel et al. (1964), who discussed temporal variations or the effect of the "biological clock" as a factor in the rate of incorporation of precursors into DNA of different cell types of normal and tumor-bearing mice. For similar observations on diurnal fluctuations in the epidermis of urodele larvae, see Scheving and Chiakulas (1965).

Determinations of the labeling index and the mitotic index in various fetal cell types of the rat at different times of the day have shown that there are no diurnal fluctuations in fetal cells (Wegener et al., 1964). Obviously diurnal fluctuations arise after birth, parallel to the functional development of the brain. Likewise, no diurnal fluctuations in the labeling or mitotic index were found in ascites tumor cells (Lennartz and Maurer, 1964; Lennartz et al., 1966). The same is true for the spontaneous mammary carcinoma of the mouse from which Ehrlich ascites tumor cells derive, although diurnal fluctuations do occur in the normal mammary epithelium of the mouse as well as in the transplanted carcinoma. There is also no diurnal fluctuation of the labeling index in human leukemic blast cells (Roll and Killmann, 1965; Mauer, 1965).

4. Investigation of the Variations in the Cycle Time within a Cell Population by Using Continuous Infusion of Thymidine-^{3}H; "Growth Fraction"

Since the studies by Mendelsohn (1962a,b, 1963, 1964b), it has been known that in some tumors only part of the cells participate in proliferation. Mendelsohn studied transplantable tumors in mice by means of continuous infusion with thymidine-^{3}H and found that even after long infusion times a variable portion of the tumor cells remain unlabeled. The portion of proliferating cells varied between 40 and 90% of all cells (see Mendelsohn, 1964b). Similar results were obtained by Hempel (1966a,b) for melanocytes after repeated injections of thymidine-^{3}H over a long period into rats with Harding-Passey melanomas. The same was found by Steel et al. (1966) in 2 tumors, the varying growth rates of which were found to be due to considerable variations in their growth fractions. A growth fraction of 90% was found for one of these tumors (BICR/M$_1$), and only 30% for the other (BICR/A$_2$). According to Lala and Patt (1966), a decrease in the growth rate of the tumor (EAT) with increasing mass is due to an increasing diminution of the growth fraction, not to a prolongation of the phases of the cell cycle. Further methods for the determination of growth fractions in tumors were discussed by Mendelsohn (1960a, 1962b, 1964a) and by Baserga et al. (1963).

Some autoradiographic determinations of the generation time suggest that even in tissue of the normal adult animal not all cells participate in proliferation to the same extent. Lesher et al. (1961a) studied the generation time of mouse crypt cells with both of the independent methods discussed in Section IID, 1, c. The length of the cell cycle was determined directly as the time interval between the corresponding points of two successive waves of percent labeled mitoses on the one hand, and from the labeling index and the duration of S on the other. The generation time calculated by the latter method was almost double that of the one measured with the first. This discrepancy can be explained by assuming that only about half of all cells participate in proliferation. Similar discrepancies were found in other cell types too, i.e., in the epithelium of mouse prestomach by Wolfsberg (1964) and in the epithelium of ear epidermis of the mouse by Pilgrim et al. (1966). Furthermore, Gracheva (1966) reported that practically all liver epithelia participate in proliferation in rat fetuses on the days 15–18 of embryonic development; but by the time of birth half of the liver epithelia no longer divide, an obvious correlation with the beginning of the functional activity. According to experiments by Post et al. (1963), only 10% of all liver cells participate in proliferation in 3-week-old rats, i.e., when the liver is still in a stage of continuous growth. Such discrepancies in the determination of the generation time have been found even in fetal cell types. For instance, Zhinkin and Andreeva (1963) concluded from their experiments that only 50%, 15%, and 5%, respectively, of the cells in rat fetal tongue muscle participate in proliferation on days 17, 19, and 21 of embryonic development.

Since most of the generation times summarized in tables are calculated from the labeling index and the duration of S, it is of great interest to know whether or not variations of the cycle time within one and the same cell type or a growth fraction exist for the cell types listed in the tables. In order to find out whether or not all cells within a cell population have the same generation time or whether a growth fraction exists, Löbbecke *et al.* (1967) studied a number of fetal cell types of the rat using continuous infusion of thymidine-^{3}H. On day 20 of pregnancy rats were given thymidine-^{3}H (2 mCi/day) continuouusly from 3 hours to 3 days. Because of their short generation times (13–40 hours) fetal cell types are especially suited for experiments with continuous infusion. Results are shown in Fig. 13. The curves depict the percentage of labeled cells as a function of the infusion time for different fetal cell types. The values for T-S are represented by the dotted line. S was determined by the percentage of labeled mitoses method, T from the labeling index and the duration of S.

In case all cells participate in proliferation with the same generation time, labeling of cells should reach 100% after continuous infusion over a time period of T-S. It can be seen from Fig. 13 that this is true for the fetal cell types a–d. Thus all cells within these cell types have the same generation time and, furthermore, this time agrees very well with that calculated from the labeling index and the duration of S. However, conditions are different in the case of fetal tongue muscle (Fig. 13f). In this cell type only 75% of all cells are labeled at T-S, which means that not all cells participate in proliferation with the same generation time. The shape of the curve (75% labeled cells at T-S and the slow approach to 100% later on) does not allow any conclusion as to whether there is a growth fraction or a wide variety of generation times in this population, since in populations with exponential growth 100% labeling will be reached after some time even in the presence of nonproliferating cells. For details and further experiments with continuous infusion of thymidine-^{3}H see the original paper and the references quoted there; see also Foot (1963). For technical procedures of continuous infusion see Eve and Robinson (1963).

E. DNA SYNTHESIS RATE AT DIFFERENT STAGES OF THE S PHASE

Several investigators have counted the number of grains over metaphases of different cell types as a function of time after a single application of thymidine-^{3}H. Because of the short availability time of thymidine-^{3}H in mouse and rat, this grain number presumably represents the DNA synthesis rate at the time of injection within the restrictions made under Chapter 4, Section I, D, 2.

Koburg and Maurer (1962) and Koburg (1963b) found the DNA synthesis rate to be quite constant during the whole DNA synthesis phase for the jejunum, ileum, and colon of the mouse. Constant DNA synthesis rates for various other cell types of the mouse were found by Pilgrim and Maurer (1965), who determined the mean grain number per nucleus in the beginning, middle, and at the end of the S phase by double labeling with

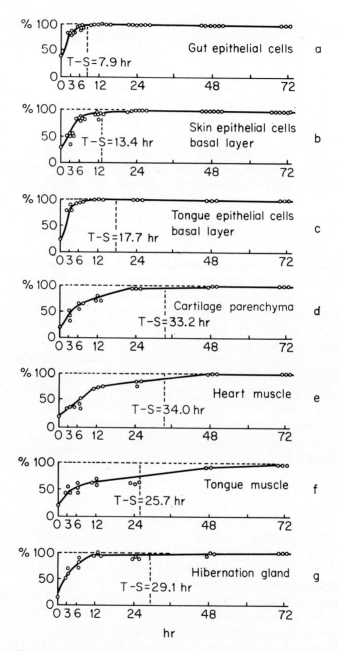

FIG. 13. Percentages of labeled cells as a function of infusion time for various fetal cell types of the rat (day 20) after continuous infusion of thymidine-³H. (From Löbbecke *et al.*, 1969.)

thymidine-³H and -¹⁴C. Wegener *et al.* (1964) examined various fetal cell types of the rat (day 20 of gravidity) and found that the DNA synthesis rate (measured by metaphase grain counts) increases slightly throughout the S phase. Bresciani (1965b) found a bimodal curve for the thymidine-³H incorporation rate into alveolar epithelia of the mammary gland of the mouse.

In *in vitro* experiments with L-strain mouse cells, Stanners and Till (1960) found evidence for a constant rate of DNA synthesis during the S period, except for a possibly slightly lower rate during the earlier stages of S. For the same cells, however, Smith (1963) found an increasing thymidine-³H incorporation rate throughout the S phase with a slight maximum near the end. In the latter experiments, the grain number was correlated with the DNA content of the nucleus (determined by Feulgen absorption) which was taken as a measure for the age of the cell within the S phase (see also Dendy and Cleaver, 1964). Kasten and Strasser (1966b) found an abrupt cessation of the nucleolar DNA synthesis and a decrease of the extranucleolar DNA synthesis 4–5 hours after the beginning of DNA synthesis in human adenocarcinoma cells CMP; thereafter both regions resumed DNA synthesis.

Even if the DNA synthetic rate of the whole nucleus in some animal cells seems to be constant during the S-phase, it may be different and independent in different parts of the nucleus or chromosomes. Thus, Gall (1959), Prescott and Kimball (1961), and Prescott (1964b) observed in the macronucleus of *Euplotes eurystomus* that DNA synthesis started at both ends of the ribbon-like nucleus and progressed toward the middle until both synthesis waves met. This replication pattern could not be correlated with individual chromosomes, since this macronucleus divides without a regular mitotic division figure.

In early pachytene nuclei of *Melanoplus differentialis* the sex chromosome forms a deeply stained block of heterochromatin and the autosomes constitute the remaining euchromatic part of the nucleus. In this stage Lima-de-Faria (1959a) reported that the heterochromatin synthesizes DNA at a different time than the euchromatin. The same was found in nuclei of cultured human male leukocytes (Lima-de-Faria and Reitalu, 1963; see also Lima-de-Faria *et al.*, 1965). Also in cultured mammary gland epithelia of the mouse DNA replication of the heterochromatin and euchromatin occurs asynchronously (Church, 1965).

During the past years many investigators have reported that an asynchronous DNA synthesis occurs in the different chromosomes. In cultured cells from Chinese hamsters an asynchronous replication of chromosomes and differences in DNA synthesis even between homologous chromosomes was observed (Taylor, 1960c, 1962a, 1963a; Hsu, 1964; Peacock, 1963).

In a cell line derived from a male embryo the Y-chromosome replicated late, whereas the short arm of the X-chromosome finished replication earlier than most of the complement. The long arm of the X-chromosome began replication in the middle of S and finished at about the same time as the Y-chromosome. In a cell line derived from a female embryo one X-chromosome showed a replication pattern similar to that in the male cells, but the other X-chromosome was still replicating in the latter half of the S phase and continued for a short period after most of the autosomes had completed replication. Furthermore, differences exist in the pattern in which various regions of both the late-replicating X- and Y-chromosome were finishing replication. Asynchronous replication and varying amounts of label per unit length in the autosomes were also found in mature sperms of the grasshopper (Taylor, 1964a). Gartler and Burt (1964) reported that the "late synthesizing Y-chromosome" begins replication after the rest of the chromosomes in cultured cells from bovine males (see also Stubblefield, 1965). In bovine leukocytes Mukherjee et al. (1967) found that both X-chromosomes begin replication almost simultaneously, but shortly thereafter, one of the X-chromosomes suspends activity, then resumes it in a great burst in DNA synthesis during the last part of the S phase. Asynchronous replication of one X-chromosome in late S was also found by Galton and Holt (1965) in cell cultures of mouse embryos (C57BL/10 Jax) and by Evans et al. (1965) in female mice. Fraccaro et al. (1954, 1965) and Tiepolo et al. (1967) reported late replication of one chromosome in spermatogonia of mice in vitro and in vivo. Asynchronous DNA synthesis in sex chromosomes was also found in marsupial species (Graves, 1967), in opossum lymphocytes (Schneider and Rieke, 1967), and in Drosophila melanogaster (Barigozzi et al., 1966, 1967). For more details on asynchronous DNA replication see Gavosto et al. (1965), Hsu and Lockhart (1964), Beermann and Pelling (1965), Pflueger and Yunis (1966).

Chromosomes in cultured human cells, like leukocytes, skin, testis, and others also show asynchronous DNA replication (Lima-de-Faria et al., 1961, 1965; Taft and Brooks, 1963; Schmid, 1963; Atkins et al., 1963; Atkins and Santesson, 1964; Atkins and Gustavson, 1964; German, 1964; Kikuchi and Sandberg, 1965; Comings, 1966, 1967a,b; Froland, 1967; Mukherjee et al., 1966; Miller et al., 1966). In human leukocytes in culture, Morishima et al. (1962) found that labeling of individual chromosomes was not uniform and that it depends on the rate of DNA synthesis at different sites at the time of exposure to thymidine-³H. The two homologous X-chromosomes in human females had different patterns of DNA replication. One continued replication for a period in the cell cycle after most of the other chromosomes in the complement had completed DNA synthesis (see also Petersen, 1964; Gilbert et al., 1962, 1965, 1966).

In human males no such differences could be detected. For further investigations, see Büchner *et al.* (1965, 1967), Pfeiffer and Büchner (1964), and Pfeiffer *et al.* (1965, 1966).

In root tips of maize, Abraham and Smith (1966) observed an asynchronous DNA synthesis of the B-chromosome in the second half of the S phase. Asynchrony in DNA replication was detected in the m-chromosome at the beginning of the S phase by Iordansky and Matushina (1966).

Apart from the observation of asynchronous duplication of chromosomes, the rate of DNA synthesis has been found to be different even in single chromosomes. In *Crepis capillaris* root tips with three haploid chromosomes, Taylor (1958a, 1960c) observed a gradient concentration of tritium after labeling with thymidine-^{3}H, suggesting progressive DNA duplication from both ends of the chromosomes toward the centromeres. Similar results were found in *Secale cereale* by Lima-de-Faria (1959b), who from the distribution of the label concluded that replication in the distal region occurs during a different time period than in the regions on both sides of the kinetochore and that there is a time period during which their replication overlaps. According to Peacock (1963), DNA synthesis in *Vicia faba* roots sometimes proceeds simultaneously in more than one segment of a chromosome arm. From the changing distribution of the label during the cycle of DNA synthesis in spermatocytes of the grasshopper *Melanoplus*, Lima-de-Faria (1961) concluded that the initiation of DNA synthesis does not take place simultaneously along the whole meiotic chromosome, but rather occurs at specific segments.

In salivary gland chromosomes of larvae of *Chironomus thumni thummi*, initiation of DNA replication occurs simultaneously in all bands, and at the end of the S phase synthesis is found only in heterochromatic structures (Keyl and Pelling, 1963). Onset of DNA synthesis at many sites in a chromosome was found also for the salivary gland chromosomes of *Drosophila* by Plaut (1963). For details on puff development and DNA synthesis in *Sciara* salivary gland chromosomes in culture, see Cannon (1965).

In cultured Chinese hamster cells, differences in DNA synthetic rate in different regions of the X- and Y-chromosome was observed by Taylor (1960d). Different intensity of the label per unit length in autosomes of mature sperms of the grasshopper (Taylor, 1964a) has already been mentioned.

F. IRRADIATION EFFECTS ON DNA SYNTHESIS

It has long been known from biochemical experiments that X irradiation reduces the incorporation of labeled precursors into DNA (Hevesy, 1948; Harrington and Lavik, 1955; Ord and Stocken, 1956; Kelly, 1957;

Nygaard and Potter, 1959; Sugino et al., 1963; Barnum et al., 1964; Skalko, 1965; Brent et al., 1966). In contrast to such biochemical studies, the autoradiographic method enables the investigator to evaluate whether this decrease in incorporation of the precursor is due to a reduction of the number of cells synthesizing DNA or to a reduction of the DNA synthetic rate. Furthermore, such interesting problems as radiation sensitivity of the different phases of the cell cycle or the effect of X irradiation on the length of the cell cycle or its phases can be studied only autoradiographically.

1. Influence on the Labeling Index

In the small intestine of mice the labeling index has been found to be slightly decreased immediately after irradiation and considerably lower several hours later. One day after irradiation with 3000 rad the labeling index was about 20% and on the second day about 9% compared to the normal of 40% in controls (Sherman and Quastler, 1960). These findings agree very well with those found by Looney (1965b) in liver epithelia of rats following partial hepatectomy, by Lajtha and Oliver (1960) in cultured human bone marrow cells, by Pelc and Howard (1955, 1956) in Vicia faba roots, by Davies and Wimber (1963) in staminal hairs of Tradescantia occidentalis and by Van't Hof and Sparrow (1965) in roots of Tradescantia paludosa. Similar results were noted in fibroblasts of chicken embryos in culture (Kuyper et al., 1962b) and in Ehrlich ascites tumor cells (Frankfurt and Lipchina, 1964). For HeLa cells and mouse fibroblasts in culture, Smith (1961) reported that the fraction of cells synthesizing DNA is not markedly affected by X-rays. On the other hand Painter and Robertson (1959) found that by 4–8 hours after irradiation almost twice the number of HeLa cells were synthesizing DNA as in control cultures. Interpreting these findings, it seems to be more probable that many cells in DNA synthesis at the time of X irradiation remained in this stage for an abnormally long time than that there was an effect on the rate at which cells enter the DNA synthesis period.

2. Influence on the DNA Synthetic Rate

In irradiation studies in which DNA synthesis is measured by short-term labeling after irradiation, Sherman and Quastler (1960) found that after a dose of 800 rads in crypt cells of the mouse intestine the grain count per labeled cell dropped to one-half its normal value within about 0.5 hour and reached very low values within a few hours. After administration of 2500 rads, half the normal grain count was reached within 20 min, and after 6–18 hours the grain count was hardly above background. A similar decrease in DNA synthetic rate to half the normal immediately after whole-body irradiation with doses of 200–3000 rads was observed by Cattaneo et al. (1960) in hair follicles of the mouse epidermis after irritation. See also Perrotta (1966). Those and other effects of X irradiation on intestinal epithelium, bone marrow, and other tissues have been discussed within a broader framework and reviewed by Patt and Quastler (1963).

Reduction of the rate of incorporation of thymidine-^{3}H by X-ray irradiation has been found also in regenerating liver (Looney et al., 1963, 1965; Looney, 1965a,b, 1966a,b; Chang et al., 1966), in crypt cells of the rat (Looney, 1966a), in HeLa S3 cells and Chinese hamster cells (Painter and Rasmussen, 1964), in mouse fibrosarcoma cells (Bose et al., 1965b), in ascites tumor cells (Crathorn and Schooter, 1964; Frankfurt and Lipchina, 1964; Kim and Evans, 1964), in HeLa cells (Smith, 1961), in cultured fibroblasts of chicken embryos (Kuyper et al., 1962b), and in Pisum sativum (Van't Hof, 1966).

The effect of partial irradiation of cell components on the DNA synthetic rate in tissue culture cells was studied by Dendy and Smith (1964) using a microbeam of α-particles or of ultraviolet light. Similar to the effect of X irradiation (Smith, 1961), the rate of DNA synthesis was reduced. A 50% reduction occurred with an α-particle dose of $\sim 15\alpha/\mu^2$. The nucleolus appeared to have no specific role in DNA synthesis, since inhibition of DNA synthesis by irradiation of the nucleolus did not differ from that produced by irradiation of an equal area of the nuclear sap.

Under different experimental conditions, namely administration of the labeled thymidine *during* exposure to X-rays, Das and Alfert (1961) reported that in root meristems of onion seedlings the thymidine-^{3}H incorporation rate was increased. Repeating those experiments, but using bean roots, Howard and Douglas (1963) were not able to confirm those results. On the contrary, they found that radiation exposure tended to decrease the DNA synthetic rate and the number of cells synthesizing DNA.

Continous irradiation of rats with 415 rads/day over 5 days led to an increased incorporation of thymidine-^{3}H into crypt cells (Wimber and Lamerton, 1963, 1965). However, it should be noted that processes examined after 5 days of continuous irradiation may be quite different from those studied shortly after a single short-term irradiation.

Apart from biochemical determinations, the effect of irradiation on the DNA synthetic rate has been studied autoradiographically by counting grains per labeled nucleus. It should be pointed out once more that a reduced number of grains per labeled nucleus cannot simply be considered to be due to a reduction in the DNA synthetic rate without knowing how irradiation influences the percental participation of thymidine-^{3}H in physiological DNA synthesis (Section I, D, 2) and the thymidine pool, since several authors have noted that pool changes occur especially after irradiation (Lajtha, in Ris et al., 1963). However, see also the experiments by Smets (1966) concerning this problem.

3. Influence on the Duration of the Cell Cycle and Its Phases

Apart from the generally observed division delay, autoradiographic studies have shown that the different phases of the cell cycle are sensitive to X-ray's to varying extents. Shortening of the whole cell cycle in crypt cells of the duodenum in mice and rats by continuous γ-irradiation was observed by Lesher et al. (1961b, 1966). Furthermore, after 1 day of irradiation the passage of the cells through mitosis is delayed because the cells are partly blocked in G_2. Similar results were obtained by Wimber and Lamerton (1963). In these experiments continuous irradiation of rats with 415 rads/day over 5 days led to a shortening of the generation time in intestinal crypt cells. Continuous irradiation of mice with 50, 84, or 176 rads per day causes increased cell production in the epithelium of the ileum; this may possibly be due to an increase in the number of proliferating cells per crypt, to a shortening of the cell cycle, or to a combination of both. Neither the duration of S nor of mitosis is influenced by these doses (Wimber and Lamerton, 1966). Shortening of the generation time by continuous irradiation would seem to be a more general effect, since it has been found also in red and white blood cell precursors (Lamerton, 1966; Lord, 1964, 1965). In embryonic tissue of the mouse (tail tip) no influence of irradiation on the duration of the cell cycle was observed, most probably because the cell cycle of those cells is extremely short (8.5 hours) (Wimber and Lamerton, 1965). Prolongation of the different phases of the cell cycle by irradiation has been observed only in G_2 phases of intestinal crypt cells. Lamerton (1966) considers differences in the capacity to tolerate continuous irradiation between intestine and bone marrow to be due to a shorter generation time of normal intestine than of bone marrow, with the result that intestinal cells take up smaller doses between two sequential divisions.

Continuous irradiation with 29 rads per day over 9 days leads to a prolongation of the cell cycle by a factor of 3–4 in *Tradescantia* root meristem cells; the DNA synthesis phase is only slightly prolonged, but G_1 and G_2 increase considerably (Wimber, 1966b). For the effect of daily exposure to γ-rays from a ^{60}Co source on root meristem cells of *Pisum*, see Van't Hof and Sparrow (1963b).

Whole-body irradiation of mice with Harding-Passey melanoma has shown that there are no big differences between "radiosensitive" intestinal epithelia and "radioinsensitive" melanocytes considering (1) the depression of the DNA synthetic rate, (2) the time until DNA synthesis is resumed; and (3) the disappearance and reappearance of mitoses. Both cell types are well suited for such a comparison since they have about the same length of generation cycle and its phases. The difference in radiosensitivity of the two types is not due to unlike influences of irradiation on the time schedules of their cell cycles (Hempel, 1966a,b).

4. Relative Radiosensitivity of the Different Phases of the Cell Cycle

In contrast to Sections 1–3 above, this section deals with the radiosensitivity of the individual phases of the cell cycle, which has been studied for a variety of cell types. Such differences in radiosensitivity between the single phases have generally been found in animal as well as in plant cells. During recent years predominantly synchronized cell cultures have been used for these studies, applying thymidine-^{3}H for the determination of S. The extent of radiation damage has been estimated by the following criteria: (1) appearance of chromosome aberrations, (2) delay of mitosis and effects on DNA synthesis, and (3) depression of division by premature differentiation or cell death. Cell death may be due mainly to the loss of damaged chromosomes or chromosome parts during mitosis.

According to Dewey and Humphrey (1962), mouse fibroblasts *in vitro* and ascites tumor cells *in vitro* and *in vivo* are more radiosensitive during the DNA synthesis phase than during G_1 or G_2 (250 rads, ^{60}Co). They found double the amount of chromosome damage if cells were irradiated during S, compared to those irradiated during G_1, and, furthermore, a considerable delay in mitosis. On the other hand, chromosome damage of cells irradiated during G_2 is greater than that in cells irradiated during G_1. Furthermore, mitotic delay is longer in cells irradiated in G_2 than in those irradiated in G_1. In synchronized HeLa S3 cell cultures, Tolmach (1961, 1963) found cells in the S phase to be twice as radiosensitive as those in other phases of the cell cycle (200–500 rad; see also Terasima and Tolmach, 1961). In more recent investigations these authors observed that the maximum of radiosensitivity lies shortly prior to the beginning of the S phase (Terasima and Tolmach, 1963a,b; Tolmach, in Ris *et al.*, 1963; Terasima, 1964). Radiation-induced mitotic delay in L cells increases from a value of 0.4–0.5 min/rad for cells irradiated in the G_1 phase to a value of 2.3–2.4 min/rad for cells irradiated in G_2; for cells partially irradiated during S, a value between these two has been obtained (Whitmore *et al.*, 1967). Biochemical studies of Nygaard and Potter (1959) on spleen, thymus, intestine, and bone marrow of the rat also suggest that the S phase is more radiosensitive than the other phases of the cell cycle. A marked increase in sensitivity to ultraviolet irradiation during S was found by Smith (1963) in L cells of the mouse. X-irradiation of *Vicia faba* with 100 r during late G_1 or early S results in a number of chromosome aberrations double that from irradiation during late S or early G_2 (same dose). Similar results are reported by Choumak (1964) in intestinal and corneal epithelia following whole-body irradiation. Here, the maximum radiosensitivity is localized during the transition from G_1 to S and from G_2 to mitosis.

Conditions seem to be different in cultured Chinese hamster cells, in which irradiation with 250 rads of ^{60}Co at a dose rate of 40 rads/min. has shown that radiosensitivity is increased by a factor of 3-4 during G_2 over that from irradiation during S (Hsu et al., 1962; Hsu, in Ris et al., 1963). Similar results have been found by Sinclair and Morton (1966); mitosis and G_2 were most radiosensitive, while G_1, early S and late S were less radiosensitive in this sequence.

In root meristem cells of Vicia faba irradiation with 50–150 rads leads to a mitotic delay in cells that are in S during irradiation, whereas cells which are in G_2 during irradiation show the highest rate of chromosome aberration (Evans and Scott, 1964; Evans, 1965). In synchronously growing Oedogonium cardiacum zoospores there is a marked increase in radiosensitivity during G_2 as measured by loss of cell reproductive capacity (Horsley et al., 1967). Similar results were obtained by Brewen (1965) for cultured human leukocytes. Irradiation with 100 rads at a dose rate of 50 to 60 r per minute showed that cells in G_2 have more chromosome aberrations per unit irradiation dose than cells in S or G_1.

With higher radiation doses, blocking of the cells in a certain phase of the cell cycle can be achieved, but this blocking of cells can be overcome after different time intervals, depending on the cell type and radiation dose. Whole-body irradiation of mice with 400 r leads to a blocking of corneal and duodenal epithelia at the transition from G_2 to M and from G_1 to S. During regeneration, first, the block between G_2 to M is removed, next DNA synthesis is normalized, and finally, the block between G_1 to S is released (Choumak, 1963b). Such an arresting of cells in certain phases of the cell cycle has been found also in uterine epithelium of the mouse after whole-body irradiation; doses from 100 to 400 rads delay the transition of the cells from G_1 to S, and doses of 2000 rads inhibit this transition completely. Whole-body irradiation with 800 r leads to an inhibition of the transition of cells from G_2 to M in implanted ascites tumor cells after 10 hours (Frankfurt and Lipchina, 1964). Whole-body irradiation of rats with 600–770 r results in a delay of S and mitosis in liver epithelia; i.e., irradiation prolongs G_1 and G_2 (Gracheva, 1964a).

Not much is known about the mechanism that leads to the various types of radiation damage, such as chromosome aberrations or changes in the duration of the generation cycle or of its phases. It is also difficult to coordinate and compare the different experiments that were performed under different conditions and with varying radiation doses. Furthermore, it is quite certain that processes occurring under continuous irradiation differ from those after single short-term irradiation.

G. CHROMOSOME REPRODUCTION AND DISTRIBUTION OF CHROMOSOMAL DNA TO THE DAUGHTER CELLS DURING MITOSIS AND MEIOSIS

In their well-known experiment Taylor, Woods, and Hughes (1957) studied the fate of newly synthesized molecular units of DNA in roots of *Vicia faba* and elucidated the mechanism of chromosome reproduction and distribution of chromosomal DNA during mitosis. Roots of *Vicia faba* were grown in a thymidine-^{3}H solution for 8 hours and then transferred to a solution containing colchicine but no thymidine-^{3}H. At the first metaphase after labeling, both sister chromatids of all labeled chromosomes were uniformly labeled. At the second metaphase after labeling, i.e., after further growth in an inactive medium containing colchicine, all chromosomes were labeled; however, only one of the two sister chromatids of each chromosome was labeled. At the metaphase of the next generation about one-half of the chromosomes had one labeled and one unlabeled chromatid, while the remaining half was completely unlabeled. These findings were recently confirmed by Iordansky (1964) and Iordansky et al. (1966). From their results Taylor et al. (1957) concluded that each chromosome consists of two subunits, along both of which DNA is synthesized as a unit that extends throughout the length of the chromosome. This newly synthesized DNA behaves as a physical entity and remains intact through succeeding replications and nuclear division, except for occasional chromatid exchanges. During mitosis the four units are separated in such a manner that each daughter cell receives one original and one newly synthesized unit (Fig. 14).

These first findings concerning the mechanism of chromosome reproduction did not remain uncontradicted. La Cour and Pelc (1958, 1959a,b) reported different results in similar experiments with *Vicia faba*. At the first metaphase after replication in the presence of thymidine-^{3}H, they found not only labeled chromosomes with both chromatids labeled, as did Taylor et al., but also some with only one of the sister chromatids labeled. After the second replication in inactive medium, La Cour and Pelc, like Taylor et al., observed metaphase chromosomes with only one sister chromatid labeled. However, unlike Taylor et al., they also found other chromosomes with both chromatids labeled. From their results, the latter authors concluded that each chromosome consists of *four* subunits and that not always are both the orig'nal and newly synthesized chromatids

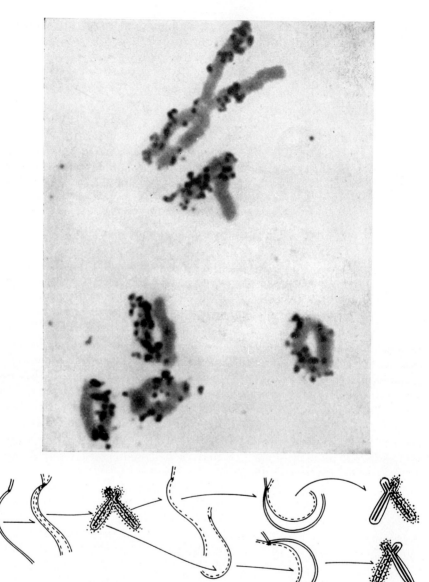

Duplication with   First c−metaphase   Duplication without   Second c−metaphase
labeled thymidine   after labeling   labeled thymidine   after labeling

FIG. 14. Autoradiogram of a group of chromosomes after one replication with thymidine-³H and one additional replication in an environment free of labeled precursor of DNA. (From Taylor, 1963c.)

segregated and transferred to the two daughter cells together. Further-more, they assumed colchicine to have an influence on the separation of the chromatids.

La Cour and Pelc's results (1958) were supported by findings of Plaut and Mazia (1956, 1957) and Plaut (1958), who labeled *Crepis capillaris* with thymidine-^{14}C and observed that the radioactivity was not dis-tributed equally between the two halves of the dividing cell. These dis-crepancies in the results were considered to be due to the less favorable resolution of ^{14}C-labeling and the consequent difficulty in distinguishing between the labels of the two chromatids. With the use of thymidine-^{3}H the discrepancies in the results were considered to be due perhaps to dif-ferential absorbance of ^{3}H-labeled β-particles by uneven squashing, even though La Cour and Pelc obtained the same results using thymidine-[14]C.

In order to check the influence of colchicine on the segregation of chromosomes, Woods and Schairer (1959) repeated La Cour and Pelc's experiments, administering colchicine during and after thymidine-^{3}H labeling and counting grains separately over the two chromatids of each chromosome. They found no difference in the results whether colchicine was administered during or after thymidine-^{3}H labeling and there was also no influence of colchicine on DNA replication. Unfortunately they did not apply colchicine before thymidine-^{3}H labeling. However, recently Peacock (1963) showed that colchicine application before, during, and after thymidine-^{3}H labeling of *Vicia faba* did not influence DNA replica-tion or segregation, nor did it alter the prospects of sister chromatid exchange.

Although the experimental results at both the chromosomal level and the molecular level indicated more and more that chromosome duplication is a semiconservative process, the mechanism of replication still remains obscure. The observation that in some cases DNA synthesis takes place simultaneously at many sites in the chromosome and that in other cases it is restricted to certain chromosomal regions, the various patterns of replication being a genetic property of the cell, has led to the following conclusion: a chromosome consists of many replication units and may be opened for replication at special operator sites. These assumptions have been supported by studies of the interruption of DNA replication by the application of fluorodeoxyuridine or aminopterin which lead to a depletion of the nucleotide thymidylate and consequently to chromosome lesions, which may be produced at many sites in the chromosome (Taylor *et al.*, 1962; Taylor, 1963a,b,c,d). Starting from these observations and con-sidering the fact that DNA synthesis is cyclic, even in tissues where nuclear divisions do not occur, Taylor (1962b, 1963a,b,c) has developed a new model of the mechanism of chromosome duplication. According to

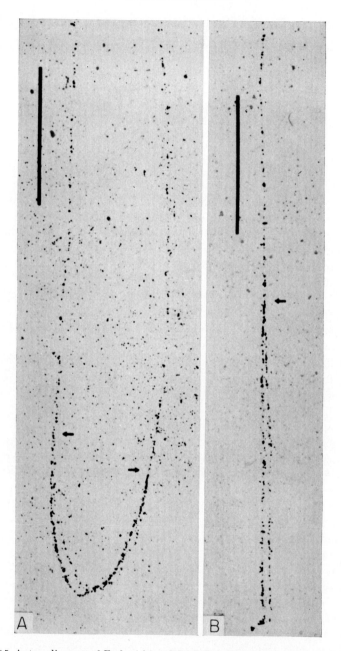

FIG. 15. Autoradiogram of *Escherichia coli* B3 DNA after incorporation of thymidine-³H for a period of 1 hour (two generations). The arrows show the point of replication; exposure time was 61 days; the scales show 100μ. (From Cairns, 1963.)

this model, the two subunits of DNA in each chromosome correspond to the two polynucleotide chains in DNA double helices. It is assumed that the chromosome is composed of tandemly linked molecules of DNA with special linkers in the DNA chain as operator sites for DNA replication. A reversal in polarity is assumed to occur at each of these linkers, a necessary prerequisite, since such a reversal would prevent deletions, duplications, inversions, and translocations from interrupting the alternating sequence of the linkers necessary for the regular segregation of new and old DNA chains. In a series of papers, Taylor has discussed how this model works considering the patterns and levels of control mechanisms (1962b, 1963a,b,c, 1964b, 1965).

DNA structures in *Escherichia coli* have been found to replicate in a semiconservative manner analogous to the behavior of DNA at the molecular and at the chromosomal level. Furthermore, DNA synthesis during normal experimental growth is virtually continuous, since it takes place through more than 80% of the division cycle (McFall and Stent, 1959; Schaechter *et al.*, 1959; Van Tubergen, 1961; Person and Osborn, 1964). A very impressive autoradiographic demonstration of bacterial chromosome replication was published by Cairns (1963; see also Bleecken *et al.*, 1966). Autoradiograms of isolated chromosomes of *E. coli* show a splitting into two daughter chromosomes, apparently in accordance with the helix model (Fig. 15).

5. RNA Synthesis

It is not the purpose of this chapter to deal with the problems of RNA synthesis in general, but to assess the role that autoradiography plays in the investigation of the cellular RNA synthesis.

I. General Aspects of Autoradiographic Studies on RNA Synthesis

A. RNA Precursors

RNA metabolism has already been studied autoradiographically using inorganic phosphate ^{32}P (Taylor, 1953; Taylor and McMaster, 1954, 1955; Odeblad and Magnusson, 1954; Vincent, 1954; McMaster-Kaye and Taylor, 1958) or ^{14}C-labeled adenine and orotic acid, respectively (Ficq, 1955a,b; Sisken, 1959; McMaster-Kaye, 1960, 1962; Prescott, 1959, 1960; Sibatani et al., 1962). However, phosphorus is not a specific RNA precursor but is incorporated in a variety of other cellular components. On the other hand, ^{14}C-labeled substances cannot be produced with a sufficiently high specific activity. Thus, the most important improvement, especially for autoradiographic purposes, was achieved by the introduction of tritium-labeled nucleosides like cytidine-^{3}H and uridine-^{3}H, as RNA precursors. Apart from the relative specificity of these precursors and the better localization of the label in the autoradiogram, because of the higher resolution of the tritium label, these compounds are available with high specific activities. However, despite this progress a specific labeling of RNA similar to that of DNA with thymidine-^{3}H cannot be achieved even with these precursors, since these nucleosides are also incorporated to a small extent into DNA. Cytosine, for instance, is also one of the bases in the DNA molecule, and uridine can be transformed via deoxyuridine into thymidine. Only uridine which is labeled solely in the 5 position can be regarded as a selective precursor for RNA, since transformation to thymidine via deoxyuridine would lead to the loss of its label. However, the portion of ^{3}H-labeled RNA precursors incorporated into DNA is small and is dependent on the rate of proliferation in the tissue under study. Cells that are in DNA synthesis are mostly recognized in autoradiograms by their heavier label, or they can be tagged by simultaneous application of ^{14}C-labeled thymidine and distinguished by their ^{14}C-tracks. Furthermore, extraction of the sections with ribonuclease also gives information on the proportion of RNA precursor that is incorporated into DNA.

B. DIFFERENT RNA FRACTIONS

In contrast to biochemical work where several RNA fractions as determined by their different base composition and their different sedimentation coefficient can be distinguished, the turnover of the sum of all RNA fractions is measured in short-time autoradiographic *in vivo* studies. Of course, the fraction with the highest turnover rate predominates.

It has been known for a long time from biochemical experiments that different RNA fractions exist within the nucleus, nucleolus, and cytoplasm. Apart from the different composition of their bases and their varying density gradients, the several fractions also clearly incorporate radioactive precursors differently, i.e., their metabolic activities also vary (Vincent, 1954, 1955a,b, 1957a,b; Vincent and Baltus, 1960; Sporn and Dingman, 1963; Sibatani *et al.*, 1962; Harris, 1965).

Most nuclear RNA is protein bound within the chromosomal and other nuclear structures. This ribosomelike RNA with sedimentation coefficients of ~33 and 19 S contains molecules of a relatively high molecular weight. The question remains open as to whether or not nuclear ribosomes actually exist—as electron microscopic studies seem to indicate.

At most only a small portion of the nuclear RNA, which makes up 15% of the total cellular RNA, is unbound. It is not certain whether the varying portion of so-called "soluble" or "transfer" RNA (with a sedimentation coefficient of 4 S) that can be isolated from some nuclei of animal cells really is nuclear RNA or whether it is a result of contamination with cytoplasm during the isolation process. In any case the portion of soluble RNA in the nucleus should not exceed 5% of the total nuclear RNA.

Cytoplasmic RNA consists essentially of two fractions—the so-called "soluble" RNA with a sedimentation constant of 4 S and the RNA contained in the ribonucleoprotein particles, the so-called ribosomes, with a sedimentation coefficient of 28 and 16 S; the latter makes up more than three-fourths of the total cytoplasmic RNA. About 50% of the ribosomes with a diameter of ~150 Å consist of RNA, and the other 50% of protein. For a report on the formation of these ribosomes and their role in transporting information from the nucleus to the cytoplasm, see Perry (1966).

Autoradiographic studies of RNA synthesis in various cell structures as a function of experimental time have shown that it is possible to differentiate between RNA fractions with varying metabolic activity. For instance, Feinendegen and Bond (1964) were able to prove the existence of 3 acid-insoluble RNA fractions with varying turnover rates in the nucleolar region of HeLa S3 cells after labeling with cytidine³H-. Three different RNA fractions with different turnover rates were also found in the nuclei of liver and pancreas cells after injection of cytidine-³H to mice by Amano et al. (1965). In contrast, the turnover only of ribosomal RNA could be measured in the cytoplasm.

C. RELATIONSHIP BETWEEN GRAIN NUMBER AND RNA SYNTHETIC RATE

Support for the assumption that actually turnover rates in the sense of *de novo* RNA synthesis are measured in autoradiographic studies was given by investigations of Schultze et al. (1961) and Schultze and Maurer (1962, 1963). Parallel investigations by these authors using cytidine-³H and uridine-³H in mice have shown that both the nucleosides have the same incorporation scheme (Fig. 16). With the same experimental times, application of both nucleosides results in the same relative grain density distribution throughout the whole organism. This suggests that nucleoside incorporation occurs based on a *de novo* synthesis of RNA. However, uridine-³H is incorporated to a much smaller extent than cytidine-³H. Under equal experimental conditions the grain density on autoradiograms with uridine-³H is about one-fifth that on autoradiograms with cytidine-³H. This was already found in biochemical studies of Hammarsten et al. (1949, 1950). Obviously uridine is catabolized and excreted to a much greater extent than cytidine.

Especially in studies of RNA synthesis with labeled nucleosides, the question arises how far the number of grains on autoradiograms is a measure of the RNA synthetic rate. In quite a number of autoradiographic studies, the incorporation of labeled nucleosides into the single cell structures was evaluated quantitatively by counting grains over the corresponding cell structures. These grain numbers correlate with the number of incorporated nucleoside molecules but are by no means a measure for the synthetic rate of RNA (amount of newly synthesized RNA per unit time). This would be the case only if the special conditions in the RNA precursor pool were known. Unfortunately this knowledge is lacking, at least for animal organisms. It is not known whether or not there is a dilution of the applied precursor by a precursor pool present in the cell, nor is there any knowledge as to whether this pool is by-passed as was described for HeLa cells by Feinendegen et al. (1961a,b).

D. FIXATION EFFECTS

Furthermore, it must be taken into account that fixation plays an important role in determining which portion of the macromolecular

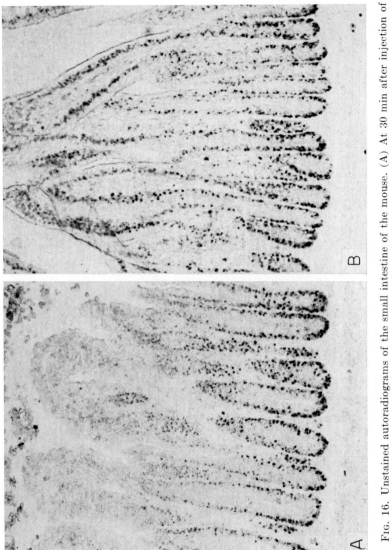

Fig. 16. Unstained autoradiograms of the small intestine of the mouse. (A) At 30 min after injection of uridine-³H. (B) At 30 min after injection of cytidine-³H. (From Schultze and Maurer, 1967.)

RNA is retained in the tissue. Grain counts are correlated only to that material which is not dissolved by the special fixation fluid.

E. INFLUENCE OF β-SELF-ABSORPTION

Even more essential to the quantitative evaluation of autoradiograms after application of ³H-labeled nucleosides is the influence of β-self-absorption. Since the dry mass per square micron differs greatly for different cell structures (in the deparaffinized water-free section), the influence of self-absorption on the grain numbers over these cell structures is also different. Short-time quantitative studies by Schultze and Maurer (1963) on the uridine-³H incorporation into mouse esophagus epithelium have shown that about 25% of the total ³H-activity is localized over the nucleolus, 70% over the caryoplasm, and up to 5% over the cytoplasm, if β-self-absorption is not taken into consideration. When the differing coefficients for β-self-absorption in the individual cell structures in sections of comparable thickness are taken into account, this relationship is practically the reverse, i.e., actual distribution of ³H-activity is then 60%:36%:∼4% for nucleolus:caryoplasm:cytoplasm. This makes it quite evident how great is the influence of β-self-absorption from the weak β-energy of ³H on the results of quantitative grain counts (see also Pollister, 1965; Arnold, 1965). Without considering the influence of β-self-absorption, Kasten and Strasser (1966b) found a relationship of 6:3:1 for nucleolus:caryoplasm:cytoplasm for the density of their label in human epithelial adenocarcinoma cells.

II. Physiological RNA Synthesis

A. INTRACELLULAR RNA SYNTHESIS

1. Site of RNA Synthesis in the Intact Cell

There is no unity of opinion in the literature on the localization of RNA synthesis within the cell. Some authors assume that RNA synthesis takes place only in the nucleolus and that RNA then migrates to the nucleus and cytoplasm; others, however, assume that RNA is synthesized in the nucleolus and caryoplasm, or in the caryoplasm only—in part combined with chromatin—before migrating to the nucleolus.

Many autoradiographic studies of cellular RNA synthesis in different biological subjects have led at least to one clear-cut result, namely, that nuclear labeling appears before cytoplasmic labeling (Taylor, 1953, 1960b; Taylor and McMaster, 1955; McMaster-Kaye and Taylor, 1958; McMaster-Kaye, 1960, 1962; Odeblad and Magnusson, 1954; Ficq, 1955b;

Vincent, 1954, 1955a,b; Fitzgerald and Vinijchaikul, 1959; Goldstein and Micou, 1959a,b; Woods, 1959, 1962; Woods and Taylor, 1959; Woods and Zubay, 1965; Zalokar, 1959, 1960a,b; Amano and Leblond, 1960; Amano et al., 1965; Leblond and Amano, 1962; Feinendegen et al., 1960a,b; Feinendegen and Bond, 1963, 1964; Bond and Feinendegen, 1964; King and Falk, 1960; Oehlert, 1961; Perry, 1960, 1964a; Perry et al., 1961a,b; Sirlin, 1960b, 1962a; Sirlin et al., 1962, 1963; Baeckeland and Chèvremont, 1961; Chèvremont and Baeckeland, 1961; Bogoroch and Siegel, 1961; Caro and Forro, 1961; Errera, 1961; Rho and Bonner, 1961; Sisken and Kinosita, 1961b; Stöcker et al., 1961a,b; Stöcker, 1962a,b, 1963a,b, 1964b; Stöcker and Altmann, 1963; Van den Broek and Tates, 1961; Kimball and Perdue, 1962; Lauf et al., 1962; Prescott, 1962a, 1963; Prescott and Bender, 1962, 1963b; Favard-Séréno and Durand, 1963a,b; Schultze and Maurer, 1963; Srinivasan et al., 1963; Chipchase and Birnstiel, 1963; Davidson, 1964; Fraser, 1964; Gracheva, 1964b; Monesi and Crippa, 1964; Welling et al., 1965; De Vitry, 1965a,b; Franklin and Granboulan, 1965; Fliedner et al., 1965; see also the review by Graham and Rake, 1963).

On the other hand, different results have been obtained by the various authors on the kinetics of labeling of nucleolar and chromosomal RNA. By virtue of the time curves of the rates of incorporation into the different cell compartments, some authors concluded (1) that the nucleolar RNA was labeled before the chromosomal RNA (Taylor, 1953; McMaster-Kaye and Taylor, 1958; McMaster-Kaye, 1960; Fitzgerald and Vinijchaikul, 1959; Pelling, 1959; Sirlin, 1960b; Oehlert, 1961); or (2) at about the same time, but in any case independently (Perry, 1960; Sisken and Kinosita, 1961b; Amano and Leblond, 1960; Schultze and Maurer, 1963); or (3) that chromosomal labeling occurred earlier than the labeling of the nucleolus (Woods, 1959, 1962; Goldstein and Micou, 1959b). These differences may be due to the different biological material investigated or perhaps may be caused by different methods of fixation, which can affect the various cell structures in different ways, as was pointed out in Chapter 2, Section I, A, 1.

Recently, the combination of electron microscopic studies with autoradiography showed that in *Ipheion uniflorum* after pulse labeling of RNA with uridine-³H a rapidly labeled RNA fraction appears in the nucleolonemata. In the light microscope the nucleolonemata appear in this species as centrally located compact skeins (La Cour and Crawley, 1965).

A combination of autoradiographic and biochemical techniques has provided evidence that transfer RNA is synthesized in the nucleolus (Birnstiel et al., 1965). In these studies selective labeling of nucleolar

RNA was achieved by incubating isolated salivary glands of *Smittia* with uridine-^{14}C in the presence of 5,6 dichloro-1-(β-D-ribofuranosyl)-benzimidazole (DRB) and of 4,5,6-trichloro derivative (TRB) both of which inhibit chromosomal and cytoplasmic RNA synthesis (Sirlin and Jacob, 1964). Extraction of this nucleolar RNA showed that it consisted, with the exception of minor activity in the 28 S RNA, entirely of small molecular RNA with sedimentation characteristics of transfer RNA.

Autoradiographic studies of the RNA synthesis in chromosomes from oocytes of *Triturus viridescens* were performed by Gall and Callan (1962) and Izawa et al. (1963), in polytene chromosomes of dipteran salivery glands by Ficq et al. (1958), Fujita and Takamoto (1963), Sirlin and Schor (1962a,b), and Pelling (1964).

Whether there is an independent RNA synthesis in the cytoplasm or not is still an open question. Most experiments indicate that, if there is an independent cytoplasmic RNA synthesis at all, it must be very small. Harris (1959) studying the incorporation of RNA precursors in tissue culture cells autoradiographically came to the conclusion that the occurrence of the cytoplasmic labeling was too rapid to be due to transfer from the nucleus only and that there is a markedly independent cytoplasmic RNA synthesis.

2. Migration of RNA from the Nucleus to the Cytoplasm

From most autoradiographic experiments, transport of nuclear RNA or RNA-like material to the cytoplasm in acid-insoluble high molecular form was assumed, because of the decrease of grain numbers over the nucleus and a corresponding increase of the number of grains over the cytoplasm, as a function of the experimental time. These results were partly interpreted as migration of messenger RNA. For references see Chapter 5, II, A, 1.

The only direct observation of an extrusion of labeled macromolecular RNA or an RNA-like substance from the nucleolus to the cytoplasm was described by Stöcker et al. (1961b) and Stöcker (1962a). Using cytidine-^{3}H, these authors examined autoradiographically the RNA synthesis of pancreas cells of normal mice and mice stimulated with pilocarpine. It could be seen on the autoradiograms that often the labeled nucleoli were situated at the nuclear membrane. In some cases these nucleoli at this position were unlabeled, but a cloud of grains could then be observed in the cytoplasm on the outside of the adjacent nuclear membrane. Grain counts showed that the number of grains in these clouds outside the nuclear membrane corresponded approximately to those normally observed over labeled nucleoli.

3. Relationship between Nuclear and Cytoplasmic RNA

a. *Studies with enucleation or nuclear transplantation.* In further eluci-
dating whether or not nuclear RNA is the precursor of cytoplasmic RNA,
an obvious choice is the investigation of unicellular subjects from which
the nuclei can be removed or transplanted into enucleate fragments. No
incorporation of labeled RNA precursors was found in enucleated cells
of *Amoeba proteus* (Prescott, 1959); *Acanthamoeba* sp. (Prescott, 1960);
Tetrahymena pyriformis (Prescott, 1962a) or in human amnion cells
(Goldstein *et al.*, 1960). In amacronucleate *Paramecium aurelia* Kimball
and Prescott (1964) reported only 2–3% incorporation of RNA precursors compared to the macronucleates.

On the other hand, enucleate *Acetabularia* have been shown to continue
synthesizing a considerable amount of RNA (Brachet *et al.*, 1955;
Schweiger and Bremer, 1960, 1961; Sutter *et al.*, 1961).

In view of these experiments with enucleate unicellular organisms, the
investigation of RNA synthesis in nucleus-free mammalian cells such as
reticulocytes is of interest. Thus, Pinheiro *et al.* (1963) have studied the
capacity of RNA synthesis of rat reticulocytes after incubation with
uridine-^{3}H and cytidine-^{3}H. They found that apparently only nucleated
cells are capable of RNA synthesis, since there was no uptake of label in
nucleus-free reticulocytes even though these cells still continue to synthesize protein (see also Schweiger, 1964; Borsook, 1964). In erythrocytes in
birds, which do not extrude their nuclei during erythrocyte maturation,
Cameron and Prescott (1963) found that the average grain count per
cell in the uridine-^{3}H treated fowl dropped rapidly during the maturation
process until no incorporation was found in the mature erythrocytes.
Thus, RNA synthesis stops in mature erythrocytes whether enucleated
or nucleated; this means that in erythrocytes enucleation is not a prerequisite for the loss of RNA synthesis. The same results were found by
Fraser (1964).

The opposite of the enucleation experiments, transplantation of
^{32}P-labeled nuclei into unlabeled enucleated or normal nucleated amoebae
resulted in the transmission of labeled material from the nucleus to the
cytoplasm as traced directly by autoradiography. Uptake of label by the
normal unlabeled nucleus did not occur (Goldstein and Plaut, 1955) when
a labeled nucleus was inserted into a nucleated organism.

In summary, the experiments mentioned above provide good evidence
that most, if not all, RNA is synthesized in the nucleus and then migrates
to the cytoplasm. For the special conditions in *Acetabularia*, see Brachet
(1961).

b. *Studies with ultraviolet microbeam techniques.* High-resolution autoradiography is also the only suitable tool in such experiments as those

performed by Perry and Errera (1960) and Perry et al. (1961a) to further demonstrate the relationship between nucleolar and cytoplasmic RNA. These authors showed that irradiation of HeLa cell nucleoli with an ultraviolet microbeam abolishes practically all subsequent incorporation of precursors into nucleolar RNA and depresses the appearance of newly formed cytoplasmic RNA by about 70%, while the RNA synthesis of the extranucleolar parts of the nucleus is depressed by about 30%. These findings are in good agreement with the experiments of Schultze and Maurer (1963) mentioned before, in that about 70% of the nuclear RNA is synthesized in the nucleolus (after correction for β-self-absorption). These results further strongly suggest that the RNA of the nucleolar-chromosomal complex is a precursor of the cytoplasmic ribosomal RNA.

c. *Application of inhibitors.* Certain inhibitors of RNA synthesis, like actinomycin D, have been applied for further investigation of intranuclear RNA synthesis. Actinomycin D in high concentrations (10^{-6} M) is known to inhibit RNA synthesis up to 99% in mammalian cells (Reich et al., 1961; Franklin, 1963; Perry, 1962b, 1963, 1964a; Sirlin, 1962b; Sirlin et al., 1962; Levy, 1963; Beermann and Clever, 1964; De Vitry, 1964, 1965c, Allfrey and Mirsky, 1963; Smith and Schlegel, 1964; Cleffmann, 1964;) as well as in cell-free systems (Hurwitz et al., 1962). At low concentrations of actinomycin D (10^{-7} and 10^{-8} M) the synthesis of nucleolar RNA is suppressed, while there is still appreciable RNA synthesis in the chromatin portion of the nucleus. The appearance of newly synthesized RNA in the cytoplasm is also considerably suppressed (Perry, 1964a; Perry et al., 1964; Stenram, 1964; Stenram and Willén, 1966). Applying actinomycin D before the labeled precursor prevents incorporation of the latter (Arnold, 1965). On the other hand, application of actinomycin D after pulse labeling, i.e., after synthesis of labeled nucleolar RNA, showed that this RNA is transformed into ribosomal RNA in the presence of the blocking agent (Perry, 1964a). However, in HeLa cells Levy (1963) did not find transport of labeled RNA to the cytoplasm in the presence of actinomycin.

Recent studies by Sirlin and Jacob (1964), Sirlin et al. (1965), and Birnstiel et al. (1965) have revealed a possibility for sequential and reversible inhibition of RNA synthesis in nucleolus and chromosomes by benzamide and substituted benzamides. This method promises new ways of studying intranuclear RNA synthesis.

In addition to actinomycin D, histones also were found to inhibit nuclear RNA synthesis, the different fractions of histones varying in their inhibitory effect (Allfrey et al., 1963; Allfrey and Mirsky, 1963; Hindley, 1963). Addition of histones, especially arginine-rich histones, to isolated thymus nuclei considerably inhibits the incorporation of RNA precursors. On the other hand, histone-depleted nuclei, obtained by digestion with trypsin, synthesize RNA at a higher rate (Allfrey and Mirsky, 1962).

d. *Relationship between RNA synthesis and DNA.* Furthermore, by means of the autoradiographic method it has been possible to shed some light on the mode of action of the inhibitory effect of actinomycin and histones. Autoradiograms of lampbrush chromosomes isolated from oocytes of *Triturus viridescens* after labeling with RNA precursors normally show heavy grain deposits over the loops (Gall and Callan, 1962; Izawa et al., 1963). Also, polytene chromosomes of dipteran salivary glands show the heaviest labeling in interbands and puffs, that is, in regions where DNA is more unfolded (Ficq et al., 1958; Fujita and Takamato, 1963; Sirlin and Schor, 1962a,b). A general relationship between the rate of RNA synthesis and the size of a puff, as shown especially in the case of Balbiani rings, was described by Pelling (1964); RNA synthesis increases with the size of these structures. Treatment with actinomycin D as well as with histones has been shown to cause very rapid condensation and retraction of the extended loop structure, and in autoradiograms considerable depletion of the label over the loops (Izawa et al., 1963; Allfrey and Mirsky, 1963). These results indicate that DNA functions as a template for RNA synthesis only in a dispersed state, and that actinomycin and histones—by combination with DNA—cause condensation of DNA and, therefore, inhibition of RNA synthesis. In the case of histones, the results suggest that this may be part of the physiological mechanism for the differential control of chromosome activity.

Close association of DNA, nuclear RNA, and protein synthesis as well as cytoplasmic RNA synthesis during interphase in cultured cells of different cell lines has been described by Seed (1966a,b,c,d). Delay of the onset of DNA synthesis, caused by X-irradiation, leads to inhibition and accumulation of RNA in the nucleus as well as to inhibition of accumulation of RNA in the cytoplasm.

The findings contained in this section are in good agreement with biochemical results of DNA removal on RNA synthesis. While removal of 70–80% of the total DNA from the nucleus is without obvious effect, removal of the last 15–20% of the DNA results in a complete blockage of RNA synthesis (Allfrey and Mirsky, 1958, 1962, 1963). This led to the conclusion that 15–20% of the DNA is active as a "primer" for RNA synthesis, while most of it is probably combined with histones and, therefore, inactive or repressed.

Consideration of the inhibitory effects of the removal of DNA as well as histones and of the addition of actinomycin D on RNA synthesis leads to the conclusion that all RNA synthesis is dependent on DNA.

B. RNA Synthesis during the Generation Cycle

1. Interphase

In contrast to DNA synthesis, RNA synthesis in the cell is not restricted to a certain period during the cell cycle. As many autoradiographic studies with RNA precursors have shown, RNA synthesis occurs during the whole interphase. On autoradiograms, all interphase nuclei are labeled (Figs. 17 and 18). [For examples of autoradiograms for mammalian tissue cultures, see Prescott (1964b) and Taylor (1960b); for animal organs, see

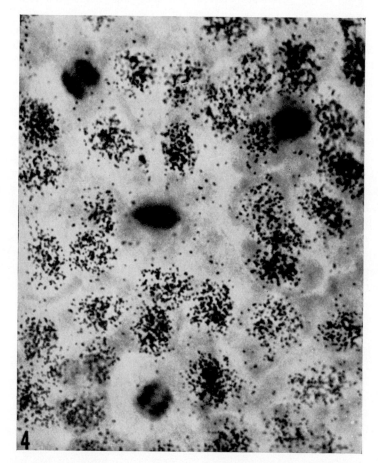

Fig. 17. Autoradiogram of mammalian tissue culture cells incubated for 15 min in uridine-³H. Nuclei of interphase cells are heavily labeled, but mitotic stages show no labeling. (From Prescott, 1964b.)

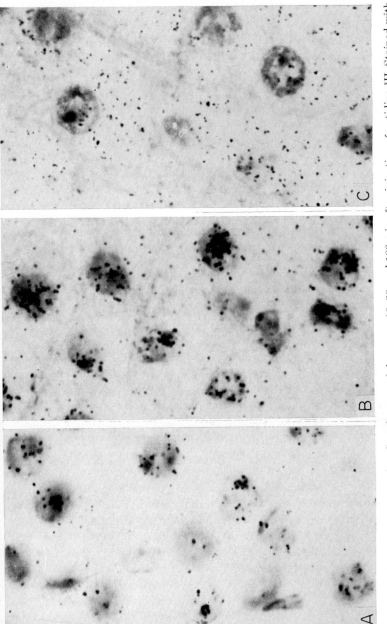

FIG. 18. Autoradiograms of the adrenal cortex of the mouse 10, 30, and 180 min after injection of cytidine-³H. Stained with hematoxylin and eosin. (A) After 10 min grains are predominantly situated over the nucleolus. (B) After 30 min, they are more diffusely distributed over the nucleus. (C) After 180 min there is decreasing grain number over the nucleus and increasing grain density over the cytoplasm.

Schultze and Maurer (1963).] Quantitative evaluation of RNA synthetic rates in short-term experiments after labeling with cytidine-^{3}H by counting grains over nuclei of different cell types of the mouse have shown that within one and the same cell type the nuclear RNA synthesis increases linearly with the increasing nuclear volume between two mitoses (Schneider and Maurer, 1963; Stöcker, 1962c). Similar results were obtained in recent experiments with cultured Chinese hamster cells CHEF by Crippa (1966), who combined uridine-^{3}H labeling of the RNA with histophotometric determination of the DNA content of the cell. The rate of chromosomal and nucleolar RNA synthesis is smallest during G_1. It increases continuously during S, parallel with the increase of the DNA content of the cell and, finally, remains constant during G_2. On the other hand, the entire RNA synthesis is more intensive during G_2 than at the beginning of the interphase (G_1 and early S). In *Paramecium caudatum* macronuclear RNA synthesis is continuous throughout the cell cycle, but micronuclear RNA synthesis is restricted to the S period (Rao and Prescott, 1967).

2. Mitosis and Meiosis

During mitosis, from about the middle to the end of the prophase, when condensation of the chromosomes has increased, RNA synthesis stops and only begins again in the middle or late telophase. This was found to be true for plant cells (Woodard et al., 1961; Das, 1963; Van't Hof, 1963; Harris and La Cour, 1963; Davidson, 1964; Kusanagi, 1964a; Kessler, 1967), for cultured cells (Taylor, 1960a; Feinendegen et al., 1960b; Prescott and Bender, 1962; Konrad, 1963; Errera and Brunfaut, 1964; Monesi and Crippa, 1964; Prescott, 1964b; Reiter and Littlefield, 1964; Crippa, 1966; Showacre et al., 1967), for tumor cells (Baserga, 1962b; Kasten and Strasser, 1966b), and for animal cells (mouse) (Linnartz-Niklas et al., 1964; Monesi, 1964) (see Fig. 17).

For more details about RNA synthesis in Chinese hamster cells during interphase and mitosis, see King and Barnhisel (1967), who found that all incorporation of uridine-^{3}H into RNA may be accounted for by cells in the interphase and that the entire label (uridine-^{3}H) may be attributed to those cells in interphase where portions of the chromosomal material are known to be already extended.

In recent experiments, Showacre et al. (1967) measured the incorporation of uridine-5-^{3}H and cytidine-5-^{3}H into nucleolar and nonnucleolar RNA in the nucleus of monkey and pig kidney cells *in vitro* during the cell cycle. Cinematographic records were made of cells during asynchronous exponential proliferation in order to identify the temporal position of individual cells in relation to the preceding mitosis, permitting correlation of the rate of RNA labeling with the position of a cell within the cycle. RNA synthesis was absent in early telophase, and rose very abruptly in rate in late telophase and in very early G_1 in both the nucleus and the reconstituting nucleolus. Thereafter, through the G_1 and S periods the rate of nuclear RNA synthesis rose gradually.

The close correlation between the condensed state of the chromosomes and the cessation of RNA synthesis has been observed also in all different cell types in the testis, from the primary spermatogonia to the spermatids of the grasshopper *Melanoplus differentialis;* thus, it applies to cells destined for mitosis as well as for meiosis (Muckenthaler, 1964).

In the literature, there is no unity of opinion on nucleolar RNA synthesis during mitosis. Das (1963) has reported that the RNA synthesis rate in root tips of *Allium* and *Nigella,* although decreasing in the condensing chromosomes during prophase, remains normal in the nucleolar fraction so long as nucleoli are maintained. In accordance with the results of Taylor (1960b), Prescott and Bender (1962) found for cultured cells that RNA synthesis stopped completely when condensation of chromosomes occurred, but before the nucleolus had disappeared and the nuclear membrane had distintegrated. This evidence is against the idea that nuclear RNA synthesis stops because of the disappearance of the nucleolus, but it supports the possibility that cessation of RNA synthesis is responsible for the disappearance of the nucleolus. In recent experiments Das and Alfert (1966) were able to show that the nucleolar apparatus is a very active center of RNA synthesis during early mitotic prophase in *Allium* and *Nigella* root meristems and during meiotic prophase in *Urechis* oocytes. In contrast to these, the nucleolar apparatus produces little or no RNA during meiotic prophase in corn anthers and in locust testis. Using cytidine-^{3}H in root tips of *Luzula,* Kusanagi (1964b) has observed that the nucleolar RNA migrates to the metaphase chromosomes during late prophase or prometaphase in order to combine with them. After disintegration of the nucleolus, the nucleolar RNA seems to be distributed in the spindle and the cytoplasm.

Most investigators only report that RNA synthesis stops during mitosis, but quantitative evaluation of the decrease in the RNA snythesis during mitosis has shown that the rate of RNA synthesis during metaphase-anaphase decreases to a minimum value of 13–16% in mammalian tissue culture cells (Konrad, 1963) or to 5–10% in mouse cells, respectively (Linnartz-Niklas *et al.,* 1964), while the decrease in protein synthesis was much less prominent. As was pointed out by the latter authors these percentages might be upper limits. Also, Taylor (1960b) mentioned that RNA synthesis at a rate comparable to a few percent of the regular interphase synthesis might be missed in autoradiographic studies. Therefore, in most studies only the complete cessation of RNA synthesis during mitosis is reported.

Cells arrested in metaphase with colchicine (Taylor, 1960a; Prescott and Bender, 1962; Konrad, 1963) do not synthesize RNA or else RNA synthesis is extremely low during this prolonged mitotic condition.

The cessation or marked decrease in RNA synthesis during mitosis further confirms the assumption that DNA can serve as a template for RNA synthesis only when in a dispersed state. This hypothesis was also supported by Taylor's (1959) findings of a decrease in RNA synthesis during meiosis in *Lilium longiflorum*. Similar results were obtained by Henderson (1963, 1964) and Das *et al.* (1965). Henderson followed the course of RNA biosynthesis autoradiographically through all stages of male meiosis in the locust *Schistocerca gregaria* using uridine-[3]H. RNA synthesis decreased progressively during diakinesis, as chromosome coiling became more and more complete and had ceased by the time nuclear membrane breakdown occurred. No RNA precursor was incorporated into any autosome during the first meta- or anaphase. During the second prophase RNA was again synthesized by the uncoiled autosomes, while synthesis decreased as chromosome coiling became more advanced and stopped at the contracted state of the second meta-anaphase. The incorporation of uridine-^{3}H into RNA also ceases in meiosis of mice from the early meiotic prophase until early pachytene, and then quickly increases to its maximum in the middle of pachytene. RNA synthesis decreases progressively during late pachytene, diplotene, and diakinesis while the chromosomal spirals tighten in order to come fully to rest at the meta-anaphase (Monesi, 1965b).

The relationship between a decreased RNA synthesis and the condensed state of DNA has been confirmed by the results of Hsu (1962), who found less labeling of the condensed heterochromatin compared to the despiralized euchromatin in interphase cells of the mouse cell line H_4C after application of uridine-[3]H. During mitosis when both euchromatin and heterochromatin condense, RNA synthesis stops. On the other hand Mitchison and Lark (1962) could not find any drop in the RNA synthesis rate during nuclear division in *Schizosaccharomyces pombé* examined with adenine-[3]H. They concluded that this difference from the behavior of cells in more highly developed organisms might well be due to the absence of condensed chromosomes as well as a true mitosis in the fission yeast. An abrupt increase in RNA synthesis was observed during mitosis of synchronized *Lactobacillus acidophilus* cells (Burns, 1961). In contrast to Baserga's experiments (1962b), Lauf *et al.* (1962) have reported that RNA synthesis continues during mitosis in ascites tumor cells.

C. RNA Synthesis in the Different Cell Types of the Mammalian Organism

In the preceding chapters only intracellular RNA synthesis was considered. However, autoradiographic studies of the RNA synthesis of organs and tissues in the mouse and rat have shown that the various cell types have different rates of RNA synthesis. The most striking result was the similarity of autoradiograms after application of labeled RNA precursors and labeled amino acids (see Chapter 6, Section II, D). Thus, cells with an intense protein turnover also have a high RNA synthetic rate (see Fig. 25 and Table XVI). Certain cell types, such as the chief cells of the stomach, intestinal epithelium, choroid plexus, and adrenal cortex have a high RNA synthetic rate, and others, such as muscle and connective tissue, have a very low one (Schultze et al., 1961; Koburg, 1961b, 1962a).

Even the state of maturation of a cell line influences RNA synthesis, as shown by *in vitro* studies of RNA and protein metabolism in normal human erythroblasts and granuloblasts (Torelli et al., 1964). For every molecule of leucine taken up into protein, immature myeloid cells synthesize a much greater amount of RNA than do mature forms. Furthermore, application of actinomycin D has shown that this RNA synthesized in immature cells is rapidly degraded. This metabolically active RNA fraction obviously does not act as a template for the simultaneously synthesized proteins, as shown in experiments with actinomycin D (Torelli et al., 1965).

For special studies of RNA synthesis in germ cells of mouse testis, see Monesi (1965a,b).

III. RNA Synthesis under Pathological Conditions

RNA synthesis has been studied under different experimentally pathological conditions, for example, regeneration and tumor initiation. RNA synthesis, measured by adenine-^{14}C uptake into isolated rat liver nuclei, recovers much more rapidly from the effects of partial hepatectomy than does protein synthesis (Logan et al., 1959b). In regenerating wound tissue of rats RNA synthesis has been studied with ^{32}P; it increases during the early stages of regeneration, but diminishes with time (Williamson and Guschlbauer, 1963).

In studies of tumor initiation a decreased incorporation of cytidine-^{3}H has been found in autoradiograms after treatment of mouse skin with carcinogenic hydrocarbon (DMBA) (Sinclair and McCarter, 1964). In contrast to these results, Oehlert et al. (1961) and Oehlert and von Pein (1963) have reported a significant rise in the RNA synthetic rate, but no change in the incorporation pattern, in the nuclei after but a single treatment of the mouse epidermis with methylcholanthrene. Induction of hepatocellular carcinoma by feeding diethylnitrosamine to rats also resulted in a relative increase of cytidine-^{3}H incorporation into the nuclei of hepatocytes, while protein synthesis and the cytoplasmic RNA content are depressed (Oehlert and Hartje, 1963a,b). Under the effects of ethionine not only does the RNA content of the cytoplasm diminish in pancreas and liver epithelia as well as in the chief cells of the stomach of the rat, but new synthesis of RNA in the cell nucleus is also inhibited. In the restoration phase (3 days after the last ethionine injection) overly abundant RNA synthesis accompanied by an enlargement of both nucleus and nucleolus becomes especially striking in liver epithelium (Beck et al., 1965).

It should be emphasized that conclusions from autoradiographic results showing incorporation of protein and RNA precursors under the influence of carcinogenic substances have to be drawn with great caution, since the extent of chemical influence of carcinogens on the precursor pool is still unknown. Thus, the question arises whether or not such experimental results are really comparable with normal synthetic rates.

The influence of several chemical substances on RNA synthesis of Langerhans' islet cells has been studied by Stöcker et al. (1966a). Using cytidine-^{3}H as a parameter for the synthesis of macromolecular RNA the nuclear incorporation was found to be higher in the B cells than in the A cells; application of insulin and tolbutamide led to increased synthesis in both cell types, whereas it decreased exclusively in the B cells after glucagon and alloxan pretreatment.

Usually the increase in size of the nucleolus is a characteristic of enhanced RNA synthesis; but the nucleolar enlargement after repeated applications of atropine is accompanied by about a 30% diminution of macromolecular RNA synthesis per unit dry mass of nucleolar material. Presumably, since there is an additional inhibition of the migration of RNA to the cytoplasm, the increase in size of the nucleolus is caused by a storage of RNA (Stöcker et al., 1967).

IV. RNA Synthesis after X-Ray Irradiation

From biochemical work it is known that irradiation with X-rays strongly decreases the uptake of ^{32}P into nuclear RNA of rat and mouse liver (Payne et al., 1952). Autoradiographic studies make it possible to examine which of the cellular structures are affected by X-ray irradiation. Thus, Vorbrodt (1962) using orotic acid-^{14}C found that X-ray irradiation with 2300 r reduces the average grain number over both nuclei and cytoplasm of Ehrlich ascites tumor cells up to 8 hours after irradiation. From these results the author concluded that X-ray irradiation probably inhibits or slows down the synthesis of that type of nuclear RNA which passes into the cytoplasm in nonirradiated cells. However, the limited resolving power of ^{14}C precluded discrimination of the effects on RNA synthesis in the nucleoli and in other parts of the nucleus. Logan et al. (1959a) also found that the incorporation of adenine-^{14}C into the RNA of isolated calf thymus nuclei is inhibited by X-ray irradiation.

Boudnitskaya et al. (1964) have reported that in prelabeled HeLa cells newly synthesized RNA is radiosensitive and that the nucleolar RNA seems to be more sensitive than that of the rest of the nucleus. Incubation of HeLa cells with cytidine-^{3}H immediately after X-ray irradiation showed more depression of RNA synthesis at the beginning of the incubation time, which suggests that damage to the mechanism of RNA synthesis can be repaired. X-ray irradiation also inhibits the transport of label from the nucleus to the cytoplasm. In recent experiments Mantyeva et al. (1966) were able to show that 2 hours after whole-body irradiation an activation of nuclear and cytoplasmic RNA synthesis in rat liver cells occurs. In mouse Ehrlich ascites tumor cells, however, an inhibition of RNA synthesis was observed.

6. Protein Synthesis

I. Correlation between Amino Acid Incorporation Rate and the Specific Activity of the Free Amino Acid

Protein synthesis in organs and tissues has been frequently studied with tracers by means of biochemical methods, results being reported for whole organs, per gram of tissue, or even per gram of isolated and fractionated cell structures. However, only autoradiography enables the investigator to study the protein synthesis in single cells and subcellular components in undisrupted cells, which reduces the risk of displacing cellular material. It has already been pointed out (Chapter 2, Section I, A, 2) that, in the histological procedure commonly used, the protein is precipitated and free amino acids are dissolved.

After injection of labeled amino acids into animals only part of the amino acids is incorporated into the proteins of the whole organism, while the rest is catabolized. For instance, it was found that about 50% of ^{3}H and/or ^{14}C-labeled leucine, l-phenylalanine, and l-tyrosine and about 20% of dl-lysine was incorporated into body proteins, while only 5% of glutaminic acid was utilized and 95% was catabolized (Citoler *et al.*, 1966c).

Before presenting results concerning the study of protein metabolism with labeled amino acids, it should be emphasized that the incorporated radioactivity measured autoradiographically may not be equated with the total amount of amino acid incorporated but depends also (1) on the specific activity of the free amino acid and (2) on the amino acid composition of the protein under investigation.

1. The autoradiographic grain density (grains per/μ^2) represents a relative measure of the amino acid activity incorporated into protein per unit volume of tissue. The following relationship exists between the incorporated amino acid activity and the incorporation rate:

Amino acid activity incorporated between
injection ($= 0$) and sacrifice ($= T$)
$$= R \cdot \int_0^T s_t \cdot dt$$
$$= R \cdot s_{\text{mean}} \cdot T$$

R is the amino acid incorporation rate (mass per unit time) per unit volume; s_t is the specific activity of the free amino acid at the site of synthesis as a function of time t. The integral can be replaced by the product: mean specific activity s_{mean} of the free amino acid between injection and sacrifice $(0-T)$ times T. (For details see Maurer, 1960; Schultze et al., 1960, 1965; Citoler et al., 1966c.) Thus, the autoradiographic grain densities represent relative amino acid incorporation rates $(= R)$, only if s_{mean} has the same value for the various cell types in the organism or in the different animals compared.

It is practically impossible to measure the specific activity at the site of amino acid incorporation. However, there is some evidence that the mixing of the labeled amino acid molecules injected with the pool of the free amino acid is a very rapid process, resulting in approximately equal values for s_{mean} in different tissues of the body. [For details and exceptions, as well as for more references, see Schultze et al. (1965), Maurer (1960), Deimel and Maurer (1961).]

The important relationship between the amount of amino acid incorporated and the mean specific activity of the free amino acid is often ignored, and the autoradiographic results in animals under different conditions (different age or nutrition, irradiated and nonirradiated) are compared without considering that possible differences in the amino acid pool size may and probably do influence the specific activity of the free amino acid and consequently the grain density.

2. It is easy to see that the turnover rates of the different amino acids correspond to the proportion of these amino acids in the protein, but only if the amino acid composition of the fast-turnover fractions of the protein is the same for the cells studied, will the grain densities over these cell types represent relative protein synthetic rates. If the fast-turnover fractions of the protein contain a higher concentration of a certain amino acid, the incorporation rate of this amino acid will be greater too, without representing a higher protein synthetic rate. [For details see Schultze et al., 1960, 1965; Citoler et al., 1966c.]

These two prerequisites just mentioned should always be kept in mind when grain densities measured autoradiographically are interpreted as protein synthetic rates.

Similar to the investigation of RNA synthesis, autoradiographic studies of the protein synthesis in the cell only measures the sum of the synthetic rates of all different protein fractions, predominantly the fast-turnover fractions, which are probably emzyme proteins.

II. Protein Synthesis under Normal Conditions

A. INTRACELLULAR PROTEIN SYNTHESIS

In contrast to labeling of DNA and short-term experiments with RNA, the application of radioactive amino acids results in simultaneous labeling of nucleus and cytoplasm (Schultze et al., 1960; Tixier-Vidal et al., 1965).

Even 2–5 minutes after injection into mice or rats both nucleus and cytoplasm of the cell become labeled. The increase in activity in the cytoplasm and nucleus as a function of experimental time are approximately equal as could be expected in view of Section I of this Chapter.

1. Cytoplasm

In cells of normal adult animals it has been generally observed that labeling of the cytoplasm is quite uniform (except during the first few minutes). In ganglionic cells cytoplasmic labeling is distributed in accordance with the stainable Nissl substance (Schultze et al., 1959; Droz, 1965b). Two minutes after injection of leucine-^{3}H grains are almost exclusively localized over the ergastoplasm of the acinar cells of rat pancreas (Warshawsky et al., 1963; Leblond, 1965a,b). In electron microscopic studies combined with autoradiography initial labeling of the ergastoplasm and subsequent migration of the label to the Golgi complex has been observed by several authors in the cells of protein-secreting organs as well as ganglionic cells (Caro, 1961b; Revel and Hay, 1963a; Nadler et al., 1964; Wellings and Philp, 1964; Van Heyningen, 1964, 1965; Droz, 1965b, 1966; Caro and Palade, 1964; Palade and Caro, 1964; Ross and Benditt, 1965; Racadot et al., 1965; Tixier-Vidal et al., 1965; Fedorko and Hirsch, 1966; Rohr et al., 1967; see also Zhinkin, 1966). The function of the Golgi apparatus is generally taken to be that of "packing" protein molecules for secretion. However, the results of more recent investigations indicate that on the one hand smaller protein molecules are combined to normal, large secretory protein molecules in the Golgi region and, on the other hand, a synthesis of carbohydrates obviously occurs in the Golgi complex. This means that the protein molecules coming from the ergastoplasm are not only given their specific size in the Golgi complex but also combined with carbohydrates there (Leblond, 1965b; Neutra and Leblond, 1966).

Droz and Bergeron (1965) have described protein synthesis as taking place also in the mitochondria of rat liver and tubular epithelia.

2. Nucleus

Within the nucleus the highest grain density is found over the nuclear membrane, obviously because of the chromatin attached to the nuclear membrane (Fig. 19) (Schultze et al., 1959; Oehlert et al., 1960; Sirlin, 1960a). In the remaining nuclear area without nucleolus the grains are preferentially localized over the stainable chromatin structures, while the unstained regions of the nucleus contain scarcely any grains at all. On condensed chromosomes the grains appear to be situated more over the chromosomal margin than directly over the chromosomal body,

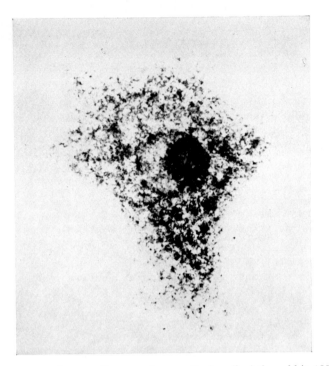

Fig. 19. Unstained autoradiogram of a ganglionic cell of the rabbit 180 minutes after application of ^{35}S-labeled thioamino acids. (From Schultze *et al.*, 1959.)

indicating that the labeled substance forms a tube around the chromosomes (Linnartz-Niklas, *et al.*, 1964). Figures from grain counts over nuclei can be found in Section II, C, 2 of this Chapter.

Transport of labeled protein from the nucleus to the cytoplasm or vice versa has not been observed in the cells of adult animals. However, transport of cytoplasmic protein to the nucleus cannot be excluded from consideration. In cell cultures during a "pulse-chase" experiment a flow of radioactive proteins from the cytoplasmic fraction to the nuclear fraction has been observed only in virus-infected cells, but not in non-infected cells, (Fujiwara and Kaplan, 1967). Many investigations like those with isolated nuclei or enzymatic studies indicate that some protein synthesis does take place in the nucleus. For instance, Kuehl (1967) concludes from the similarity in the time courses of the specific activity of total protein in nucleus and cytoplasm that protein synthesis occurs in the nucleus as well as in the cytoplasm, and that the two rates of protein synthesis are roughly comparable. Patel and Wang (1965) were able to show that the DNA-RNA-protein complex isolated from the nuclear residual protein of the thymus is an active site of protein synthesis.

Experiments studying amino acid incorporation into nuclear protein by the aggregate enzyme of Weiss suggest that the site of nuclear protein synthesis is the nucleoprotein, i.e., the chromatin (Sekeris *et al.*, 1966). In experiments with isolated calf thymus nuclei Allfrey *et al.* (1964) found that labeled amino acids (^{14}C-L-alanine) are actively incorporated into characteristically chromosomal proteins such as the arginine-rich and lysine-rich histones. These authors were able to show that amino acid incorporation occurs within the nucleus and is not due to cytoplasmic contamination. Nonetheless, far less is known about the mechanism of nuclear protein synthesis than about cytoplasmic protein synthesis.

Completely different results have been found in unicellular organisms which suggest that in amoebae only part of the nuclear protein is synthesized in the nucleus itself whereas the other part migrates into the cell nucleus from the cytoplasm. In *Amoeba proteus*, Goldstein and his group (Goldstein, 1958, 1963, 1965; Byers *et al.*, 1963a,b; Goldstein and Prescott, 1967) demonstrated autoradiographically that transplantation of single-labeled nuclei from donors into unlabeled whole host cells results in the concentration of label in both host cell and donor nuclei, while the cytoplasmic labeling is relatively low. From the striking constancy in the distribution of the label between the two nuclei, donor nucleus radioactivity:host nucleus radioactivity = 2.5:1, it was concluded that there must be two major classes of protein. One fraction, about 40% of the proteins in the nucleus, rapidly migrates back and forth between the nucleus and the cytoplasm, so-called "cytonucleoproteins." These rapidly migrating proteins (RMP) are 25–50 times more concentrated in the nucleus than in the cytoplasm, and migration into the nucleus therefore occurs against a high concentration differential. The other fraction, the remaining 60% of nuclear proteins, has been classified as slow-turnover proteins (STP), since all of them ultimately undergo turnover. During division all protein is released to the cytoplasm, but it returns to the interphase nuclei of the daughter cells, where it remains concentrated at least for 4 generations. Also, nuclei of *A. chaos chaos* host cells concentrate label acquired from implanted labeled *A. proteus* nuclei.

Similar results were obtained by Prescott and Bender (1963b), Prescott (1963), and Stone and Prescott (1965), who labeled *A. proteus* with different tritiated amino acids and found the nucleus consistently more heavily labeled than the cytoplasm. Cutting of the cytoplasm prevented cell division and led to a slow reduction in the nuclear label, whereby the ratio of nuclear to cytoplasmic label became steadily greater. The persistence of a slight cytoplasmic labeling led to the assumption that a gradual net displacement of radioactivity from nucleus to cytoplasm takes place. All nuclear protein was found to turn over continuously during experimentally prolonged interphase. If the cells were allowed to divide, the protein localized in the nucleus during interphase became evenly dispersed throughout the cytoplasm.

Goldstein and Prescott tend to interpret all these results as being due to migrating proteins. On the other hand, considering that protein molecules can be synthesized in seconds to minutes, the experimental results could equally well be interpreted to represent breakdown of nuclear proteins and reutilization of breakdown products for cytoplasmic protein synthesis.

In *Acetabularia* considerable incorporation of amino acids occurs in the nucleus. With methionine-^{35}S an extremely high incorporation into the nucleolus was found, and labeling of the cytoplasm increased after transfer of the algae to a medium containing unlabeled methionine, suggesting that part of the cytoplasmic protein originates in the nucleolus. Anucleate *Acetabularia* cytoplasm is capable of protein synthesis, and under favorable conditions this protein synthesis can be even more rapid. However, after 1–2 weeks protein synthesis in anucleate fragments ceases (Olszewska and Brachet, 1960, 1961; see aslo Brachet, 1961).

3. Nucleolus

Contradictory results have been obtained with respect to the labeling of the nucleolus. Autoradiograms of animal tissue have always shown more dense labeling over the nucleolus-associated chromatin. For interpretation of autoradiographic results concerning nucleolar labeling, it should be kept in mind that it is difficult to distinguish between labeling of the nucleolus and of the nucleolus-associated chromatin.

For *somatic cells of the adult animal* very slight amino acid incorporation or none at all are reported in a number of investigations (Droz and Verne, 1959; Schultze et al., 1959; Carneiro and Leblond, 1959a; Oehlert et al., 1960; Oehlert, 1961; Mortreuil-Langlois, 1961; Leblond and Amano, 1962; Erb and Hempel, 1962; Stenram, 1962b). More recent studies by Stöcker (1962a, 1963c) have shown that there is amino acid incorporation into the larger liver nucleoli of normal rats, into rat liver nucleoli experimentally enlarged by application of thioacetamide (TAA), as well as into mouse pancreas nucleoli experimentally enlarged by stimulation with pilocarpine. The enlargement of the nucleoli obviously is an expression of their increased functional state. Koburg (1962b) and Sandborn (1963) found amino acid incorporation also into the nucleoli of certain ganglionic cells. These results may be interpreted to indicate that nucleolar protein synthesis perhaps depends on the functional state of the cell.

Completely different conditions were found in *generative and embryonic cells.* Quite heavy labeling of the nucleolus was reported for oocytes of echinoderms and frogs by Ficq (1953, 1955a,b, 1959b), Ficq and Errera (1955b, 1959), Pantelouris (1958), Erb and Hempel (1962), and Erb and Maurer (1962). In myoblasts of amphibian embryos labeling of the nucleolar apparatus (nucleolus and nucleolus-associated chromatin) with methionine-^{35}S was described by Sirlin and Elsdale (1959). In chick embryos, labeled and unlabeled nucleoli were observed after application of methionine-^{35}S by Sirlin and Waddington (1956). Some observations seem to indicate that nucleolar protein synthesis decreases relatively with increasing maturation of cells like oocytes of sea urchin (Erb and Hempel, 1962) or mesoderm cells of amphibian embryos (Waddington and Sirlin, 1959).

Uniform uptake of labeled amino acids has been found in nucleoli of chironomids (Ficq, 1959b; Sirlin, 1960a), the labeling of which appears before chromosomal labeling (Sirlin and Knight, 1958; Sirlin, 1960b, 1962b).

In *cell cultures* moderate labeling of the nucleolus of HeLa cells after application of lysine-^{3}H was reported by Errera *et al.* (1961). On the other hand the finding of minimal histidine-^{3}H incorporation into nucleoli of HeLa cells and cultured hamster cells led Prescott and Bender (1962) to the conclusion that there is no evidence of a higher rate of protein synthesis in the nucleolus.

In *plants*, labeling of the nucleolus was observed in root tip cells of *Vicia faba* after application of lysine-^{3}H (Mattingly, 1963). Leucine-^{3}H uptake in nonisolated nuclei of *Rhynchosciara angelae* was reported to be slightly greater in nucleolar material than in chromosomes (Sirlin and Schor, 1962b).

B. PROTEIN SYNTHESIS DURING INTERPHASE, MITOSIS, AND MEIOSIS

1. Interphase

Protein is synthesized during the whole interphase of the cell in both nucleus and cytoplasm. Different protein synthetic rates were observed during various phases of the interphase for a number of biological subjects. The same nuclear protein synthetic rate per unit volume has been found in the cells of the normal adult mouse and rat from the beginning of the G_1 phase until the end of the S phase. This is probably true also for the G_2 phase (Gerbaulet *et al.*, 1961, 1963; Schultze *et al.*, 1965). In ascites tumor cells Baserga (1962a) found a higher incorporation rate of leucine-^{14}C during the DNA synthesis period. In special experiments Kasten and Strasser (1966a) have studied amino acid incorporation into various cell structures of synchronized human tumor cells during the cell cycle. During the S period arginine is incorporated into the chromatin and nucleolus and during G_2 into the chromatin only. During G_1 all 5 ^{3}H-labeled amino acids examined (arginine, lysine, leucine, tryptophan, and glycine) are incorporated into the nucleolus, obviously due to synthesis of arginine-rich histones in the nucleolus. Incorporation of lysine into the nucleus is 1.5–3 times greater than into the cytoplasm. The content of lysine bound to chromatin and nucleolus increases, especially at the end of the S phase. These lysine-rich proteins may be connected with the combination of histones with DNA or with the initiation of mitosis.

Recent experiments by Prescott (1966) have shown that in *Euplotes eurystomus* the synthesis of histones starts together with DNA synthesis and finishes with the end of DNA synthesis, i.e., that there is a close connection between the synthesis of histones and DNA. Protein synthesis in the macronucleus, however, occurs during the whole cell cycle.

In plant cells amino acid incorporation varies with respect to the stage of interphase. Higher incorporation rates were observed in G_2 cells in *Vicia faba* (Woodard *et al.*, 1961) and pea root meristem cells (Van't Hof, 1963) than in either S- or G_1 cells. Bloch *et al.* (1967) have studied DNA synthesis and synthesis of histones as a function of time in onion root meristem cells and found that synthesis of DNA and of histones is closely correlated prior to cell division. Similar results were obtained by Robbins and Borun (1967) in HeLa cells.

Autoradiographic studies using double labeling techniques revealed that incorporation of phenylalanine-^{3}H into *Acetabularia* occurs throughout the interphase (Olszewska, 1964).

Treatment of cultured human amnion cells with puromycin, which reduces the protein synthetic rate to 20% of the control value, prevents cells from entering mitosis. These findings suggest that protein synthesis 30–60 minutes prior to metaphase is necessary for the commencement of mitosis (Donnelly and Sisken, 1967). Furthermore, synthesis of a certain amount of G_1 protein is also necessary for the start of DNA synthesis, as found in cultured mammalian cells by Terasima and Yasukawa (1966).

2. Mitosis

Similar to RNA synthesis, protein synthesis is reduced during mitosis although the drop of the protein synthetic rate does not reach values as low as that of RNA. Linnartz-Niklas *et al.* (1964) reported a reduction of chromosomal protein synthesis in metaphase to about 15% of the interphase value for liver and intestinal epithelium of the mouse. The corresponding cytoplasmic protein synthetic rate, however, was only reduced to about 60% at the same time. Sims (1965) found no protein synthesis at all in the chromosomes of rat epidermis and tongue epithelium during metaphase, anaphase, and early telophase.

In Chinese hamster cells Taylor (1960b) has reported that the protein synthesis—measured as amino acid incorporation into cytoplasm—is not affected by the division stage. For hamster and HeLa cells, Prescott and Bender (1962) found a decline of the protein synthetic rate (histidine-^{3}H) during mitosis until a value of about 25% of the average interphase level was reached at telophase. By late telophase the rate of protein synthesis began to rise again. In contrast to these results, Konrad (1963) observed a 42% increase in protein synthesis during prophase and a subsequent return to the average interphase value during meta-anaphase for cultured hamster cells. On the other hand, human amnion cells showed no significant change of the protein synthetic rate at prophase, but there was a drop of 52–56% in protein synthesis at meta-anaphase as compared to the average interphase synthetic rate (Konrad, 1963). Mammalian tissue culture cells arrested at metaphase with colchicine continued to incorporate amino acids, but at a lower rate. After several hours the protein synthetic rate dropped to about 5–15% of the interphase level (Prescott and Bender, 1962; Konrad, 1963). In ascites tumor cells Baserga (1962a) and Baserga and Kisieleski (1962b) have observed that the protein synthetic rate decreases as DNA synthesis ceases and drops to a minimum during actual cell division.

High amino acid incorporation rates into chromosomal proteins during prophase have been reported for root tip cells of *Vicia faba* (Woodard *et al.*, 1961) and pea root meristem cells (Van't Hof, 1963). The mitotic division during which a marked loss of chromosomal and nucleolar protein occurs has been characterized as the catabolic phase (Woodard *et al.*, 1961). On the other hand, Mattingly (1963) observed that at later stages of mitosis chromosomes of *Vicia faba* incorporate some of the labeled amino acids. For root tip cells of *Allium cepa* Jensen (1957) has reported that nuclear and nucleolar incorporation of phenylalanine-^{14}C rises during cell division, while the cytoplasmic incorporation is unaffected. Prensky and Smith (1964) using arginine-^{3}H have observed incorporation of the labeled amino acid into cytoplasm and into all nuclei during interphase and mitosis. Strikingly, there was a high proportion of unlabeled chromosomes in the second division, indicating that there might be a complete turnover of an arginine-rich fraction of nuclear protein during one division cycle.

3. Meiosis

In *Lilium longiflorum* a relatively rapid protein synthesis occurs during premeiotic interphase and leptotene, and during the remainder of the prophase protein synthesis continues, but at a much lower rate (Taylor, 1959).

Recent experiments of Stafford and Iverson (1964) have shown that the mitotic apparatus from sea urchin eggs isolated at metaphase and placed in seawater containing leucine-^{14}C incorporated the label in such a way that it was not removable by washing or chasing.

Mangan et al. (1965) have reported incorporation of labeled amino acid in the region of the mitotic apparatus in sea urchin eggs and shown that the specific activity of proteins from the isolated mitotic apparatus is more than 3 times that of the protein from the rest of the cell.

Labeling of the forming spindle in early cleavage of sea urchin eggs after application of leucine-^{3}H has been interpreted by Gross and Cousineau (1963) as synthesis of protein important for the mitotic apparatus. Labeling of the spindle has also been observed by Linnartz-Niklas et al. (1964) in adult mouse cells.

C. QUANTITATIVE EVALUATION OF PROTEIN SYNTHESIS IN THE VARIOUS CELL TYPES OF MAMMALS

1. Mean Protein Synthetic Rate in Various Cell Types

Protein synthesis in the various cell types of normal animals has been studied by means of autoradiography after labeling with a variety of amino acids by Bélanger (1955b, 1956a), Bélanger et al. (1956), Niklas and Oehlert (1956), and Leblond et al. (1957) using methionine-^{35}S; and by Ficq and Brachet (1956) using phenylalanine-[14]C. In recent studies similar autoradiographic pictures for the different cell types in rat and mouse have been obtained using 12 different ^{3}H-labeled amino acids and 5 ^{14}C-amino acids (Schultze et al., 1960, 1965; Schultze and Maurer, 1967; Citoler et al., 1966c). The similarity of the autoradiograms using so many different labeled amino acids strongly suggests that the autoradiographic grain density actually represents protein synthesis, i.e., relative protein turnover rates. For more quantitative details see the original papers.

Summarizing the results of these studies, it was generally found that there are certain cell types in the organism with high protein turnover per unit volume, others with a moderate turnover, and still others with a very low one. The chief cells of the stomach, exocrine pancreas epithelia, cells of the adrenal cortex, cells of the reticuloendothelial system, and ganglionic cells (regardless of their localization in the body) and the epithelium of the choroid plexus, belong to the group of cells with the highest protein turnover rates in the organism. Intestinal crypt cells, hair root cells, cells of the basal layer of the epidermis, cells of the columnar cartilage and liver epithelium are of the intermediate type, with a protein synthetic rate about one-third that of the above. Finally, there is a group of cells with a very low protein turnover per unit volume, like muscle cells, bone and cartilage, connective tissue and glia; these cell types differ from those of the group with the highest protein turnover by a factor of 30 to 70. For more details, see Citoler et al. (1966c). These differences in the protein synthetic rates for the various cell types are shown in Fig. 20 and in Table XII. Table XII contains mean values for

TABLE XII

RELATIVE MEAN GRAIN DENSITY OVER DIFFERENT CELL TYPES OF THE MOUSE 60 MIN AFTER APPLICATION OF ^{3}H-LABELED AMINO ACIDS; LIVER CELLS = 100[a,b]

Cell type	Density	Cell type	Density
1. Cells of the intestinal tract		Kidney, cortex,	
Chief cells (stomach)	304	(convoluted tubules)	97
Lieberkühn's crypts	294	Kidney, cortex (Henle's	
Pancreas, exocrine	274	loops)	94
Prestomach, stratified		Spermatogonia	50
epithelia	219	Kidney, medulla	
Colon, mucosa	210	(collecting tubules)	47
Villus epithelium	151	Glomerulum epithelium	37
Tongue, stratum spinosum	150		
Brunner's glands	137	5. Cells of the respiratory tract	
Liver, parenchymal cells	= 100	Bronchial epithelium	73
Salivary glands, serous	95	Alveolar epithelium	32
Parietal cells, stomach	70		
		6. Skin, muscle, and	
2. Cells of the nervous system		connective tissue	
Myenteric plexus	300	Sebaceous glands	60
Nucleus dentatus	120	Smooth muscle	50
Purkinje cells	100	Fat cells	41
Nucleus olfactorius	80	Skin, stratum basale	41
Glia	12	Connective tissue,	
White matter	9	subcutaneous	34
		Heart muscle	29
3. Cells of the endocrine glands		Tongue muscle	23
Adrenal cortex (fascicular		Skeletal muscle	12
layer)	117	Cartilage	12
Epiphysis	110		
Pancreas, endocrine	102	7. Cells of the inflammatory	
Adenohypophysis	100	infiltration	
Adrenal medulla	88	Plasmocytes	275
Neurohypophysis	70	Histiocytes	140
		Lymphocytes	37
4. Cells of the genitourinary			
tract			
Epididymis epithelium	136	8. Erythrocytes	~0

[a] From Citoler et al. (1966c).
[b] Mean values from experiments with ^{3}H-labeled l-tyrosine, l-phenylalanine, dl-lysine, dl-arginine, and dl-tryptophan.

the relative grain density of mouse cell types after application of various amino acids (l-tyrosine-^{3}H, dl-tryptophan-^{3}H, dl-arginine-^{3}H, dl-lysine-^{3}H, and l-phenylalanine-^{3}H). These values are a relative measure for cellular ^{3}H-labeled amino acid incorporation per unit volume in the corresponding cell type. Similar results have already been obtained for ^{35}S- and ^{14}C-labeled amino acids (Schultze and Maurer, 1962). These results have been confirmed by biochemical studies (Citoler et al., 1966c).

Special studies on protein metabolism in bones have been performed with a variety of labeled amino acids by Bélanger (1956a, 1958), Leblond et al. (1950, 1959a), Greulich (1956), Carneiro and Leblond (1959b), Carneiro (1965), Koburg (1961a, 1962a, 1963a), Tonna (1961, 1962, 1964a,b, 1965), Tonna and Cronkite (1962a), Tonna et al. (1962, 1963a), Young (1962a,b,c, 1963), Campo and Dziewiatkowski (1963), and Tanzer and Hunt (1964). It was concurrently observed that amino acid incorporation was highest in active osteoblasts. With increasing experimental time the radioactivity appeared in the adjacent matrix, indicating that osteoblasts produce a matrix precursor within their cytoplasm, which is then released to the prebone where it can be seen later as a radioactive band formed at the time of injection, separating the older unlabeled bone from the newer, weakly labeled bone. Osteocytes and fibroblasts showed lower amino acid incorporation. In epiphyseal cartilage amino acid incorporation was highest in proliferating and hypertrophic chondrocytes with subsequent secretion of the labeled material into the matrix.

Autoradiographic studies of the protein metabolism in teeth has revealed that there is rapid amino acid incorporation into odontoblasts and that the radioactivity is later released into the predentinal and later the dentinal matrix. Similarly in the enamel organ protein synthesis occurs in the ameloblasts and is later released to preenamel (Carneiro and Leblond, 1959b; Karpishka et al., 1959; Hwang et al., 1962, 1963; Greulich and Slavkin, 1965).

In the central nervous system ganglionic cells have a much higher amino acid incorporation rate than the surrounding white substance. All ganglionic cells of one and the same nuclear area of cranial nerves have a similar grain density, except the Purkinje cells where weakly labeled cells are situated near heavily labeled ones; the latter finding indicates that the cells are in a different functional state. Ganglionic cells in the motor and vegetative cranial nerve nuclei have a very high protein turnover, while sensory cells have a turnover only one-fourth to one-fifth as great. Those ganglionic cells with the highest protein turnover of all were also found to be cells for which a high oxygen consumption, high sensitivity against oxygen deficiency, and a strong tendency for autolysis have been demonstrated. Special studies of protein metabolism in the CNS

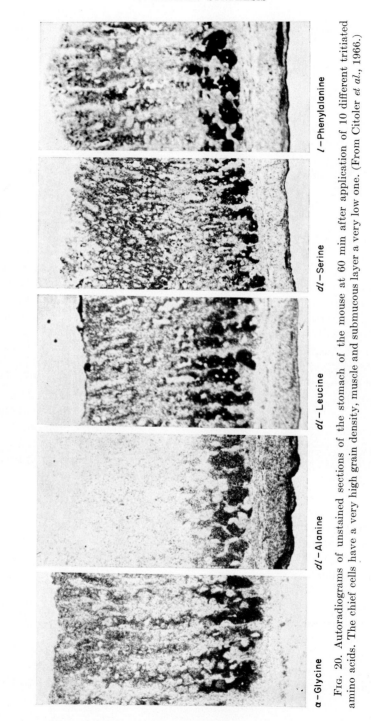

Fig. 20. Autoradiograms of unstained sections of the stomach of the mouse at 60 min after application of 10 different tritiated amino acids. The chief cells have a very high grain density, muscle and submucous layer a very low one. (From Citoler *et al.*, 1966.)

α – Glycine   *dl* – Alanine   *dl* – Leucine   *dl* – Serine   *l* – Phenylalanine

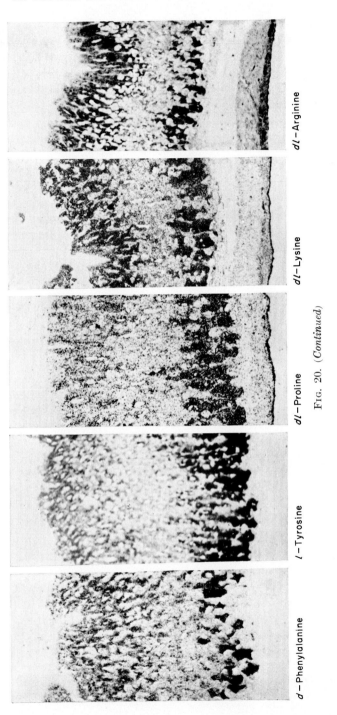

Fig. 20. (Continued)

were performed by Fischer *et al.* (1956), Gracheva (1957, 1964c), Oehlert *et al.* (1958), Schultze *et al.* (1959, 1960), Koburg (1962b), Altman and Altman (1962), Altman (1963a,b), Altman and Das (1964), and Rhodes *et al.* (1964). In interesting studies Droz and Leblond (1962) and Droz (1965a) distinguished two kinds of protein in ganglionic cells: the so-called "stationary" proteins, which turn over within about 2 weeks, and the so-called "migrating" proteins, which leave the cell's body within 1 day. Proteins synthesized in the ergastoplasm of the Nissl substance migrate to the Golgi apparatus, accumulate there, move on to the originally unlabeled axon hillock, and finally migrate downward inside the axons. The speed of this last migration has been estimated to be 0.6–0.9 mm/day in adult rats and 2.0–2.5 mm/day in young, growing rats. Similar results have been obtained for the olfactory nerve in toads and in mice with leucine-^{3}H (Weiss and Holland, 1967), for the optic nerve in mice (Taylor and Weiss, 1965), as well as for isolated nerve preparations (Weiss, 1967). Here too the observed rate of movement was a few millimeters per day. The experiments indicate that there is a daily movement down the axon of between 1.5 to 3 times the volume of ganglionic mass.

High amino acid incorporation rates have been found in the epithelia of the exocrine *pancreas*, while there is much less incorporation into the cells of the Langerhans islets (Niklas and Oehlert, 1956; Schultze *et al.*, 1960; Hansson, 1959; Warshawsky and Leblond, 1961; Warshawsky *et al.*, 1963; Citoler *et al.*, 1966c). From quantitative grain counts over the different cell structures Warshawsky *et al.* (1963) estimated that the protein of the ergastoplasm in the pancreatic cell has a life span of only about 5–6 minutes. This time span includes not only the time necessary for protein synthesis, but also that for migration of the newly synthesized protein out of the ergastoplasm.

In the *liver* there is a relatively uniform incorporation of labeled amino acids. The observation of Ficq and Errera (1955a) and Ficq (1959a) that amino acid incorporation into the nucleus is four times higher than into cytoplasm could not be confirmed by other investigators (Schultze *et al.*, 1960, 1965). Kupffer cells are always more heavily labeled than liver epithelia (Niklas and Oehlert, 1956; Citoler and Maurer, 1963a).

In *spleen* and *lymph nodes* high amino acid incorporation has been found in the follicle centers, the areas of lymphopoiesis. In the follicular border zones and the basophilic islets of the red splenic pulp, higher incorporation rates have been observed in younger immature cells (Tischendorf and Linnartz-Niklas, 1958a,b, 1961, 1962; Meneghelli, 1960).

Autoradiographic studies of the *thyroid*, partly in combination with the electron microscope, have shown that the protein component of the thyroglobulin is synthesized in the ergastoplasm of the follicle epithelium.

Only after the colloid has been transported into the follicle lumen does the glycoprotein component combine with iodine to form the final thyroglobulin (Nadler et al., 1960; Nadler, 1965).

In *ovary* and *uterus* high amino acid incorporation has been observed in the liquor-secreting granulosa cells and in theca and lutein cells, and a lower incorporation has been noted in the growing follicle cells of the secondary follicles and in the uterine mucosa. For more details and autoradiographic studies of protein metabolism in blastogenesis and embryogenesis, see Müller (1961, 1964).

In the *eye* epithelial and endothelial cells of the cornea, epithelia of the iris and the ganglionic cells of the retina have a very high protein turnover, while the stroma of the cornea, the sclera, and other cells of the retina show a much lower one (Schultze and Nover, 1959; Nover and Schultze, 1960). Droz (1963) has demonstrated migration of labeled protein newly synthesized in the inner segment of the rods toward the outer segment.

In the inner *ear* high protein synthesis has been found in the cochlear ganglionic cells, a moderate one in Corti's organ, and a very low protein synthesis or none at all in the membrana tectoria (Bélanger, 1956b; Meyer zum Gottesberge, 1961; Meyer zum Gottesberge and Plester, 1961; Koburg and Plester, 1962; Plester et al., 1962; Koburg and Hempel, 1965; Berger, 1966). For a review concerning protein synthesis in the ear, see Maurer and Koburg (1964).

In contrast to the very numerous thymidine studies in *bone marrow cells*, the number of investigations on the protein metabolism of blood and bone marrow cells is much smaller. In general it has been found that the early, less differentiated cells of the different cell lines incorporate considerable amounts of amino acid which decreases with increasing maturation. In the erythropoietic line, reticulocytes synthesize protein even after cessation of RNA synthesis, whereas mature erythrocytes do not synthesize protein (Gavosto and Rechenman, 1954; Gavosto et al., 1954; Pinheiro et al., 1963; Cameron and Prescott, 1963; Torelli et al., 1963). For protein synthesis in lymphocytes, see Everett et al. (1965). Studies combining autoradiography and electron microscopy on protein synthesis in rabbit reticulocytes have shown that ribosomes and polyribosomes are not decisive in determining the extent of hemoglobin synthesis (Miller and Maunsbach, 1966).

Protein metabolism in the *red and white muscle fibers* of the mouse and rat was studied by Citoler et al. (1966a,b) using 8 different ^{3}H-labeled amino acids. According to these authors, the oxidative metabolism of red fibers in skeletal muscle as well as in heart and tongue muscle is correlated with a 3–5 times higher protein turnover than is the predominantly glycolytic metabolism of white skeletal muscle fibers.

2. Nuclear Protein Synthetic Rate

Quantitative evaluation of nuclear protein synthesis in various organs of the mouse, rat, and rabbit after application of various labeled amino acids have shown that the rate of nuclear protein synthesis per unit nuclear volume, i.e., per unit dry weight, is very similar in all cell types. This is especially remarkable considering the large differences in the synthetic rate per unit volume cytoplasm between various cell types.

a. Nuclear protein synthetic rate within one cell type. Grain numbers per nucleus were counted on autoradiograms of several hundred cells of one cell type, and their corresponding nuclear areas were measured with an ocularmicrometer (Schultze *et al.*, 1965; Citoler *et al.*, 1966c). Figure 21 illustrates the grain number per nucleus as a function of nuclear area in square microns within different cell types of the mouse. Each individual nucleus is represented by one point on the curve. The linearity of the relationship between grain number per nucleus and nuclear area is quite obvious, as the extended straight line indicates. However, this means that the incorporated ^{3}H-activity of the nuclei, i.e., of the nuclear disk in the histological section, increases linearly with the increase in size of this nuclear disk. Thus, the ^{3}H-activity per unit nuclear volume is equal in all nuclei. Consequently, nuclear protein synthesis in the whole nucleus is proportional to its volume. The same results were obtained for a whole series of cell types with all the amino acids used. For more details see the original papers.

Similar results have been obtained for cell types of animals under experimentally changed conditions (Hempel *et al.*, 1962; Citoler and Maurer, 1963a). The same seems to be true for the nucleolus too (Stöcker and Altmann, 1963) and has been found also in cell cultures by means of a combination of cytophotometric and autoradiographic methods (Killander and Zetterberg, 1965; Zetterberg and Killander, 1965a,b; Zetterberg, 1966). Meristem cells of *Vicia faba* have approximately the same grain density over their nucleolus and nuclear chromatin, independent of their position in the generation cycle (Woodard *et al.*, 1961).

b. Mean nuclear protein synthetic rate in different cell types. Such a linear relationship between the grain number per nucleus and the nuclear area has been found not only for cells of one and the same cell type but also for cells of different cell types. This is illustrated in Fig. 22 which expresses the mean grain number per nucleus as a function of mean nuclear area for 39 different types of mouse cells (*l*-tyrosine-^{3}H). Here, each cell type is represented by one point for which several hundred individual cells of that type were evaluated. Deviations from linearity are greater in this case (Fig. 22) than in studies of nuclear protein synthesis in one and the same cell type. However, as compared with the great differences in *cytoplasmic* grain density over different cell types, these deviations from linearity are relatively small. Thus, grain density over the nuclei of

200

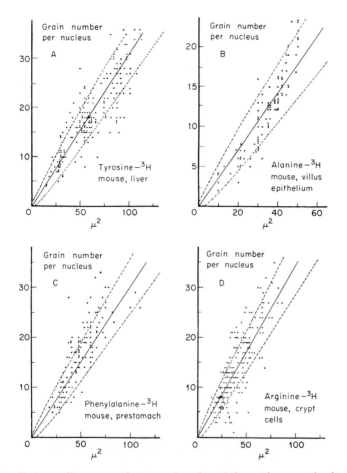

FIG. 21. Grain number per nucleus as a function of the nuclear area in the section for individual nuclei within one cell type. Each point represents one nucleus; 60-min experiments for 4 different tissues with 4 different amino acids; similar results were obtained for pancreas epithelium and smooth muscle of the mouse and for liver of rat and rabbit with 4 further amino acids. (From Schultze *et al.*, 1965.)

various cell types can be considered approximately "constant." Keeping that in mind, ^{3}H-amino acid incorporation per unit nuclear volume can be considered "equal" in all types of nuclei in the organism. This also means that ^{3}H-amino acid incorporation into the whole nucleus is actually proportional to the volume of the nucleus in all different types of cells. Accordingly, large nuclei, like those of ganglionic cells, have high protein turnover, whereas small nuclei, like those of muscle and connective tissue, only have low protein turnover, always related to the whole nucleus. For more details see Schultze *et al.* (1965), Citoler *et al.* (1966c), Schultze and Maurer (1967), and also Oehlert and Schultze (1960, 1962).

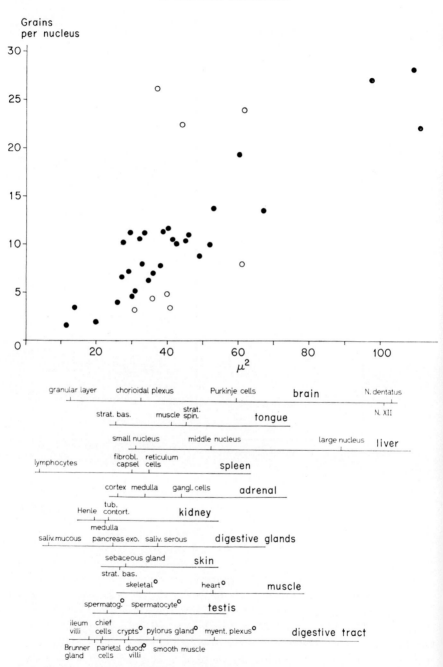

FIG. 22. Mean grain number per nucleus as a function of the mean nuclear area in the section for 39 different cell types. Each point represents one cell type; 60-min experiment with *l*-tyrosine-³H; for the open circles see 3 bottom lines of key. (From Schultze *et al.*, 1965.)

3. Cytoplasmic Protein Synthetic Rate

Table XIII contains values for the ratio between ³H-labeled amino acid incorporation into the whole cytoplasm and that into the whole nucleus of the cell for different mouse cell types as well as for different amino acids. It can be seen in the table that the ratio of incorporation of ³H-labeled amino acid into the whole cytoplasm to that into the whole nucleus of a cell is surprisingly constant. For instance, the ³H-activity in liver epithelium is on an average 7.5 times greater in cytoplasm than in the nucleus. Arginine is the only exception in all cell types. For arginine the ratio is always about 1.3 times smaller. Considering the different self-absorption coefficients for nucleus and cytoplasm these values will be somewhat higher. See the original papers for details, exceptions, and information on the method of investigation.

The amazing constancy in the relationship of amino acid incorporation into all the cytoplasm to that into the whole nucleus is true, however, not only for the various cell types in one and the same animal, but also for different species of animals as shown with various amino acids in Table XIV.

In view of these approximately constant ratios, the question arises whether or not local synthesis actually is measured or whether these values only express a diffusion equilibrium in proteins migrating between cytoplasm and the nucleus. In order to elucidate this problem, these ratios were measured as a function of experimental time between 5 and 210 minutes after application of the labeled amino acid. It can be seen in Fig. 23 that the ratios remain for the most part constant. Therefore, it is unlikely that the values of the ratios are due to a diffusion equilibrium in labeled protein. If this were the case, completely different values should be expected for muscle cells with their big cytoplasmic volume.

It is interesting to note that the rather constant value for the ratio of cytoplasmic to nuclear incorporation obviously tends to decrease in all cells with an increased metabolic function (Table XV). Thus, lower values

TABLE XIV

RATIO OF TOTAL CYTOPLASMIC TO TOTAL
NUCLEAR AMINO ACID INCORPORATION
FOR THE LIVER OF MOUSE, RAT, RABBIT,
AND PIGEON AFTER APPLICATION OF
DIFFERENT ³H-LABELED AMINO ACIDS[a]

Animal	Amino acid	Liver
Mouse	Mean value of 8 different ³H-amino acids	7.5
Rat	l-Tyrosine-³H	7.1
Pigeon	dl-Leucine-³H	6.8
	dl-Lysine-³H	6.8
Rabbit	dl-Leucine-³H	7.4

[a] From Citoler et al. (1966).

TABLE XIII

RATIO OF AMINO ACID INCORPORATION INTO THE WHOLE CYTOPLASM OF A CELL TO THAT INTO THE WHOLE NUCLEUS LISTED FOR DIFFERENT CELL TYPES OF THE MOUSE AND RAT AFTER APPLICATION OF DIFFERENT TRITIATED AMINO ACIDS[a]

Nuclear vol. in % of cell vol.	Cells	Mouse										Rat
		I Alanine	II Leucine	III Serine	IV Phenylalanine	V Tyrosine	VI Tryptophan	VII Proline	VIII Lysine	Mean I–VIII	IX Arginine	X Tyrosine
30	Lieberkühn's crypts	—	2.3	2.2	—	—	—	—	—	2.4	—	—
20	Choroid plexus	5.3	4.8	4.2	4.2	4.5	—	—	4.3	4.6	—	4.2
20	Ganglionic cells (CNS)	—	5.1[b]	—	7.4[d]	6.9[c]	—	—	6.2[b]	6.4	—	8.4[b]
15	Villi epithelia, small intestine	5.0	5.4	—	5.1	5.4	5.1	—	4.5	5.1	3.1	4.6
14	Pylorus glands	3.1	4.0	4.2	3.8	3.3	—	—	3.5	3.7	2.2	4.2
14	Adrenal medulla	—	7.3	5.7	3.1	3.5	4.3	—	—	4.9	2.9	4.5
14	Pancreas, endocrine	6.1	5.0	4.9	6.5	—	4.5	—	—	5.4	—	5.0
14	Salivary gland, serous	6.9	7.2	7.5	—	7.2	—	7.5	6.8	7.1	6.9	6.0
12	Brunner's glands	5.8	5.6	7.3	7.2	5.2	—	—	5.4	6.1	5.5	5.1
12	Adrenal cortex	5.3	5.8	6.4	6.1	7.4	6.0	—	6.1	6.3	4.9	5.6
9	Kidney medulla	5.6	—	4.5	6.1	4.4	4.2	—	5.5	5.1	3.0	5.4
9	Liver	7.6	7.9	6.8	8.0	7.7	7.5	—	7.1	7.5	5.8	7.1
8	Kidney cortex	6.6	—	6.4	6.4	6.3	5.7	—	6.0	6.2	4.1	5.2
8	Kidney, loops of Henle	6.0	8.5	—	6.8	6.5	6.8	—	6.1	6.9	3.6	6.8
8	Pancreas, exocrine	13.5	13.4	12.5	17.5	15.8	16.5	13.4	—	14.7	9.6	15.0
5	Salivary gland, mucous	6.9	7.1	—	7.6	8.3	—	—	6.8	7.3	6.9	7.3
4	Smooth muscle	7.0	7.2	7.1	6.5	6.0	6.4	—	6.1	6.8	3.6	6.0
3	Heart muscle	6.1	10.5	7.7	8.4	6.7	9.5	—	6.1	7.6	6.6	6.9
1.3	Skeletal muscle	6.3	7.1	7.1	8.4	9.2	7.1	—	7.8	7.6	—	6.7

[a] From Citoler et al. (1966).
[b] Nucleus dentatus.
[c] Nucleus XII.
[d] Nucleus olfactorius.

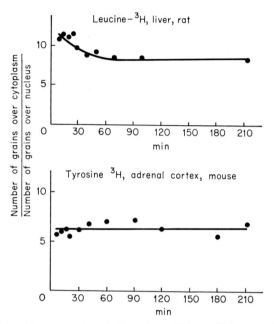

Fig. 23. Ratio of incorporation of ³H-amino acid into all the cytoplasm of a cell to that into the whole nucleus as a function of experimental time. (From Schultze and Maurer, 1967.)

for this ratio were found in regenerating liver, in strained heart muscle compared to normal, in fetal heart muscle compared to that of the mother animal, and especially in carcinoma cells.

4. Consequences

Considering these results for nuclear and cytoplasmic protein synthesis of the cell, an incorporation scheme can be derived that is applicable to all cells in the organism. The protein synthesis of the total nucleus depends on the volume of the nucleus: a large nucleus has a high protein turnover; a small nucleus, a low one. On the other hand, the protein synthesis in the entire cytoplasm of a cell is a very similar multiple of that in the whole nucleus for practically all cells in the organism. This means, therefore, that total cytoplasmic protein synthesis is proportional to the nuclear volume. From this it can be concluded that the protein synthetic rate per unit cell volume in a certain cell type depends only on the proportion of nuclear volume in the whole cellular volume. Thus, those cells with a large nucleus and a proportionally small cytoplasmic volume, like ganglionic cells, have a high protein synthetic rate, while cells with a small proportion of nuclear volume in the whole cellular volume, like muscle cells, have a low protein synthetic rate.

TABLE XV
RATIO OF AMINO ACID INCORPORATION INTO THE WHOLE CYTOPLASM
OF A CELL TO THAT INTO THE WHOLE NUCLEUS IN DIFFERENT
CELL TYPES OF MOUSE AND RAT UNDER NORMAL AND
PATHOLOGICAL CONDITIONS AS WELL AS IN TUMOR CELLS

| | | | | Tumors | | |
| | | Normal | | | Ade-
noma | Carci-
noma | |
Tissue	1	2	3	4	5	Reference
Mouse						
Liver, after applica- cation of CCl$_4$ (central:normal: peripheral, 1:2:3)	13.2	7.5	6.6	—	—	Citoler and Maurer (1963b)
Hepatitis (central:normal: peripheral, 1:2:3)	9.1	7.5	7.7	—	—	Citoler and Maurer (1963b)
Spontaneous mam- mary carcinoma (hypertrophic glands: adenoma:carci- noma, 3:4:5)	—	—	3.0	2.1	1.2	Citoler and Maurer (1963a)
Rat						
Hepatectomy (control:hepatec- tomy, 2:3)	—	7.5	5.9	—	—	Busanny- Caspari and Maurer (unpub- lished)
Heart muscle (control:training, 2:3)	—	7.5	6.1	—	—	Müller and Maurer (1965)
Heart muscle (mother:fetus, 2:3)	—	7.5	5.6	—	—	Müller and Maurer (1965)
Butter yellow carcinoma (DAB-liver:ade- noma:carcinoma, 3:4:5)	—	—	6.5	2.4	0.94	Hempel *et al.* (1962), Maurer *et* *al.* (1963)

That the incorporation of ^{3}H-labeled amino acid per unit cell volume
(i.e., autoradiographic grain density over a certain cell type) depends
on the nucleus:cell volume ratio is confirmed in Fig. 24. Here, the mean
grain density over a certain cell type was plotted as a function of the
corresponding nucleus:cell volume ratio of this cell type. As the curve

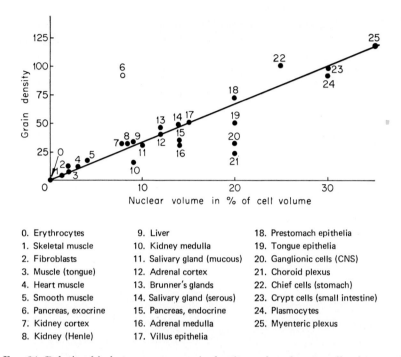

0. Erythrocytes	9. Liver	18. Prestomach epithelia
1. Skeletal muscle	10. Kidney medulla	19. Tongue epithelia
2. Fibroblasts	11. Salivary gland (mucous)	20. Ganglionic cells (CNS)
3. Muscle (tongue)	12. Adrenal cortex	21. Choroid plexus
4. Heart muscle	13. Brunner's glands	22. Chief cells (stomach)
5. Smooth muscle	14. Salivary gland (serous)	23. Crypt cells (small intestine)
6. Pancreas, exocrine	15. Pancreas, endocrine	24. Plasmocytes
7. Kidney cortex	16. Adrenal medulla	25. Myenteric plexus
8. Kidney (Henle)	17. Villus epithelia	

FIG. 24. Relationship between mean grain density and nucleus to cell volume ratio of the corresponding cell type for 26 different cell types. Each point represents one cell type as indicated; grain density = average of the relative grain density for tyrosine, phenylalanine, arginine, lysine, and tryptophan. (From Citoler *et al.*, 1966.)

shows, the relationship is quite linear. Deviation from linearity of the values for any particular cell type defines the limits of validity for this incorporation scheme. This regulatory function of the nucleus:cell volume ratio is remarkable. Obviously, the individual cell types differ far less in their protein metabolism than would be expected considering the great differences in their morphology and function.

D. RELATIONSHIP BETWEEN PROTEIN AND RNA SYNTHESIS IN DIFFERENT CELL TYPES OF THE ORGANISM

1. Protein Synthesis and RNA Content

The fundamental statement of Caspersson and of Brachet, that cells with an intensive protein metabolism also contain a high amount of RNA, has been fully confirmed by quantitative studies of protein metabolism and the RNA content in the animal cell. Niklas and Oehlert (1956) studied autoradiographically the incorporation rates of ^{35}S-labeled amino acids and found a strong proportionality between the protein synthetic rate and RNA content for the different cell types of the rat. Similar results were reported for various cell types of the mouse using phenylalanine-[14]C (Ficq and Brachet, 1956). The proportionality between protein turnover and RNA content of a cell can be expressed as follows:

$$\text{Protein turnover} = c_1 \cdot \text{RNA content}$$

2. Protein Synthesis and RNA Synthesis

Autoradiographic investigations comparing protein and RNA metabolism in tissue of normal adult mice and rats have led to very similar results (Schultze *et al.*, 1961, 1965; Schultze and Maurer, 1962, 1967). Apart from the different intracellular distribution of the grains—situated predominantly over the nucleus in the case of RNA, and localized over both nucleus and cytoplasm in the case of protein—a very similar distribution of the autoradiographic grain density distribution pattern is obtained in short-term experiments after application of labeled amino acids and RNA precursors, cytidine and uridine (Fig. 25). Quantitative

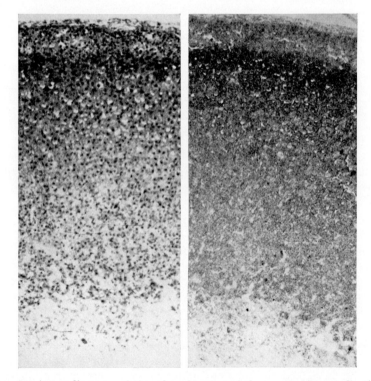

Fig. 25. Autoradiograms of the adrenal cortex of the mouse after application of (A) tritiated cytidine, 180 min; (B) tritiated leucine, 60 min. Both sections stained with hematoxylin and eosin. (From Schultze *et al.*, 1965.)

evaluation by counting grains per unit area leads to coinciding relative grain density values for both RNA precursors and amino acids for different cell types (Table XVI).

These results can be interpreted as indicating that the incorporation rate of amino acids per unit volume is proportional to that of RNA precursors per unit volume. Thus, there is not only a proportionality between protein synthesis and RNA *content*, but also between protein synthesis and RNA *synthesis*. The latter can be expressed as follows:

$$\text{Protein turnover} = c_2 \cdot \text{RNA turnover}$$

This proportionality leads to the conclusion that the ratio between protein and RNA synthetic rates should be approximately equal for all cells in the organism. The value for c_2 can be calculated, if protein and RNA synthetic rates are known for one tissue in the organism. According to protein and RNA synthetic rates for rat liver measured biochemically (Niklas *et al.*, 1958; Ernst, 1956), the ratio between protein and RNA turnover (c_2) was calculated to be approximately 20. That means that

TABLE XVI

RELATIVE GRAIN DENSITIES OVER VARIOUS TISSUES OF THE MOUSE (LIVER = 100) AFTER INJECTION OF LABELED AMINO ACIDS AND RNA PRECURSORS[a,b]

Tissue	(1) Leucine-^{3}H	(2) Lysine-^{14}C	(3) ^{35}S-Thio-amino acids	(4) Cyti-dine-^{3}H	(5) Uridine-^{3}H
Pancreas epithelium	440	530	400	150	75
Epithelium (small intestine)	410	300	300	440	500
Choroid plexus	205	163	210	215	—
Salivary gland	160	—	—	230	—
Liver	=100	=100	=100	=100	=100
Adrenal cortex	234	250	223	280	270
Adrenal medulla	84	88	77	92	95
Tongue, stratum spinosum	—	280	—	300	235
Tongue, muscle	31	33	50	30	29
Muscular layer, small intestine	—	24	23	21	35
Muscular layer, stomach	—	49	21	36	32
Skeletal muscle	20	—	—	—	—

[a] From Schultze *et al.* (1961).
[b] Time of sacrifice: (1) 45 min, (2) 90 min, (3) 75 min, (4) 180 min, (5) 40 min.

the protein synthetic rate should be about 20 times higher than the RNA synthetic rate in practically all cells in the organism.

A further conclusion can be drawn from the results described above concerning the mean life span of the RNA as can be demonstrated by division of the two equations:

$$\frac{\text{RNA content}}{\text{RNA turnover}} = \frac{c_1}{c_2} = \text{constant} = \text{mean life span of RNA}$$

Because c_1 and c_2 are constant in the organism, the mean life span of RNA should be approximately constant in the whole organism too. Biochemical investigations (Hammarsten and Hevesy, 1946) indirectly support this conclusion.

If the mean life span is not related to all the cellular RNA, but only to nuclear RNA, its value should be 10 times smaller, because the nucleus contains only about one-tenth of the cell's total RNA. That means that the mean life span of nuclear RNA should be only about half a day in most cell types. This agrees very well with autoradiographic observations that show that the migration of RNA from the nucleus to the cytoplasm takes about the same time in all cell types examined.

Proportionality between protein synthesis and RNA synthesis has been found also for the cells of cartilage and bone in rats (Koburg, 1961b, 1962a; Young, 1963), for the cochlea of the mouse (Koburg, 1961b), for the pancreas of the mouse (Stöcker et al., 1961a), and for human bone marrow cells incubated in vitro (Gavosto, 1962). Even during the process of cancerization, a parallelism between protein synthesis and RNA synthesis has been observed. Treatment of mouse epidermis cells with methylcholanthrene led to a parallel increase in both RNA synthesis and protein synthesis in the cell (Büchner, 1961; Oehlert et al., 1961; Oehlert and von Pein, 1963).

III. Protein Synthesis under Special Conditions

A. BASIC COMMENTS ON THE COMPARABILITY OF RESULTS WITH VARIOUS ANIMALS

It has already been pointed out in Section I, that the amino acid *activity* incorporated into the tissue is not simply proportional to the rate of protein turnover in that tissue (protein mass per unit time); rather it is also dependent on the specific activity of the free amino acid. The relationship is as follows:

$$\frac{\text{Incorporated amino acid activity (in 1 ml)}}{} = \text{Protein turnover rate (mass/unit time in 1 ml)} \cdot s_{\text{mean}} \cdot T$$

Experimental time T can be held constant. However, the mean specific activity of the free amino acid need by no means be equal in a normal and in an experimental animal. In this case autoradiographic grain density is *not* a measure of the protein turnover rate sought.

If, for example, the *amount* of free amino acid present in the organism of an animal is diminished under the special experimental condition, application of the same amount of amino acid activity to (1) a normal animal and (2) an experimental one will lead to higher specific activity of the free amino acid in the experimental animal. This, however, causes more activity to be incorporated, even if both animals have the same protein turnover rate. In this case it would be wrong to interpret higher incorporation of activity as being the same as a higher rate of protein turnover.

This example shows that it is absolutely necessary to know the specific activity of the free amino acid at the site where protein synthesis is being investigated in both animals. However, it takes much time and effort to measure directly the specific activity of free amino acids.

Müller and Maurer (1965) have described a method that can often be used to circumvent this problem. This method includes choosing reference organs of which it is known that they are uninfluenced by experimental conditions applied. If the amino acid incorporation into reference organs of both animals is equal, the value of the specific activity of the free amino acid as a function of time should be the same in both animals. Since free amino acids reach diffusion equilibrium very rapidly, both animals will have the same specific activity in their experimentally changed organs too. This procedure does not cause considerably more work, and it results in knowledge of s_{mean} necessary in interpreting changes in grain densities. For more details see the original paper.

Of course questions of this nature do not arise when comparing normal animals with each other, and generally not even when comparing grain densities within one and the same animal (for instance, in studying healing wounds). Furthermore, in cell cultures the specific activity of free amino acids can be measured directly. These problems can, however, be of basic significance when experimental animals and control animals are compared and when the influence of feeding, aging or irradiation on protein synthesis is being examined. Thus, they are most meaningful in the interesting problems of pathological conditions.

The fact that in such cases incorporated amino acid activity is equal to the product of *two* factors (given a constant experimental time T) has often been neglected in the literature. Only if one of the factors (s_{mean}) is constant or changes in a known manner, is it possible to make an unobjectionable interpretation of the observed grain density.

B. REGENERATION

In studying protein synthesis during regenerative processes, increased incorporation of tritiated amino acids has been found in fibroblasts in *healing wounds* from skin incisions. Due to this increased synthesis in fibroblasts, the protein synthesis in granulation tissue is much more intensive than that in connective tissue of normal animals (Kindler, 1962a,b, 1963). Ross and Benditt (1962) and Ross (1965a) have studied proline-^{3}H incorporation into wounds from normal and scorbutic guinea pigs by quantitative autoradiography and concluded that proline is first incorporated into fibroblasts, from which it is then excreted into the collagen. The mechanism of its passage has not yet been clarified; there are two possibilities: either proline passes from the ergastoplasm to the Golgi zone, then to the peripheral cytoplasm and then to the extracellular regions or it moves from the ergastoplasm directly to the extracellular surroundings.

Besides numerous biochemical investigations of protein metabolism after *hepatectomy* and quite a number of autoradiographic studies on DNA synthesis, autoradiographic studies of the protein synthesis after hepatectomy are rare. Twenty hours after partial (two-thirds) hepatectomy of rats, a maximum of the amino acid incorporation into the remainder of the liver is reached, coinciding with the maximum in the mitotic wave and preceded by a peak in the thymidine-^{3}H labeling index. This maximum is obviously due to growth of the remainder of the liver. However, another maximum of amino acid incorporation of unknown significance has been observed 10 hours after hepatectomy (Busanny-Caspari and Maurer, unpublished). This first maximum is interpreted as synthesis of enzymes which are produced before the start of a rapid proliferation. Maxima in glycine-^{14}C incorporation into acid-soluble nuclear proteins at 19 and 37–43 hours after partial hepatectomy were observed in rats by Holbrook et al. (1962).

Similar results have been obtained after unilateral *nephrectomy* in rats (Müller, 1963; Müller and Maurer, 1965). Four days after nephrectomy, there was a maximum of amino acid incorporation into the remaining kidney which coincided with the mitotic maximum and was interpreted as an expression of hypertrophy. Similar to the results after hepatectomy a pronounced maximum occurred at 12 hours, which, in contrast to hepatectomy, was found for cytoplasmic but not for nuclear incorporation. After metabolic equilibrium was reached, some weeks after nephrectomy, the amino acid incorporation rate in the remaining kidney was found to be twice that of one normal kidney of a pair.

Under the influence of tubercle bacteria reticulohistiocytary cell elements in *tuberculous granulation tissue* differentiate into epithelioid cells with an intensive protein synthesis (Wolfart, 1964). Also giant cells of the Langhans type show a high protein synthetic rate.

Using ^{35}S-labeled thio amino acids, Oehlert (1959) examined protein metabolism in cells of *inflammatory* tissue in a rat infected with *Aspergillus*. Plasma cells and Langhans' giant cells had the highest protein turnover rate, corresponding to that of cells that are secreting protein, i.e., those cells with the very highest protein turnover in the organism. The turnover rate in fibrocytes, histiocytes, and reticulum cells in the spleen and of epithelioid cells is about 3 times lower and corresponds to that in cells which grow and divide quite actively, like intestinal crypt epithelium. Mature leukocytes and lymphocytes have the lowest protein turnover rate. It corresponds to that of cells with the lowest protein metabolism in the organism, like muscle and connective tissue.

During *regeneration in amphibians,* increased incorporation of labeled amino acids into the regenerate has been generally found. During the first few days after amputation of the forelimb in *Triturus* only the epidermis produces an intense autoradiographic reaction, whereas muscle and Schwann cells react somewhat later. On the fifth day the periosteum shows concentration of label. The protein synthetic rate of the different cell types was found to be increased 2- to 5-fold (Bodemer and Everett, 1959; Anton, 1961, 1965).

During the transformation of the dorsal iris into lens, which occurs upon removal of the lens from the newt eye, an increased protein synthesis in the regenerating cells is observed when compared to that in the dorsal iris of the unoperated eye (Yamada and Takata, 1963).

C. INFLUENCE OF VARIOUS SUBSTANCES ON PROTEIN SYNTHESIS

As Citoler and Maurer (1963a) showed, treatment with CCl_4 causes drastic changes in the autoradiographic grain density pattern of the mouse liver after labeling with ^{3}H-amino acids. While the grain densities over the center and the periphery of the liver lobules are similar in normal animals, CCl_4 intoxication causes a significant decrease in the grain density by a factor of 10 over the parenchymal cells of the center and an increase over that of the periphery of the lobules (see Fig. 26). As to the whole liver, the incorporation rate of amino acids differs only slightly from the normal value. The grain density over Kupffer cells is equal in periphery and lobule center and is comparable to that in normal animals. This would indicate that the strong changes in the protein synthetic rate in liver epithelia between periphery and center of the lobules is not due to a change in the specific activity of the free amino acids. The transition from the very low grain density over the lobule's center to the high one in its periphery is abrupt, practically from one cell to the next. The changes are repaired, and no differences could be seen after 5 days. Similar experiments using glycine-^{14}C in rats had already been performed by Moyson (1956). Citoler and Maurer (1963a) also found changes in protein metabolism within the liver lobules similar to that following CCl_4 poisoning in an unspecific hepatitis of the mouse.

Application of thioacetamide (TAA) leads to an enlargement of rat

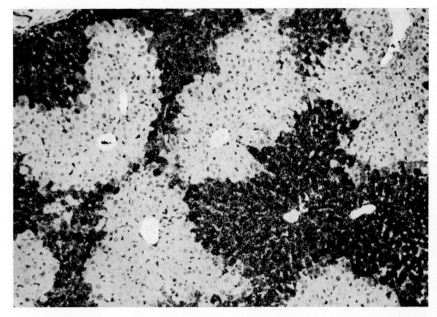

FIG. 26. Autoradiogram of the mouse liver 2 hours after CCl₄; 60 min after tritiated l-phenylalanine; high grain density over the parenchymal cells of the lobule periphery, 10 times less over the center. Note the sharp border line. (From Citoler and Maurer, 1963a.)

liver nuclei. According to autoradiographic and morphological criteria, a functional and a pathological swelling are distinguished by Stöcker (1964a, 1966a). While the incorporation rate of phenylalanine-³H is proportional to the enlarged nuclear volume in functional swelling, it is much lower in pathological swelling.

In the Langerhans' islets of rats, blocking of the cytoplasmic incorporation of phenylalanine-³H into B cells has been found after administration of alloxan. Alloxan pretreatment also reduces the autoradiographic phenylalanine-³H labeling over the zymogen granules, whereas it is only locally reduced by insulin application. After *glucagon* and *tolbutamide* administration, nuclear protein synthesis increases in the B cells and less so in the A cells of the Langerhans islets. In the B cells the cytoplasmic protein synthesis was also found to be increased (Stöcker *et al.*, 1965a,b, 1966a). Application of atropine leads to decreased cytoplasmic protein synthesis (Stöcker *et al.*, 1967).

Incorporation of cystine-³⁵S into hair follicles of mice has been found to be unaffected by cortisone, epinephrine, and methylthiouracil (Davis, 1962). Ethionine has been found to inhibit the uptake of methionine-³⁵S into the different tissues of chick embryos (Feldman and Waddington, 1955). See Beck *et al.* (1965) on protein metabolism in the different cell types of rat following ethionine intoxication.

Under the influence of actinomycin D, not only is RNA synthesis in cytoplasm strongly inhibited and that in the nucleolus practically eliminated, but protein synthesis in the nucleolus is also markedly inhibited (Stenram and Willén, 1966).

D. Influence of Feeding, Aging, and Other Conditions on Protein Synthesis

The influence of protein deficiency in food as well as starvation on the protein synthesis in the different cell types in mice and rats has been studied autoradiographically by grain counting (Stenram, 1962b; Stenram and Hirschman, 1965). The authors observed during protein inanition a shift of protein synthesis from less essential organs, such as the spleen, to more essential ones, such as the liver. However, one should be aware that these changed nutritional conditions may affect the specific activity of the precursors in an unknown way.

In the course of aging, the incorporation of glycine-^{3}H into the cells of the mouse skeletal system diminishes. Compared to other cells, osteoblasts are not so strongly influenced (Tonna, 1964b).

Protein metabolism in the brain has been investigated in rats under various experimental conditions, like visual or motor training, using leucine-^{3}H. The results indicate that such experimental conditions do not necessarily lead to increased protein synthesis in the brain of the experimental animals (Altman and Das, 1966; Altman *et al.*, 1966; Das and Altman, 1966).

Experimental brain edema leads to a distinct increase in grain density over the glial cells in the subcortical edematous area after application of *l*-tyrosine-^{3}H to adult cats (Kleihues and Schultze, 1967).

E. Protein Synthesis during Cancerization and in Tumor Cells

After application of butter yellow (DAB) to rats, the protein synthetic rate was found to increase by a factor of 2.5 in the course of development from liver parenchymal cells to adenoma cells to carcinoma cells (Lennartz *et al.*, 1961; Hempel *et al.*, 1962).

A single treatment with methylcholanthrene leads to a considerable increase in cytoplasmic protein synthesis in epidermal cells. Further increase of protein synthesis has been observed in the papillomatous stage and in the fully developed carcinoma, the synthetic rate being highest in the periphery of the tumor (Oehlert *et al.*, 1961; Oehlert and Hartje, 1963a,b).

In the spontaneous mammary carcinoma of the mouse, protein synthesis is slightly enhanced in the hyperplastic cells, diminished in the adenoma cells, and distinctly increased in the carcinoma cells (Citoler and Maurer, 1963b).

For autoradiographic studies with ^{3}H- or ^{14}C-labeled dioxyphenylalanine (DOPA) on the melanine metabolism in melanoma cells of the mouse (type Harding-Passey), in melanomatous fishes, and in agouti pigment cells, see Hempel and Erb (1962), Greenberg and Kopac (1963), and Cleffmann (1964).

F. PROTEIN SYNTHESIS UNDER THE INFLUENCE OF IRRADIATION

Biochemical studies have shown that protein synthesis is quite resistant to X-irradiation. From the few autoradiographic studies in this field, only Logan (1959) and Logan *et al.* (1959a) have reported a reduction in the incorporation rate of phenylalanine-^{14}C into isolated nuclei of rabbit and rat tissue after irradiation with 50–900 r measured by track autoradiography. In accordance with biochemical results, Gerbaulet *et al.* (1961, 1963) found that whole-body irradiation with doses up to 800 r had no influence on nuclear protein synthesis in intestinal crypt epithelium in mice (2 hours after irradiation), although DNA synthesis dropped to about one-fourth of normal. This was found to be true for cells in the S phase as well as in the G_1 phase, which could be distinguished by simultaneous injection of thymidine-^{14}C and ^{3}H-labeled amino acids. In similar studies on intestinal crypt cells of mice, Lipkin *et al.* (1963a) observed no reduction in leucine-^{3}H incorporation into nuclei or cytoplasm during the first day after whole-body irradiation with doses up to 2500 r. However, a reduction in leucine uptake was recorded 2–3 days after irradiation, at a time when cells are morphologically damaged, since they were irradiated during their proliferative phase.

7. Lipid Synthesis

Autoradiographic methods for studying lipid synthesis are still in the beginning of their development. This is due partly to the difficult technique but also to the difficulties in the interpretation of the autoradiographic results. Up to 1967 there are only six publications on autoradiographic studies of lipid synthesis, mostly in combination with the electron microscope (Stein and Stein, 1966a,b, 1967; Przelecka and Dutkowski, 1965; Jersild, 1966, 1968; Hokin and Huebner, 1967).

8. Electron Microscopic Autoradiography

I. General Considerations of the Method

High-resolution autoradiography with tritium in conjunction with the light microscope has made the autoradiographic method a very favorable tool in studying metabolic processes at the cellular level with a resolution of better than 1 μ. In order to extend these investigations into subcellular structures it is necessary to use an electron microscope to improve morphological resolution. However, autoradiographic resolving power must be improved simultaneously in order to exactly coordinate grains and subcellular structures. To this end, special emulsions with very small silver halide crystals are applied to ultrathin sections in monolayers of AgBr crystals. By underdevelopment, i.e., a combination of short developing time and specific fine-grain developers, a short silver thread is produced from a developable silver bromide crystal (instead of a coil); the shorter the thread, the better the resolving power.

The ultrathin sections used in electron microscopic autoradiography necessitate very high concentrations of radioactivity per unit volume tissue. Depending on the type of investigation, this may be a limiting factor in the use of electron microscopic autoradiography, if the necessary amount of labeled substances exceeds the physiological limits or if the specific activity of the labeled precursor is insufficient. Because of the higher specific ionization of tritium the radioactivity necessary for ^{3}H-labeled substances is somewhat smaller than that for those labeled with higher β-energetic isotopes.

First efforts to apply the electron microscope to autoradiography were made by Liquier-Milward (1956) and O'Brien and George (1959).

II. Technique

A. Preparation of Sections

Tissue samples are fixed with fixatives commonly used in electron microscopy (osmium tetroxide, dehydrated alcohol, etc.), embedded in methacrylate or other embedding media, and cut with the ultramicrotome about 0.1 μ thick in the usual manner for preparing sections for electron microscopic observation. Thereafter the sections are either placed directly on the grids covered with a collodion of Formvar film and a thin carbon layer (Caro, 1961b) or put onto a standard microscope slide coated with a collodion layer, stripped off after development, and then transferred to the grids (Bachmann and Salpeter, 1964a,b,c, 1965; Salpeter and Bachmann, 1964). Sections can also be placed on thin Formvar membranes covering holes in plastic slides through which grids can be applied to the underside of the Formvar membrane after autoradiographic processing (Pelc et al., 1961; Budd and Pelc, 1964). Bachmann and Salpeter (1964a,b,c) recommend coating the section with a 50 Å carbon layer for protection of the latent image from oxidation by the biological material of the tissue section, for protection of the section from destaining during development, and for obtaining a quite uniform emulsion coating.

B. Emulsions

Special emulsions have been developed for electron microscopic autoradiography which combine very small silver halide crystals with the highest possible sensitivity. The most commonly used types of emulsions are Ilford L 4 nuclear track emulsion with a silver halide crystal size of 1200–1600 Å, Ilford K 5 with a slightly larger grain size, Eastman Kodak NTE with an undeveloped grain size of 300–500 Å, Gevaert Scientia Nuc. 3.07 with a grain size of 700 Å, an emulsion type Lipmann (Granboulan and Audran, 1964) from which grain sizes of 300–350 Å can be obtained by centrifugation, and a modified Kodak emulsion with a grain size of 470 Å (Bachmann and Salpeter, 1964c). Gevaert Nuc 3.07, Ilford L 4, and Kodak NTE emulsions have been assessed for their qualities in electron microscopic autoradiography by Hülser and Rajewsky (1966).

C. Various Procedures for Applying the Emulsion

Several techniques have been used in order to obtain an emulsion monolayer of closely and uniformly packed silver halide crystals. Some investigators recommend centrifugation of the emulsion in order to get close packing of only the small silver halide crystals by removing most of the gelatin (Bachmann and Salpeter, 1964a,b,c; Salpeter and Bachmann, 1964; Dohlman et al., 1964; Granboulan and Audran, 1964; Granboulan, 1965). From the melted and/or diluted emulsion—centrifuged or not—a monolayer is brought onto the specimen by a thin wire loop which is dipped into the emulsion (Caro and van Tubergen, 1962; Revel and Hay, 1961; Hay and Revel, 1963a,b; Haase and Jung, 1964; Moses, 1964; Fromme, 1964; Rechenmann, 1967). In order to get a very uniform distribution of silver halide crystals and to prevent artifacts from drying, Caro and van Tubergen (1962) suggested the production of thin collodion-emulsion membranes by bringing the emulsion onto a collodion-covered agar surface with the wire loop. The collodion-emulsion membrane is then floated on a water surface and lifted out of the water with the grids. Other methods for covering the specimen with a monolayer of emulsion consist in dropping the emulsion onto the slides and draining the excess or spreading it out with a camel hair brush (Bachmann and Salpeter, 1964a,b,c; Salpeter and Bachmann, 1964; Pelc et al., 1961; Budd and Pelc, 1964; Przybylski, 1961; Granboulan et al., 1962), or even dipping the slides into diluted or undiluted emulsion and simply letting any superfluous liquid drip off (Hay and Revel, 1963a,b; Young and Kopriwa, 1964). A semiautomatic instrument for the coating with emulsion was described by Kopriwa (1967a). A completely different technique for applying a uniformly thin layer of photographic emulsion by means of a centrifugal spreading mechanism was described by Koehler et al. (1963). A similar method was reported by Dohlman et al. (1964) and Sprey (1968).

D. Exposure

Exposure conditions do not differ greatly from those of light microscopic autoradiography except that because of the thinness of the sections and the emulsions electron microscopic autoradiography is far less sensitive and much longer exposure times are needed. Caro and van Tubergen (1962) estimated a factor of about 10 for the difference in sensitivity of the two methods. Thus, electron microscopic autoradiography requires more radioactivity and longer exposure times.

E. Development

For details on fine-grain development procedures with the most frequently used microdol or additional gold latensification as well as for comparison of the different methods, see the original publications (Caro and van Tubergen, 1962; Salpeter and Bachmann, 1964; Moses, 1964). The influence of development on the number and appearance of grains in electron microscopic autoradiography was studied by Kopriwa (1967b). After appropriate development, treatment with NaOH is proposed by Revel and Hay (1961) and Hay and Revel (1963a,b) since NaOH removes most of the visible gelatin of the emulsion and makes the specimen more transparent. However, precaution has to be taken in applying this method, since the silver grains may be displaced.

Critical reviews of the technique of electron microscopic autoradiography have been given by Sawicki (1964), Bachmann and Salpeter (1965), Salpeter and Bachmann (1964), Ross (1965b), and Rechenmann (1967). Problems of electron microscopic autoradiography are discussed also by Lettré and Paweletz (1966). For a calibration method for measuring absolute autoradiographic sensitivities under various experimental conditions, see Bachmann and Salpeter (1967), who found that the highest ratio of developed grains to radioactive decay in the specimen in mono-layers of emulsions were $\frac{1}{8}$ for ^{3}H and $\frac{1}{21}$ for ^{35}S (see also Table II). For a detailed description of an electron microscopic method and the control of the different techniques involved see Rechenmann (1967b).

F. RESOLUTION

When combining autoradiography and electron microscopy, ultrathin sections as well as emulsions consisting of a monolayer of uniformly dis-tributed silver bromide crystals are used. Theoretical considerations have shown that autoradiographic geometric resolving power depends on the thickness of the section and the emulsion as well as the distance between the two. If both have the same thickness and are in close contact, the resolving power is approximately equal to the thickness of the section or emulsion provided that the range of β-particles is greater than the thickness of either the emulsion or the section. This is true for the rela-tively thick sections prepared for light microscopic observation, but also for extremely thin sections used in the electron microscope. Although in light microscopic autoradiography, tritium yields better resolution than other isotopes, since only a small part of the histological section and of the emulsion contribute to the autoradiographic reaction, there is no difference between the various isotopes, including tritium, in electron microscopic autoradiography using ultrathin sections. In this case all β-particles, including those of tritium, are "long range" particles com-pared to the thickness of the section. Therefore, the only advantage in tritium consists in its higher ionization per centimeter, which makes its probability of "hitting" a silver halide crystal higher. This implies shorter exposure times.

Underdevelopment and the use of fine-grain developers resulting in short single filaments further improves autoradiographic resolution. The shorter the filament, the better the resolving power. It is known that the latent image is situated near the surface of the crystal, regardless of the site of ionization inside the crystal. Therefore, the middle of the filament and the site of ionization in the crystal may differ by approximately one-half of the crystal diameter. For the influence of development on the grain size, see Lettré and Paweletz (1966).

The resolution obtainable with electron microscopic autoradiography using emulsions of a monolayer of silver bromide crystals was calculated theoretically and measured experimentally by Caro (1962, 1964). On the basis of the geometry of the ^{3}H-labeled preparations used and the dis-tribution of the ^{3}H-particle ranges, a resolution of about 0.1 μ can be expected. Measurement of the resolution was performed using Ilford L 4 emulsion and—as suitable "point" sources—heads of bacteriophage T2 labeled with thymidine-^{3}H. Corrections were made for the finite thickness of those phage heads. A resolution of about 0.1 μ was actually measured with those objects; this agrees closely with the calculated one. Resolutions of the same order were also found for extended sources like nuclear regions of *Bacillus subtilis* in autoradiograms of thin cross sections (Fig. 27).

In order to obtain the highest possible resolving power, it is necessary on the one hand to use the smallest possible silver bromide crystals; on the other hand, these must be large enough to absorb as much energy as is necessary to produce a developable latent image. With an energy of about 100 eV, the silver halide crystals should have a minimum size of 0.1 μ for ^{35}S and ^{14}C and of 0.01–0.05 μ for ^{3}H (Pelc *et al.*, 1961). Thus, silver bromide crystals with a diameter of 100 Å should still react to ^{3}H-particles. This would make an improvement of the resolving power up to about 0.03 μ possible with even finer-grained emulsions than used up to now (Bachmann and Salpeter, 1965). In recent investigations, Caro and Schnös (1965) compared resolving power and sensitivity between ^{3}H and ^{32}P in electron microscopic autoradiography. These investigations are all the more valuable because the β-energy of all isotopes generally

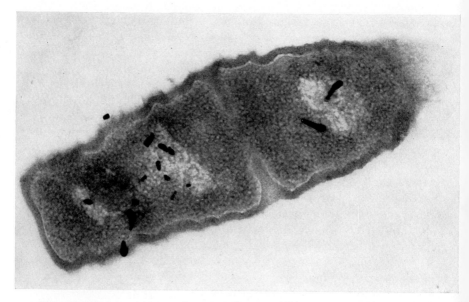

Fig. 27. Electron microscopic autoradiogram. Thin section of *Bacillus subtilis* labeled fully with thymidine-^{3}H, stained in uranyl acetate. Development in fine-grain "physical" developer. Notice small size and good localization of the grains with respect to the nuclear regions. ×58,000. (From Caro and Van Tubergen, 1962.)

used lies between that of ³H and ³²P. In contrast to ³H, the resolving power calculated for ³²P did not agree with the empirical values, whose distribution was considerably broader. Nonetheless, with a ³²P radiation source having a diameter of 1.0 μ, 61% of the grains were still found over the source, 75% within 1 μ of it, and 87% within a distance of 0.2 μ outside of it. Compared to the resolving power of 0.1 μ unobtainable with tritium, the resolving power of ³²P was approximately 0.3 μ. Since practically all isotopes in use have less β-energy than does ³²P, their resolving power with Ilford L 4 emulsion lies between 0.1 and 0.3 μ.

For a review of electron microscopic autoradiography and its resolution problems, see also Sawicki (1964).

III. Application of Electron Microscopic Autoradiography

A. DNA Synthesis

Electron microscopic autoradiography of cells labeled with thymidine-³H has been used partly for testing the usefulness and possibilities of this method and partly for better coordination of the labeling to subcellular structures. In most studies the grains were found to be confined to the nucleus (Caro, 1961a); however, in HeLa cells (Moses, 1964) and LLG-MK₂ monkey kidney cells (Silk et al., 1961), cytoplasmic labeling was observed and DNA or polynucleotide synthesis in the cytoplasm was discussed. Within the nucleus, grains were observed to be situated over nuclear regions containing microfibroblasts (Moses, 1964), or a meshwork of fine filaments, possibly deoxynucleoproteins (Revel and Hay, 1961; Hay and Revel, 1963a), or, in the blue-green alga *Anabaena* sp., in nucleoplasmic areas containing fibrils about 25–30 Å in diameter that possibly correspond to the DNA macromolecules (Leak, 1965). For more details, see van Tubergen (1961), Przybylski (1961), Hampton and Quastler (1961), Granboulan et al. (1962), Koehler et al. (1963), Gothié et al. (1963), Zadjela and Moreno (1963), Littau et al. (1964), Swartzendruber and Hanna (1965), Gaudecker (1966), Wolstenholme (1966), and Nougarède and Bronchart (1967).

In virus-infected cells only a small part of the grains is associated with the viral aggregates. Since methodical errors could be excluded, it has been assumed that the labeled DNA was mainly excess viral DNA that is known to accumulate in adenovirus-infected cells (Harford and Hamlin, 1965; Harford et al., 1966).

B. RNA Synthesis

The well-known observation that RNA synthesis preferentially occurs in the nucleolus, but also in the caryplasm, and its migration within the nucleus and to the cytoplasm has been confirmed and defined more exactly by a series of authors using electron microscopic autoradiography after labeling with uridine-^{3}H. For liver cells, this was found by Noorduyn and de Man (1966), de Man and Noorduyn (1967), and Pogo et al. (1967); for monkey kidney cells in culture, by Geuskens and Bernhard (1966); during amphibian embryogenesis, by Karasaki (1965); for insect salivary gland cells, by Jacob and Sirlin (1964); for bacteria, by Franklin and Granboulan (1965); and for Trillium microspores, by Kemp (1966). In isolated calf thymus nuclei (Littau et al., 1964), in cultured monkey kidney cells (Granboulan and Granboulan, 1964), and in mouse hepatic cells (Noorduyn and de Man, 1966) RNA synthesis was found to occur in the regions of dispersed chromatin, while the condensed chromatin is inactive in RNA synthesis. In the nucleolus (Granboulan and Granboulan, 1964, 1965), the active site of RNA synthesis is localized in the nucleolus-associated chromatin and in the intranucleolar chromatin. La Cour and Crawley (1965) found a rapidly labeled RNA fraction in the nucleolonemata in root meristem cell of Ipheion uniflorum.

In virus-infected cells, electron microscopic autoradiography showed that the greater part of actively incorporated uridine was localized in the masses of virus particles (Hibino and Matsui, 1964; Zhdanov et al., 1964); see also Granboulan and Franklin, 1966).

C. Protein Synthesis

Studies of the kinetics of protein synthesis in the acinar cells of the pancreas after application of tritiated amino acids have shown that newly synthesized protein first appears in the ergastoplasm of the basal half of the cell close to the outer walls of the ergastoplasmic vesicles. Later, the newly synthesized protein was found in the Golgi complex, from where it migrates to the zymogen granules in the apical half of the cell (Caro, 1961b; Caro and Palade, 1961, 1964; Palade and Caro, 1964; Ghiara, 1962; Van Heyningen, 1964; Jamienson and Palade, 1967).

Similar conditions were found in hepatic cells of the rat (Droz, 1966), in lactating cells of the mouse mammary gland (Wellings and Philp, 1964; Fiske et al., 1966), and in rabbit myelocytes (Fedorko and Hirsch, 1966). In neurons of rats after application of leucine-^{3}H, the newly synthesized protein appears first over the Nissl bodies of the neurons and then migrates and accumulates in the Golgi region (Droz, 1965b, 1966; Racadot et al., 1965).

A very similar scheme of synthesis and secretion into extracellular protein is followed during collagen formation in healing wounds of guinea pigs (Ross and Benditt, 1962; Ross, 1964; see also Hay, 1964). Studies of collagen synthesis using proline-^{3}H during bone formation in rats have shown that collagen synthesis takes place in the endoplasmic reticulum;

later the entire proline-^{3}H activity is situated over the cisternae, and finally it appears in the preosseous zone (Rohr, 1965). In contrast to all other studies, only weak labeling of the Golgi zone was found by this author throughout the experimental interval.

In studies of the collagen synthesis in cartilage of *Ambystoma* larvae after labeling with proline-^{3}H, Revel and Hay (1963a,b) were able to show that the label was first localized over the ergastoplasm and was still associated with the cisternae of the endoplasmic reticulum, but had also appeared in the Golgi zone where the newly synthesized protein accumulated within large vacuoles. These vacuoles subsequently moved toward the surface of the cell and discharged their labeled contents into the extracellular space.

Studies of the synthesis and fate of proteins of the basement lamella of regenerating salamander limbs with electron microscopic autoradiography were interpreted to indicate that the collagen of the basement lamella and other proline-rich proteins were secreted by fibroblasts and by the epidermis and accumulated at the epidermal-lamellar junction (Hay and Revel, 1963b; Revel, 1965).

Further problems studied by means of electron microscopic autoradiography are those of protein synthesis in mitochondria of rat liver cells and cells of the convoluted tubules (Droz and Bergeron, 1965), in rabbit reticulocytes (Miller and Maunsbach, 1966), in granular cells of the mouse esophagus and forestomach (Rowden and Budd, 1967); as well as studies of hair keratin synthesis in mice, (Nakai, 1964), amelogenesis in rats (Johnson, 1967), amyloid formation in spleen explants (Cohen *et al.*, 1965), and transport of ^{3}H-labeled histidine through the Schwann and myelin sheaths into the axon of peripheral nerves in newts (Singer and Salpeter, 1966a,b).

D. OTHER PROBLEMS

Studies of the *sulfate uptake* into chondrocytes (Godman and Lane, 1964) as well as into goblet cells of the rat (Lane *et al.*, 1964) have shown that the Golgi apparatus is the actual site of sulfation.

Iodine uptake into the thyroid gland using ^{125}I but also ^{131}I has been studied by Kayes *et al.* (1962), Stein and Gross (1963), Sheldon *et al.* (1964), Lupulescu *et al.* (1964), Lupulescu and Petrovici (1965, 1966), and Bauer and Meyer (1965).

Glucose-^{3}H was used to study the glycogenolytic effect of amylase (Coimbra, 1967), the mucopolysaccharide synthesis in Brunner's gland of mice (Schmalbeck and Rohr, 1967), and the site of glycogen synthesis in rat liver cells (Coimbra and Leblond, 1966) and the incorporation into the cell wall of growing plant cells (Ray, 1967). Using ^{3}H-labeled glucose and galactose, Neutra and Leblond (1966) and Droz (1967) were able to demonstrate that carbohydrate synthesis and formation of glycoproteins takes place in the Golgi complex in goblet cells as well as in neurons of the rat.

Localization of *serotonin*-^{3}H in rat brain (Aghajanian and Bloom, 1967a), of *digoxin*-^{3}H in the myocardial cells of frogs and dogs (Smith and Fozzard, 1963), of 5-*hydroxytryptamine*-3-^{14}C in rabbit blood platelets (Davis and Kay, 1965), and of *hemoglobin absorption* by proximal tubule cells of the rabbit kidney (Neustein and Maunsbach, 1966) was studied with electron microscopic autoradiography. Diisopropylfluorophosphate-^{3}H (DFP) was used to phosphorylate *acetylcholinesterase* and to demonstrate its distribution within the motor end plate of mouse sternomastoid muscle (Salpeter, 1967). Localization of *norepinephrine*-^{3}H in rat brain was studied by Aghajanian and Bloom (1966, 1967b) and the incorporation of *norepinephrine*-^{3}H and 5-*hydroxytryptophan*-^{3}H into nerve fibers, epiphysis, and cervical ganglion by Taxi and Droz (1966a,b) and into the locus niger, the substantia grisea periventricularis, as well as the locus coeruleus, by Descarries and Droz (1968).

Melanin synthesis was studied by Nakai and Shubik (1964) and by Hirsch *et al.* (1965) using ^{14}C- and ^{3}H-labeled DOPA.

Intercellular synthesis and storage of *catecholamines* was studied by Elfvin *et al.* (1966) and Hempel and Kraft (1968).

Since an improvement of the autoradiographic resolution by a factor of about 10 can be achieved with electron microscopic autoradiography, solutions to many problems of metabolic processes connected with subcellular structures are accessible with this method and in the future will improve our knowledge of intracellular metabolic processes.

9. Autoradiographic Methods in Cytochemistry

Dalgaard used a modified Gomori technique as early as 1948 in order to locate phosphatase in the tissue. Tissue sections were incubated with ^{32}P-labeled glycerophosphate and calcium nitrate. In this early work, the amount of labeled calcium phosphate was measured with a Geiger-Müller counter. The advantage of this method consists in the simplicity of its quantitation. More recently, Hempel (1963b) treated sections of mouse skin with tritiated n-phenylmaleiamide in order to locate and quantitate sulfhydryl groups. This substance binds to the sulfhydryl groups, which then are located and quantitatively determined by grain counting in high-resolution autoradiography. Ostrowski *et al.* (1963) and Barnard and Ostrowski (1964) were able to localize acetylcholinesterase within the motor end plates of the mouse diaphragm by making use of its reaction with tritiated diisopropanylphosphorofluoridate and following autoradiographic demonstration of the tritium distribution in the section. With the same labeled-inhibitor method, Ostrowski *et al.* (1964) studied the distribution of nonspecific esterases in the mouse kidney.

This method of "staining" chemical groups or enzymes with ^{3}H-labeled substances is very promising and may be applied in cases where proper staining methods are not available.

References

Abraham, S., and Smith, H. H. (1966). *J. Heredity* **57**, 78.

Adams, J. E., Martin, W. E., and Pomerat, C. M. (1965). *Texas Rept. Biol. Med.* **23**, Suppl. 1, p. 191.

Adelstein, S. J , Lyman, C. P., and O'Brien, C. (1964). *Comp. Biochem. Physiol.* **12**, 223.

Adolphe, M., Boue, A., and Deysson, G. (1968). *Rev. Franc. Etud. Clin. Biol.* **13**, 76.

Adrian, E. K., and Walker, B. E. (1962). *J. Neuropathol. Exptl. Neurol.* **21**, 597.

Aghajanian, G. K., and Bloom, F. E. (1966). *Science* **153**, 308.

Aghajanian, G. K., and Bloom, F. E. (1967a). *J. Pharmacol. Exptl. Therap.* **156**, 23.

Aghajanian, G. K., and Bloom, F. E. (1967b). *J. Pharmacol. Exptl. Therap.* **156**, 407.

Albouy, G., and Faraggi, H. (1949). *Compt. Rend.* **228**, 68.

Alfert, M., and Das, N. K. (1962). *Acta Histochem.* **14**, 321.

Allfrey, V. G., and Mirsky, A. E. (1958). *Trans. N. Y. Acad. Sci.* **21**, 3.

Allfrey, V. G., and Mirsky, A. E. (1962). *Proc. Natl. Acad. Sci. U.S.* **48**, 1590.

Allfrey, V. G., and Mirsky, A. E. (1963). *Cold Spring Harbor Symp. Quant. Biol.* **28**, 247.

Allfrey, V. G., Littau, V. C., and Mirsky, A. E. (1963). *Proc. Natl. Acad. Sci. U.S.* **49**, 414.

Allfrey, V. G., Littau, V. C., and Mirsky, A. E. (1964). *J. Cell Biol.* **21**, 213.

Altman, J. (1962). *Exptl. Neurol.* **5**, 302.

Altman, J. (1963a). *J. Histochem. Cytochem.* **11**, 741.

Altman, J. (1963b). *Nature* **199**, 777.

Altman, J., and Altman, E. (1962). *Exptl. Neurol.* **6**, 142.

Altman, J., and Das, C. D. (1964). *Anat. Record* **148**, 535.

Altman, J., and Das, G. D. (1966). *Physiol. Behavior* **1**, 105.

Altman, J., Das, G. D. and Chang, J. (1966). *Physiol. Behavior* **1**, 111.

Amano, M. (1962). *J. Histochem. Cytochem.* **10**, 204.

Amano, M., and Leblond, C. P. (1960). *Exptl. Cell Res.* **20**, 250.

Amano, M., Messier, B., and Leblond, C. P. (1959). *J. Histochem. Cytochem.* **7**, 153.

Amano, M. Leblond, C. P., and Nadler, N. J. (1965). *Exptl. Cell Res.* **38**, 314.

Ames, I. H., and Mitra, J. (1967). *J. Cell Physiol.* **69**, 253.

Amprino, R. (1951). *Boll. Soc. Ital. Biol. Sper.* **27**, 1713.

Amprino, R. (1952a). *Experientia* **8**, 20.

Amprino, R. (1952b). *Z. Zellforsch. Mikroskop. Anat.* **37**, 240.

Amprino, R. (1952c). *Experientia* **8**, 380.

Amprino, R. (1953a). *Experientia* **9**, 291.

Amprino, R. (1953b). *Chir. Orani Movinento* **38**, 139.

Amprino, R. (1954a). *Gaz. Med. Port.* **7**, 212.

Amprino, R. (1954b). *Compt. Rend. Assoc. Anat.* **41**, 633.

Amprino, R. (1955a). *Acta Anat.* **24**, 121.

Amprino, R. (1955b). *Experientia* **11**, 65.

Amprino, R. (1955c). *Experientia* **11**, 19.

André, T. (1956). *Acta Radiol. Suppl.* **142.**

Andreeva, L. P. (1964). *In* "A Study of Cell Cycles and Metabolism of Nucleic Acids During Differentiation of the Cells" (L. N. Zhinkin and A. A. Zavarzin, eds.), p. 136. Nauka, Moscow and Leningrad.

Andresen, N., Chapman-Andresen, C., Holter, H., and Robinson, C. V. (1953). *Compt. Rend. Trav. Lab. Carlsberg, Ser. Chim.* **28,** 499.

Andrews, G. A., Root, S. W., Kniseley, R. M., and Kerman, H. D. (1953). *Radiology* **61,** 922.

Andros, G., and Wollman, S. H. (1964). *Proc. Soc. Exptl. Biol. Med.* **115,** 775.

Andros, G., and Wollman, S. H. (1965). *J. Histochem. Cytochem.* **13,** 390.

Antipova, M. P. (1966). *Arch. Anat. Histol. Embriol.* **50,** 34.

Anton, H. J. (1961). *Arch. Entwicklungsmech. Organ.* **153,** 363.

Anton, H. J. (1965). *Regeneration Animals Related Probl., Intern. Symp., Athens, 1964,* p. 377.

Antoni, F., Köteles, G. J., Hempel, K., and Maurer, W. (1965). *Histochemie* **5,** 210.

Appelgren, L.-E., Erigsson, Y., and Ullberg, S. (1961). *Acta Physiol. Scand.* **53,** 339.

Appelgren, L.-E., Söremark, R., and Ullberg, S. (1963a). *Biochim. Biophys. Acta* **66,** 144.

Appelgren, L. E., Nilsson, A., and Ullberg, S. (1963b). *Acta Radiol.* **1,** 459.

Appleton, T. C. (1964). *J. Roy. Microscop. Soc.* **83,** 277.

Appleton, T. C. (1966). *J. Histochem. Cytochem.* **14,** 414.

Arnold, G. (1965). *J. Morphol.* **116,** 65.

Arnold, J. S. (1952). *Federation Proc.* **11,** 5.

Arnold, J. S. (1953). *Federation Proc.* **12,** 383.

Arnold, J. S., and Jee, W. S. S. (1954a). *Stain Technol.* **29,** 49.

Arnold, J. S., and Jee, W. S. S. (1954b). *Stain Technol.* **29,** 225.

Arnold, J. S., and Jee, W. S. S. (1954c). *Proc. Soc. Exptl. Biol. Med.* **85,** 658.

Arnold, J. S., Johnson, K., and Jee, W. S. S. (1954). *Federation Proc.* **13,** 421.

Arnold, J. S., Stover, B. J., and van Dilla, M. A. (1955). *Proc. Soc. Exptl. Biol. Med.* **90,** 260.

Arnold, J. S., Jee, W. S. S., and Johnson, K. (1956). *Am. J. Anat.* **99,** 291.

Asling, C. W., Johnston, M. E., Durbin, P. W., and Hamilton, J. G. (1957). "Biology and Medicine," UCRL–8024. At. Energy Comm., 1957.

Atkins, L., and Gustavson, K.-H. (1964). *Hereditas* **51,** 135.

Atkins, L., and Santesson, B. (1964). *Hereditas* **51,** 67.

Atkins, L., Gustavson, K.-H., and Hansson, O. (1963). *Cytogenetics* **2,** 208.

Atkinson, W. B. (1952). *Science* **116,** 303.

Atlas, M., and Bond, V. P. (1965). *J. Cell Biol.* **26,** 19.

Austoni, M. E. (1954a). *Proc. Soc. Exptl. Biol. Med.* **85,** 48.

Austoni, M. E. (1954b). *Wien. Z. Inn. Med. Grenzg.* **4,** 151.

Austoni, M. E. (1956). *Proc. Soc. Exptl. Biol. Med.* **92,** 6.

Austoni, M. E., and Ziliotto, D. (1956). *Kongr. Europae. Ges. Haematol., 5, Freiburg, 1956* p. 134.

Austoni, M. E., Ziliotto, D., Candiani, G., and Carenza, P. (1956). *Haematologica* *(Pavia)* **41,** 469.

Axelrod, D. J. (1947). *Anat. Record* **98,** 19.

Axelrod, D. J., and Hamilton, J. G. (1947). *Am. J. Pathol.* **23,** 389.

Bachmann, L., and Salpeter, M. M. (1964a). *Proc. 3rd European Reg. Conf. Electron Microscopy, Prague,* p. 15.

Bachmann, L., and Salpeter, M. M. (1964b). *Tagungsber. Deut. Ges. Biophysik Schweiz. Ges. Strahlenbiologie, Wien* p. 217.

Bachmann, L., and Salpeter, M. M. (1964c). *Naturwissenschaften* **51**, 237.

Bachmann, L., and Salpeter, M. M. (1965). *Lab. Invest.* **14**, 303/1041.

Bachmann, L., and Salpeter, M. M. (1967). *J. Cell Biol.* **33**, 299.

Bachmann, R., Harbers, E., and Neumann, K. (1950). *Verhandl. Anat. Ges.* **48**, 154.

Bade, E. G., Sadnik, I. L., Pilgrim, C., and Maurer, W. (1966). *Exptl. Cell Res.* **44**, 676.

Baeckeland, E., and Chèvremont, M. (1961). *Bull. Assoc. Anat.* **47**, 80.

Ball, C. R., Connors, T. A., Cooper, E. H., and Topping, N. E. (1967). *Neoplasma* **14**, 253.

Banerjee, M. R., and Walker, R. J. (1967a). *J. Cell Physiol.* **69**, 133.

Banerjee, M. R., and Walker, R. J. (1967b). *J. Nat. Cancer Inst.* **39**, 551.

Banerjee, S. N., and Horsley, R. J. (1968). *Am. J. Bot.* **55**, 514.

Barigozzi, C., Dolfini, S., Fraccaro, M., Raimondi, G. R., and Tiepolo, L. (1966). *Exptl. Cell Res.* **43**, 231.

Barigozzi, C., Dolfini, S., Fraccaro, M., Halfer, C., Raimondi, G. R., and Tiepolo, L. (1967). *Atti Assoc. Genet. Ital.* **12**, 291.

Barnard, E. A., and Ostrowski, K. (1964). *Exptl. Cell Res.* **36**, 28.

Barnum, C. P., Scheller, S., and Herman, N. P. (1964). *Cancer Res.* **24**, 1155.

Barr, H. J. (1963). *J. Cellular Comp. Physiol.* **61**, 119.

Baserga, R. (1961). *J. Histochem. Cytochem.* **9**, 586.

Baserga, R. (1962a). *Biochim. Biophys. Acta* **61**, 445.

Baserga, R. (1962b). *J. Cell Biol.* **12**, 633.

Baserga, R. (1963). *Arch. Pathol.* **75**, 156.

Baserga, R. (1965). *Cancer Res.* **25**, 581.

Baserga, R., and Banks, D. (1962). *J. Pathol. Bacteriol.* **84**, 239.

Baserga, R., and Heffler, S. (1967). *Exptl. Cell Res.* **46**, 571.

Baserga, R., and Kisieleski, W. E. (1962a). *J. Natl. Cancer Inst.* **28**, 331.

Baserga, R., and Kisieleski, W. E. (1962b). *Atompraxis* **8**, 386.

Baserga, R., and Kisieleski, W. E. (1963). *Lab. Invest.* **12**, 648.

Baserga, R., and Nemeroff, K. (1962a). *Stain Technol.* **37**, 21.

Baserga, R., and Nemeroff, K. (1962b). *J. Histochem. Cytochem.* **10**, 628.

Baserga, R., Kisieleski, W. E., and Halvorsen, K. (1960). *Cancer Res.* **20**, 910.

Baserga, R., Henegar, C. C., Kisieleski, W. E., and Lisco, H. (1962a). *Lab. Invest.* **11**, 360.

Baserga, R., Lisco, H., and Kisieleski, W. E. (1962b). *Proc. Soc. Exptl. Biol. Med.* **110**, 687.

Baserga, R., Tyler, S. A., and Kisieleski, W. E. (1963). *Arch. Pathol.* **76**, 9.

Baserga, R., Estensen, R. D., and Petersen, R. O. (1965). *Proc. Natl. Acad. Sci. U.S.*, **54**, 1141.

Baserga, R., Lisco, H., and Kisieleski, W. E. (1966). *Radiation Res.* **29**, 583.

Bateman, A. J., and Chandley, A. C. (1962). *Nature* **193**, 705.

Bauer, G. C. H. (1954a). *Acta Orthopaed. Scand.* **23**, 169.

Bauer, G. C. H. (1954b). *Acta Orthopaed. Scand.* **23**, 192.

Bauer, W. C., and Meyer, J. S. (1965). *Lab. Invest.* **14**, 1795.

Beck, V., Kramsch, D., and Oehlert, W. (1965). *Beitr. Pathol. Anat. Allgem. Pathol.* **132**, 241.

Beermann, W., and Clever, U. (1964). *Sci. Am.* **210**, 50.

Beermann, W., and Pelling, C. (1965). *Chromosoma* **16**, 1.

Beischer, D. E. (1953). *Nucleonics* 11(12), 24.
Bélanger, L. F. (1950). *Anat. Record* 107, 149.
Bélanger, L. F. (1951). *Anat. Record* 109, 268.
Bélanger, L. F. (1952a). *Anat. Record* 114, 529.
Bélanger, L. F. (1952b). *J. Natl. Cancer Inst.* 13, 238.
Bélanger, L. F. (1952c). *Nature* 170, 625.
Bélanger, L. F. (1953). *J. Dental Res.* 32, 168.
Bélanger, L. F. (1954a). *Can. J. Biochem. Physiol.* 32, 161.
Bélanger, L. F. (1954b). *Anat. Record* 118, 755.
Bélanger, L. F. (1955a). *Proc. Soc. Exptl. Biol. Med.* 88, 150.
Bélanger, L. F. (1955b). *Anat. Record* 121, 262.
Bélanger, L. F. (1956a). *Anat. Record* 124, 555.
Bélanger, L. F. (1956b). *Science* 123, 1074.
Bélanger, L. F. (1957a). *J. Histochem. Cytochem.* 5, 65.
Bélanger, L. F. (1957b). *J. Dental Res.* 36, 595.
Bélanger, L. F. (1958). *J. Histochem. Cytochem.* 6, 146.
Bélanger, L. F. (1961). *Stain Technol.* 36, 313.
Bélanger, L. F., and Leblond, C. P. (1946). *Endocrinology* 39, 8.
Bélanger, L. F., and Leblond, C. P. (1950). *Proc. Soc. Exptl. Biol. Med.* 73, 390.
Bélanger, L. F., and Magner, D. (1957). *Cancer* 10, 1110.
Bélanger, L. F., and Migicovsky, B. B. (1958). *J. Exptl. Med.* 107, 821.
Bélanger, L. F., Bélanger, C., Burke, P., and Tremblay, P. de C. (1954a). *J. Histochem. Cytochem.* 2, 467.
Bélanger, L. F., and Lotz, W. E., Visek, W. J., and Comar, C. L. (1954b). *Anat. Record* 119, 53.
Bélanger, L. F., Gilbert, A. E., Crevier, M., and Bélanger, C. L. (1956). *Anat. Record* 124, 257.
Bélanger, L. F., Visek, W. J., Lotz, W. E., and Comar, C. L. (1957). *J. Biophys. Biochem. Cytol.* 3, 559.
Benes, L., Soska, J., and Lukasova, E. (1965). *Folia Biol. (Prague)* 11, 123.
Bennett, L. L., Simpson, L., and Skipper, H. E. (1960a). *Biochim. Biophys. Acta* 42, 237.
Bennett, L. L., Skipper, H. E., Simpson, L., Wheeler, G. P., and Wilcox, W. S. (1960b). *Cancer Res.* 20, 62.
Berger, F. (1966). *Acta Histochem.* 23, 141.
Bergström, I., Magnusson, G., Odeblad, E., and Ziliotto, D. (1955). *Acta Physiol. Scand.* 35, 36.
Berman, I., and Newby, E. J. (1963). *Stain Technol.* 38, 62.
Berman, I., Winter, S. R., and Newby, E. J. (1966). *Anat. Record* 154, 635.
Bernier, G., and Jensen, W. A. (1966). *Histochemie* 6, 85.
Berry, R. J., Oliver, R., and Reiskin, A. B. (1966). *Health Phys.* 12, 1461.
Bertalanffy, F. D., and Lau, C. (1962). *Cancer Res.* 22, 627.
Bettendorf, G., Künkel, H. A., and Maass, H. (1960). *Z. Ges. Exptl. Med.* 133, 87.
Bianchi, N. O., and Molina, O. J. (1967). *Chromosoma (Berl.)* 21, 387.
Bianchi, N., Lima-de-Faria, A., and Jaworska, H. (1964). *Hereditas* 51, 207.
Biddulph, S. F. (1967). *Planta* 74, 350.
Birnstiel, M. L., Sirlin, J. L., and Jacob, J. (1965). *Biochem. J.* 94, 10.
Black, B. M., Woolner, L. B., and Blockburn, C. M. (1953). *J. Clin. Endocrinol.* 13, 1378.
Blank, H., McCarthy, P. L., and DeLamater, E. D. (1951). *Stain Technol.* 26, 193.

Bleecken, S. (1961). *Atompraxis* **7**, 321.

Bleecken, S. (1967). *Atompraxis* **13**, 190.

Bleecken, S., Strohbach, G., and Sarfert, E. (1966). *Z. Allgem. Mikrobiol.* **6**, 121.

Blenkinsopp, W. K. (1967a). *J. Cell Sci.* **2**, 33.

Blenkinsopp, W. K. (1967b). *Nature* **214**, 930.

Bloch, D. P., MacQuigg, R. A., Brack, S. D., and Wu, J.-R. (1967). *J. Cell Biol.* **33**, 451.

Block, P., Seiter, I., and Oehlert, W. (1963). *Exptl. Cell Res.* **30**, 311.

Board, F. A. (1951). *J. Cellular Comp. Physiol.* **38**, 377.

Bodemer, C. W., and Everett, N. B. (1959). *Develop. Biol.* **1**, 327.

Bogoroch, R. (1951). *Stain Technol.* **26**, 43.

Bogoroch, R., and Siegel, B. V. (1961). *Acta Anat.* **45**, 265.

Bogoroch, R., and Timiras, P. (1951). *Endocrinology* **49**, 548.

Bogoroch, R., Israelovitch, M., and Leblond, C. P. (1951). *J. Natl. Cancer Inst.* **12**, 255.

Boll, J. (1957). *Acta Haematol.* **18**, 390.

Boll, J. (1960). *Z. Krebsforsch.* **63**, 330.

Boll, J., and Mehl, H.-G. (1958). *Phot. Wiss.* **7**, 25.

Bond, V. P., and Feinendegen, L. E. (1964). *Federation Proc.* **23**, 634.

Bond, V. P., and Feinendegen, L. E. (1966). *Health Phys.* **12**, 1007.

Bond, V. P., Fliedner, T. M., Cronkite, E. P., Rubini, J. R., and Robertson, J. S. (1959). *In* "The Kinetics of Cellular Proliferation" (F. Stohlman, ed.), p. 188. Grune & Stratton, New York.

Bond, V. P., Feinendegen, L. E., and Cronkite, E. P. (1962a). *Tritium Phys. Biol. Sci., Proc. Symp. Detection Use, Vienna, 1961* **2**, 227.

Bond, V. P., Odartchenko, N., Cottier, H., Feinendegen, L. E., and Cronkite, E. P. (1962b). *In* "Erythropoiesis" p. 173. Grune & Stratton, New York.

Bond, V. P., Fliedner, T. M., and Archambeau, J. O. (1965). "Mammalian Radiation Lethality." Academic Press, New York.

Bootsma, D. (1965). *Exptl. Cell Res.* **38**, 429.

Borsook, H. (1964). *Ann. N. Y. Acad. Sci.* **119**, 523.

Bose, S., Coutinho, W. G., and Ranadive, K. J. (1964). *Indian J. Exptl. Biol.* **2**, 167.

Bose, S., Coutinho, W. G., and Ranadive, K. J. (1965a). *Indian J. Exptl. Biol.* **3**, 20.

Bose, S., Ranade, S. S., and Ranadive, K. J. (1965b). *Naturwissenschaften* **52**, 497.

Bose, S., Coutinho, W. G., and Ranadive, K. J. (1966). *Indian J. Exptl. Biol.* **4**, 69.

Boström, H. (1952). *J. Biol. Chem.* **196**, 477.

Boström, H. (1953). *Arkiv Kemi* **6**, 43.

Boström, H., and Gardell, S. (1953). *Acta Chem. Scand.* **7**, 216.

Boström, H., and Jorpes, E. (1954). *Experientia* **10**, 392.

Boström, H., and Mansson, B. (1953). *Arkiv Kemi* **6**, 23.

Boström, H., and Odeblad, E. (1953a). *Anat. Record* **115**, 505.

Boström, H., and Odeblad, E. (1953b). *Arkiv Kemi* **6**, 39.

Boström, H., Odeblad, E., and Friberg, U. (1952). *Arch. Biochem. Biophys.* **38**, 283.

Boström, H., Odeblad, E., and Friberg, U. (1953). *Acta Pathol. Microbiol. Scand.* **32**, 516.

Boudnitskaya, E. V., Brunfaut, M., and Errera, M. (1964). *Biochim. Biophys. Acta* **80**, 567.

Bourne, G. H. (1948). *Nature* **162**, 495.

Boyd, G. A. (1955). "Autoradiography in Biology and Medicine." Academic Press, New York.

Boyd, G. A., and Board, F. A. (1949). *Science* **110**, 586.
Boyd, G. A., and Levi, H. (1950). *Science* **111**, 58.
Boyd, G. A., and Williams, A. I. (1948). *Proc. Soc. Exptl. Biol. Med.* **69**, 225.
Boyd, G. A., Casarett, O. W., and Williams, A. T. (1950). *Stain Technol.* **25**, 13.
Brachet, J. (1958). *Exptl. Cell Res. Suppl.* **6**, 78.
Brachet, J. (1961). *In* "The Cell" (J. Brachet and A. E. Mirsky, eds.), Vol. 2, p. 771. Academic Press, New York.
Brachet, J., and Shaver, J. R. (1948). *Stain Technol.* **23**, 177.
Brachet, J., Chantrenne, H., and Vanderhaeghe, F. (1955). *Biochim. Biophys. Acta* **18**, 544.
Brahma, S. K., Bose, A., and Bose, S. (1961a). *Naturwissenschaften* **48**, 436.
Brahma, S. K., Bose, A., and Bose, S. (1961b). *Exptl. Cell Res.* **25**, 472.
Brahma, S. K., Bose, A., and Bose, S. (1961c). *Naturwissenschaften* **48**, 582.
Branton, D., and Jacobson, L. (1962). *Stain Technol.* **37**, 239.
Brattgård, S.-O., and Lindqvist, T. (1954). *J. Neurol.* **17**, 11.
Brenner, R. M. (1963). *Am. J. Anat.* **112**, 81.
Brent, T. P., Butler, J. A. V., and Crathorn, A. R. (1966). *Nature* **210**, 393.
Bresciani, F. (1964). *Science* **146**, 653.
Bresciani, F. (1965a). *Exptl. Cell Res.* **38**, 13.
Bresciani, F. (1965b). *In* "Cellular Radiation Biology" p. 547. Williams & Wilkins, Baltimore, Maryland.
Bresnick, E., and Karjala, R. J. (1964). *Cancer Res.* **24**, 841.
Brewen, J. C. (1965). *Intern. J. Radiation Biol.* **9**, 391.
Brière, N., and Isler, H. (1966). *Can. J. Physiol. Pharmacol.* **44**, 451.
Brown, H. O., Levine, M. L., and Lipkin, M. (1963). *Am. J. Physiol.* **205**, 868.
Bruce, W. R., and Meeker, B. E. (1965). *J. Natl. Cancer Inst.* **34**, 849.
Bryant, B. J. (1962). *Exptl. Cell Res.* **27**, 70.
Bryant, B. J. (1963a). *J. Cell Biol.* **18**, 515.
Bryant, B. J. (1963b). *Exptl. Cell Res.* **32**, 209.
Bryant, B. J. (1965). *Exptl. Cell Res.* **37**, 490.
Bryant, B. J. (1966). *J. Cell Biol.* **29**, 29.
Buck, R. C. (1955). *J. Histochem. Cytochem.* **3**, 435.
Buckaloo, G. W., and Cohn, D. V. (1956). *Science* **123**, 333.
Budd, G. C., and Pelc, S. R. (1964). *Stain Technol.* **39**, 295.
Büchner, F. (1961). *Verhandl. Deut. Ges. Pathol.* **45**, 37.
Büchner, F., and Hara, H. (1966). *Beitr. Pathol. Anat. Allgem. Pathol.* **134**, 166.
Büchner, T., Pfeiffer, R. A., and Stupperich, E. (1965). *Klin. Wochschr.* **43**, 1062.
Büchner, T., Wilkens, A., and Pfeiffer, R. A. (1967). *Exptl. Cell Res.* **46**, 58.
Burns, V. W. (1961). *Exptl. Cell Res.* **23**, 582.
Bury, H. P. R., and Crane, W. A. J. (1965). *Nature* **204**, 301.
Busanny-Caspari, W., and Maurer, W. (1968). Unpublished.
Buscher, H. P., Feit, J., and Oehlert, W. (1968). *Z. Krebsforschg.* **70**, 287.
Byers, T. J., Platt, D. B., and Goldstein, L. (1963a). *J. Cell Biol.* **19**, 453.
Byers, T. J., Platt, D. B., and Goldstein, L. (1963b). *J. Cell Biol.* **19**, 467.
Cairnie, A. B., Lamerton, L. F., and Steel, G. G. (1965a). *Exptl. Cell Res.* **39**, 528.
Cairnie, A. B., Lamerton, L. F., and Steel, G. G. (1965b). *Exptl. Cell Res.* **39**, 539.
Cairns, J. (1963). *J. Mol. Biol.* **6**, 208.
Cameron, I. L. (1964). *J. Cell Biol.* **20**, 185.
Cameron, I. L. (1966). *Nature* **209**, 630.
Cameron, I. L., and Cleffmann, G. (1964). *J. Cell Biol.* **21**, 169.
Cameron, I. L., and Greulich, R. C. (1963). *J. Cell Biol.* **18**, 31.

Cameron, I. L., and Nachtwey, D. S. (1967). *Exptl. Cell Res.* **46**, 385.

Cameron, I. L., and Prescott, D. M. (1963). *Exptl. Cell Res.* **30**, 609.

Campbell, D. (1951). *Nature* **167**, 274.

Campbell, D., and Persson, B. H. (1951). *Experientia* **7**, 304.

Campo, R. D., and Dziewiatkowski, D. (1963). *J. Cell Biol.* **18**, 19.

Cannon, G. B. (1965). *J. Cellular Comp. Physiol.* **65**, 163.

Canny, M. J. (1955). *Nature* **175**, 857.

Carneiro, J. (1965). *Symp. Intern. Soc. Cell Biol.* **4**, 247.

Carneiro, J., and Leblond, C. P. (1959a). *Science* **129**, 391.

Carneiro, J., and Leblond, C. P. (1959b). *Exptl. Cell Res.* **18**, 291.

Caro, L. G. (1961a). *J. Biophys. Biochem. Cytol.* **9**, 539.

Caro, L. G. (1961b). *J. Biophys. Biochem. Cytol.* **10**, 37.

Caro, L. G. (1962). *J. Cell Biol.* **15**, 189.

Caro, L. G. (1964). *In* "Methods in Cell Physiology" (D. M. Prescott, ed.), Vol. 1, p. 327. Academic Press, New York.

Caro, L. G., and Forro, F. (1961). *J. Biophys. Biochem. Cytol.* **9**, 555.

Caro, L. G., and Palade, G. E. (1961). *Compt. Rend. Soc. Biol.* **155**, 1750.

Caro, L. G., and Palade, G. E. (1964). *J. Cell Biol.* **20**, 473.

Caro, L. G., and Schnös, M. (1965). *Science* **149**, 60.

Caro, L. G., and van Tubergen, R. P. (1962). *J. Cell Biol.* **15**, 173.

Carpenter, E., Beattie, J., and Chambers, R. D. (1954). *J. Exptl. Zool.* **127**, 249.

Casarett, L. J. (1959). "Biology and Medicine," 15th Ed., TID–4500, UR–557. University of Rochester, Rochester, N. Y.

Casarett, L. J. (1964a). *Radiation Res. Suppl.* **5**, 187.

Casarett, L. J. (1964b). *Radiation Res. Suppl.* **5**, 93.

Casarett, L. J., and Morrow, P. E. (1964). *Radiation Res. Suppl.* **5**, 175.

Cattaneo, S. M., Quastler, H., and Sherman, F. G. (1960). *Radiation Res.* **12**, 587.

Cattaneo, S. M., Quastler, H., and Sherman, F. G. (1961). *Nature* **190**, 923.

Cave, N. D. (1966). *Hereditas* **54**, 338.

Chang, L. O., and Looney, W. B. (1965). *Cancer Res.* **25**, 1817.

Chang, L. O., Williams, S. S., and Looney, W. B. (1966). *Nature* **211**, 300.

Chapman-Andresen, C. (1953). *Compt. Rend. Trav. Lab. Carlsberg* **28**, 529.

Chavin, W. (1956). *J. Exptl. Zool.* **133**, 259.

Chèvremont, M. (1961). *Chemotherapia* **2**, 191.

Chèvremont, M. (1962). *Biochem. J.* **85**, 25.

Chèvremont, M., and Baeckeland, E. (1960). *Compt. Rend. Acad. Sci.* **251**, 1097.

Chèvremont, M., and Baeckeland, E. (1961). *Arch. Biol. (Liege)* **72**, 461.

Chèvremont, M., Baeckeland, E., and Chèvremont-Comhaire, S. (1959). *Compt. Rend. Acad. Sci.* **249**, 1392.

Chèvremont, M., Baeckeland, E., and Chèvremont-Comhaire, S. (1960). *Bull. Acad. Roy. Med. Belg.* **25**, 349.

Chibon, P. (1968). *Compt. Rend. Acad. Sci., Paris,* Ser. D. **267**, 203.

Chipchase, M. I. H., and Birnstiel, M. L. (1963). *Proc. Natl. Acad. Sci. U.S.* **50**, 1101.

Choné, B. (1963). *Folia Haematol.* **8**, 1.

Choné, B., and Frischbier, H.-J. (1961). *Strahlentherapie* **116**, 242.

Choné, B., and Frischbier, H.-J. (1962). *Nucl. Med.* **2**, 240.

Choné, B., and Frischbier, H.-J. (1963). *Strahlentherapie, Sonderbaende* **4**, 52, 156.

Choné, B., and Wentz, R. (1965). *Strahlentherapie* **126**, 407.

Choumak, M. G. (1963a). *Dokl. Akad. Nauk SSSR, Otd. Zytol.* **149**, 960.

Choumak, M. G. (1963b). *Radiobiologiya* **3**, 866.

Choumak, M. G. (1964). *Dokl. Akad. Nauk SSSR, Otd. Zytol.* **159**, 1144.

Christopherson, W. M., Berg, H. F., Kyker, G. C., and Brucer, M. (1956). *A.M.A. Arch. Pathol.* **62,** 441.

Christopherson, W. M., Kyker, G. C., Berg, H. F., and Brucer, M. (1957). *Proc. Soc. Exptl. Biol. Med.* **95,** 750.

Church, K. (1965). *Genetics* **52,** 843.

Citoler, P., and Maurer, W. (1963a). *Beitr. Pathol. Anat. Allgem. Pathol.* **129,** 73.

Citoler, P., and Maurer, W. (1963b). *Beitr. Pathol. Anat. Allgem. Pathol.* **128,** 359.

Citoler, P., Benitez, L., and Maurer, W. (1966a). *Naturwissenschaften* **53,** 42.

Citoler, P., Benitez, L., and Maurer, W. (1966b). *Exptl. Cell Res.* **45,** 195.

Citoler, P., Citoler, K., Hempel, K., Schultze, B., and Maurer, W. (1966c). *Z. Zellforsch. Mikroskop. Anat.* **70,** 419.

Clarkson, B. D., Ota, K., and Karnofsky, D. A. (1962). *Proc. Am. Assoc. Cancer Res.* **3,** 311.

Cleaver, J. E. (1965). *Exptl. Cell Res.* **39,** 697.

Cleaver, J. E. (1967). *In* "Thymidine Metabolism and Cell Kinetics" (A. Neuberger and E. L. Tatum, eds.), North-Holland Res. Monographs, Vol. 6. North-Holland Publ., Amsterdam.

Cleaver, J. E., and Holford, R. M. (1965). *Biochem. Biophys. Acta* **103,** 654.

Cleffmann, G. (1964). *Exptl. Cell Res.* **35,** 590.

Cleffmann, G. (1967). *Z. Zellforsch. Mikroskop. Anat.* **79,** 599.

Clowes, F. A. L. (1965). *New Phytologist* **64,** 355.

Coe, G. E. (1954). *Botan. Gaz.* **115,** 342.

Cohen, A. S., Gross, E., and Shirahama, T. (1965). *Am. J. Pathol.* **47,** 1079.

Cohen, J., Maletskos, C. J., Marshall, J. H., and Williams, J. B. (1957). *J. Bone Joint Surg.* **39A,** 561.

Cohen, M. M., Sandberg, A. A., Takali, N., and MacGillivray, M. H. (1967). *Cytogenetics* **6,** 254.

Cohen, Y., and Delassue, H. (1959). *Compt. Rend. Soc. Biol.* **153,** 999.

Coimbra, A. (1967). *J. Histochem. Cytochem.* **14,** 898.

Coimbra, A., and Leblond, C. P. (1966). *J. Cell Biol.* **30,** 151.

Colfer, H. F., and Essex, H. E. (1946). *Proc. Soc. Exptl. Biol. Med.* **63,** 243.

Collins, D. H., and Meachim, G. (1961). *Ann. Rheumatic Diseases* **20,** 117.

Collins, G. B. (1968). *J. Heredity* **59,** 13.

Comar, C. L., Lotz, W. E., and Boyd, G. A. (1952). *Am. J. Anat.* **90,** 113.

Comings, D. E. (1966). *Science* **154,** 1463.

Comings, D. E. (1967a). *Cytogenetics* **6,** 120.

Comings, D. E. (1967b). *Cytogenetics* **6,** 20.

Conger, A. D., and Fairchild, M. (1953). *Stain Technol.* **28,** 281.

Cook, J. R. (1966). *J. Cell. Biol.* **29,** 369.

Cooper, E. H., and Milton, J. D. (1964). *Brit. J. Cancer* **18,** 701.

Cooper, E. H., Hughes, D. T., and Topping, N. E. (1966). *Brit. J. Cancer* **20,** 102.

Cooper, E. H., Peckham, M. J., Millard, R. E., Hamlin, I. M. E., and Gerard-Marchant, R. (1968). *Europ. J. Cancer* **4,** 287.

Copp, D. H., Axelrod, D. J., and Hamilton, J. G. (1947). *Am. J. Roentgenol. Radium Therapy Nucl. Med.* **58,** 10.

Cormack, D. V. (1955). *Brit. J. Radiol.* **28,** 450.

Cosmos, E., and van Kien, L. K. (1961). *Intern. J. Appl. Radiation Isotopes* **12,** 118.

Couceiro, A., and Vieira, L. G. (1944). *Rev. Brasil. Biol.* **4,** 323.

Cowdry, E. V. (1952). *In* "Cowdry's Problems of Ageing" (A. I. Lansing, ed.). Williams & Wilkins, Baltimore, Maryland.

Craddock, C. G. (1965). *Acta Haematol.* **33,** 19.

Crane, W. A. J., and Dutta, L. P. (1963). *J. Pathol. Bacteriol.* **86**, 83.

Crane, W. A. J., and Dutta, L. P. (1964). *J. Endocrinol.* **28**, 341.

Crane, W. A. J., and Ingle, D. J. (1964). *Arch. Pathol.* **78**, 209.

Crane, W. A. J., and Ingle, D. J. (1965). *Arch. Pathol.* **79**, 169.

Crane, W. A. J., Dutta, L. P., and Ingle, D. J. (1965). *Proc. Soc. Exptl. Biol. Med.* **119**, 167.

Crathorn, A. R., and Shooter, K. V. (1960). *Nature* **187**, 614.

Crathorn, A. R., and Shooter, K. V. (1964). *Intern. J. Radiation Biol.* **7**, 575.

Crippa, M. (1966). *Exptl. Cell Res.* **42**, 371.

Cronkite, E. P. (1964). *Medicine* **43**, 635.

Cronkite, E. P., and Fliedner, T. M. (1964). *New Engl. J. Med.* **270**, 1347.

Cronkite, E. P., Bond, V. P., Fliedner, T. M., and Rubini, J. R. (1959a). *Lab. Invest.* **8**, 263.

Cronkite, E. P., Fliedner, T. M., Bond, V. P., and Robertson, J. S. (1959b). *In* "The Kinetics of Cellular Proliferation" (F. Stohlman, ed.), p. 1. Grune & Stratton, New York.

Cronkite, E. P., Fliedner, T. M., Bond, V. P., Rubini, J. R., Brecher, G., and Quastler, H. (1959c). *Ann. N. Y. Acad. Sci.* **77**, 803.

Cronkite, E. P., Bond, V. P., Fliedner, T. M., Rubini, J. R., and Killmann, S.-A. (1961a). *Intern. Congr. Radiol. Trans., 9th, Munich, 1959* p. 894.

Cronkite, E. P., Greenhouse, S. W., Fliedner, T. M., Brecher, G., and Bond, V. P. (1961b). *Nature* **189**, 153.

Cronkite, E. P., Fliedner, T. M., Killmann, S. A., and Rubini, J. R. (1962). *Tritium Phys. Biol. Sci., Proc. Symp. Detection Use, Vienna, 1961* **2**, 189.

Daoust, R., and Clermont, Y. (1955). *Am. J. Anat.* **96**, 255.

Das, G. D., and Altman, J. (1966). *Physiol. Behavior* **1**, 109.

Das, N. K., (1963). *Science* **140**, 1231.

Das, N. K., and Alfert, M. (1961). *Proc. Natl. Acad. Sci. U.S.* **47**, 1.

Das, N. K., and Alfert, M. (1966). *Natl. Cancer Inst. Monograph* **23**, 337.

Das, N. K., Siegel, E. P., and Alfert, M. (1965). *Exptl. Cell Res.* **40**, 178.

Davidson, D. (1964). *Exptl. Cell Res.* **35**, 317.

Davies, D. R., and Wimber, D. E. (1963). *Nature* **200**, 229.

Davies, D. V., and Young, L. (1954a). *J. Anat.* **88**, 174.

Davies, D. V., and Young, L. (1954b). *Nature* **173**, 448.

Davis, B. K. (1962). *Acta Endocrinol.* **41**, Suppl. 71, 3.

Davis, R. B., and Kay, D. (1965). *Nature* **207**, 650.

Dawson, K. B., Field, E. O., and Stevens, G. W. W. (1962). *Nature* **195**, 510.

Defendi, V., and Manson, L. A. (1961). *Pathol. Biol. Semaine Hop.* **9**, 525.

Defendi, V., and Manson, L. A. (1963). *Nature* **198**, 259.

Deimel, M., and Maurer, W. (1961). *Biochem. Z.* **334**, 462.

de Man, J. C. H., and Noorduyn, N. J. A. (1967). *J. Cell Biol.* **33**, 489.

Dendy, P. P., and Cleaver, J. E. (1964). *Intern. J. Radiation Biol.* **8**, 301.

Dendy, P. P., and Smith, C. L. (1964). *Proc. Royal Soc. (London)* **B160**, 328.

de Rooij, D. G. (1968). *Z. Zellforschg. Mikroskop. Anat.* **89**, 133.

Descarries, L., and Droz, B. (1968). *Compt. Rend. Acad. Sci., Paris*, Ser. D, **266**, 2480.

Devik, F. (1962). *Intern. J. Radiation Biol.* **5**, 59.

Devik, F., and Halvorsen, K. (1963). *Nature* **197**, 148.

De Vitry, F. (1964). *Develop. Biol.* **9**, 484.

De Vitry, F. (1965a). *Bull. Soc. Chim. Biol.* **47**, 1325.

De Vitry, F. (1965b). *Bull. Soc. Chim. Biol.* **47**, 1353.

De Vitry, F. (1965c). *Bull. Soc. Chim. Biol.* **47**, 1375.

Dewey, W. C., and Humphrey, R. M. (1962). *Radiation Res.* **16**, 503.

Dewey, W. C., Humphrey, R. M., and Jones, B. A. (1965). *Radiation Res.* **24**, 214.

Dhom, G., and Stöcker, E. (1964a). *Symp. Deut. Ges. Endokrinol.*, **11**, *Düsseldorf* p. 298. Springer, Berlin.

Dhom, G., and Stöcker, E. (1964b). *Experientia* **20**, 384.

Diderholm, H., and Hellman, B. (1960). *Acta Pathol. Microbiol. Scand.* **49**, 82.

Diderholm, H., Fichtelius, K.-E., and Linder, O. (1962). *Exptl. Cell Res.* **27**, 431.

Diment, A. V. (1966). *Arch. Anat. Histol. Embriol.* **50**, 29.

Dixon, F. J., and Warren, S. (1950). *Am. J. Med. Sci.* **219**, 414.

Dobyns, B. M., and Lennon, B. (1948). *J. Clin. Endocrinol.* **8**, 732.

Dobyns, B. M., and Maloof, F. (1951). *J. Clin. Endocrinol.* **11**, 1323.

Dörmer, P. (1967). *Histochemie*, **8**, 1.

Dörmer, P., Tulinius, H., and Oehlert, W. (1964). *Z. Krebsforsch.* **66**, 11.

Dörmer, P., Brinkmann, W., Stieber, A., and Stich, W. (1966). *Klin. Wochschr.* **44**, 477.

Dohlman, G. F., Maunsbach, A. B., Hammarström, L., and Appelgren, L.-E. (1964). *J. Ultrastruct. Res.* **10**, 293.

Domingues, F. J., Sarko, A., and Baldwin, R. R. (1956). *Intern. J. Appl. Radiation Isotopes* **1**, 94.

Dondua, A. K. (1967). *Tsitologiya* **9**, 1057.

Dondua, A. K., and Dondua, G. K. (1964). *In* "A Study of Cell Cycles and Metabolism of Nuclear Acids During Differentiation of the Cells" (L. N. Zhinkin and A. A. Zavarzin, eds.). p. 5. Nauka, Moscow and Leningrad.

Dondua, A. K., and Fedorova, J. E. (1964). *In* "A Study of Cell Cycles and Metabolism of Nucleic Acids During Differentiation of the Cells" (L. N. Zhinkin and A. A. Zavarzin, eds.) p. 83. Nauka, Moscow and Leningrad.

Doniach, I., and Logothetopoulos, J. H. (1955). *J. Endocrinol.* **13**, 65.

Doniach, I., and Pelc, S. R. (1949). *Proc. Roy. Soc. Med.* **42**, 957.

Doniach, I., and Pelc, S. R. (1950). *Brit. J. Radiol.* **23**, 184.

Donnelly, G. M., and Sisken, J. E. (1967). *Exptl. Cell Res.* **46**, 93.

Dontenwill, W., and Wiebecke, B. (1964). *Z. Krebsforsch.* **66**, 321.

Downes, A. M., Chapman, R. E., Till, A. R., and Wilson, P. A. (1966). *Nature* **212**, 477.

Drenckhahn, F.-O., and Meissner, J. (1956). *Arch. Exptl. Pathol. Pharmakol.* **227**, 444.

Drew, R. M., and Commerford, S. L. (1967). *Radiation Res.* **30**, 455.

Drew, R. M., and Painter, R. B. (1959). *Radiation Res.* **11**, 535.

Drew, R. M., and Painter, R. B. (1962). *Radiation Res.* **16**, 303.

Droz, B. (1963). *Anat. Record* **145**, 157.

Droz, B. (1965a). *Symp. Intern. Soc. Cell Biol.* **4**, 159.

Droz, B. (1965b). *Compt. Rend. Acad. Sci.* **260**, 320.

Droz, B. (1966). *Compt. Rend. Acad. Sci.* **262**, 1654.

Droz, B. (1967). *J. Microscopie* **6**, 419.

Droz, B., and Bergeron, M. (1965). *Compt. Rend. Acad. Sci.* **261**, 2757.

Droz, B., and Leblond, C. P. (1962). *Science* **137**, 1047.

Droz, B., and Verne, J. (1959). *Proc. 4th Intern. Congr. Biochem., Vienna, 1958* 72.

Droz, B., and Verne, J. (1959). *Acta Neuroveget. (Vienna)* **20**, 372.

Droz, B., and Warshawsky, H. (1963). *J. Histochem. Cytochem.* **11**, 426.

Dubinko, G. A. (1966). *Arch. Anat. Histol. Embriol.* **50**, 47.

Dudley, H. C., Imirie, G. W., and Istock, J. T. (1950). *Radiology* **55**, 571.

Dudley, R. A., and Dobyns, B. M. (1949). *Science* **109**, 327.

Dudley, R. A., and Pelc, S. R. (1953). *Nature* **172**, 992.

Duffy, B. J., and Fitzgerald, P. J. (1950a). *Cancer* **3**, 1018.

Duffy, B. J., and Fitzgerald, P. J. (1950b). *J. Clin. Endocrinol.* **10**, 1296.

Dumont, A. E., Ayvazian, J. H., and McCluskey, R. T. (1962). *Nature* **194**, 193.

Duthie, R. B. (1954). *J. Pathol. Bacteriol.* **68**, 296.

Duthie, R. B., and Barker, A. N. (1955). *J. Bone Joint Surg.* **37B**, 304.

Dziewiatkowski, D. D. (1951a). *J. Biol. Chem.* **189**, 187.

Dziewiatkowski, D. D. (1951b). *J. Exptl. Med.* **93**, 451.

Dziewiatkowski, D. D. (1951c). *Federation Proc.* **10**, 178.

Dziewiatkowski, D. D. (1952a). *J. Exptl. Med.* **95**, 489.

Dziewiatkowski, D. D. (1952b). *Metab. Interrelations, Trans. 4th Conf.* p. 74.

Dziewiatkowski, D. D. (1953). *J. Exptl. Med.* **98**, 119.

Dziewiatkowski, D. D. (1954a). *J. Exptl. Med.* **100**, 11.

Dziewiatkowski, D. D. (1954b). *J. Exptl. Med.* **99**, 283.

Dziewiatkowski, D. D. (1957). *J. Exptl. Med.* **105**, 69.

Dziewiatkowski, D. D. (1958). *Intern. Rev. Cytol.* **7**, 159.

Dziewiatkowski, D. D. (1964). *Biophys. J.* **4**, 215.

Dziewiatkowski, D. D., Bronner, F., di Ferrante, N., and Archibald, R. M. (1957). *J. Biophys. Biochem. Cytol.* **3**, 151.

Ebbe, S., and Stohlman, F. (1965). *Blood* **26**, 20.

Edwards, J. L., and Klein, R. E. (1961). *Am. J. Pathol.* **38**, 437.

Edwards, J. L., and Koch, A. (1964). *Lab. Invest.* **13**, 32.

Edwards, J. L., Koch, A. L., Youcis, P., Freese, H. L., Laite, M. B., and Donalson, J. T. (1960). *J. Biophys. Biochem. Cytol.* **7**, 273.

Edwards, L. C. (1955). *Stain Technol.* **30**, 163.

Eisen, V. D., and Harris, F. T. C. (1957). *Nature* **180**, 440.

Elfvin, L.-G., Appelgren, L. E., and Ullberg, S. (1966). *J. Ultrastruct. Res.* **14**, 277.

Elgjo, K. M., and Skjaeggestad, Ö. (1965). *Acta Pathol. Microbiol. Scand.* **64**, 185.

Endicott, K. M., and Yagoda, H. (1947). *Proc. Soc. Exptl. Biol. Med.* **64**, 170.

Engfeldt, B. (1953). *Acta Pathol. Microbiol. Scand.* **32**, 529.

Engfeldt, B., and Westerborn, O. (1960). *Acta Pathol. Microbiol. Scand.* **49**, 73.

Engfeldt, B., and Zetterström, R. (1954). *Endocrinology* **54**, 506.

Engfeldt, B., Engström, A., and Zetterström, R. (1952). *Biochim. Biophys. Acta* **8**, 375.

Engfeldt, B., Björnerstedt, R., Clemedson, C.-J., and Engström, A. (1954). *Acta Orthopaed. Scand.* **24**, 101.

Epifanova, O. I. (1963). *Dokl. Akad. Nauk SSSR, Otd. Zytol.* **149**, 424.

Epifanova, O. I. (1964a). *Arch. Anat. Histol. Embriol.* **46**, 27.

Epifanova, O. I. (1964b). *Usp. Sovrem. Biol.* **58**, 33.

Epifanova, O. I. (1965a). *Tsitologiya* **7**, 5.

Epifanova, O. I. (1965b). *In* "Hormones and Cell Replication" (A. A. Prokofjeva-Belgovskaja, ed.), Nauka, Moscow.

Epifanova, O. I. (1966). *Exptl. Cell Res.* **42**, 562.

Epifanova, O. I. (1967). *Tsitologiya* **9**, 1033.

Epifanova, O. I., and Smolenskaya, I. N. (1963). *Bull. Exptl. Biol.* **11**, 111.

Epifanova, O. I., Kurskaya, M. A., and Valejeva, N. V. (1963). *Tsitologiya* **5**, 656.

Eränkö O. (1957). *J. Histochem. Cytochem.* **5**, 408.

Erb, W., and Hempel, K. (1962). *Ann. Histochim.* **7**, Suppl. 2, 71.

Erb, W., and Maurer, W. (1962). *Z. Naturforsch.* **17b**, 268.

Eriksson, T. (1967). *Physiol. Plantarum* **20**, 348.

Ernst, H. (1956). Ph. D. Thesis, Univ. of Cologne.

Errera, M. (1961). *J. Cellular Comp. Physiol.* **58**, Suppl. 1, 209.

Errera, M., and Brunfaut, M. (1964). *Exptl. Cell Res.* **33**, 105.

Errera, M., Hell, A., and Perry, R. P. (1961). *Biochim. Biophys. Acta* **49**, 58.

Evans, H. J. (1964). *Exptl. Cell Res.* **35**, 381.

Evans, H. J. (1965). *Radiation Botany* **5**, 171.

Evans, H. J., and Scott, D. (1964). *Genetics* **49**, 17.

Evans, H. J., Ford, C. E., Lyon, M. F., and Cray, J. (1965). *Nature* **206**, 900.

Evans, T. C. (1947). *Proc. Soc. Exptl. Biol. Med.* **64**, 313.

Eve, C., and Robinson, S. H. (1963). *J. Lab. Clin. Med.* **62**, 169.

Everett, N. B., and Simmons, B. S. (1953). *Anat. Record* **117**, 25.

Everett, N. B., Reinhardt, W. O., and Yoffey, J. M. (1960). *Blood* **15**, 82.

Everett, N. B., Caffrey, R. W., Rieke, W. O., and Schwarz, M. R. (1965). *Symp. Intern. Soc. Cell Biol.* **4**, 143.

Falk, G. J., and King, R. C. (1963). *Radiation Res.* **20**, 466.

Fang, S. C., and Butts, J. S. (1957). *Plant Physiol.* **32**, 253.

Favard-Séréno, C., and Durand, M. (1963a). *Develop. Biol.* **6**, 184.

Favard-Séréno, C., and Durand, M. (1963b). *Develop. Biol.* **6**, 206.

Feder, N., and Sidman, R. L. (1958). *J. Biophys. Biochem. Cytol.* **4**, 593.

Fedorko, M. E., and Hirsch, J. G. (1966). *J. Cell Biol.* **29**, 307.

Feinendegen, L. E. (1967). *In* "Tritium-Labeled Molecules in Biology and Medicine" (J. R. Olive, ed.) Academic Press, New York.

Feinendegen, L. E., and Bond, V. P. (1962). *Exptl. Cell Res.* **27**, 474.

Feinendegen, L. E., and Bond, V. P. (1963). *Exptl. Cell Res.* **30**, 393.

Feinendegen, L. E., and Bond, V. P. (1964). *Atomkernenergie* **9**, 283.

Feinendegen, L. E., Bond, V. P., and Cronkite, E. P. (1960a). *Blood* **15**, 418.

Feinendegen, L. E., Bond, V. P., Shreeve, W. W., and Painter, R. B. (1960b). *Exptl. Cell Res.* **19**, 443.

Feinendegen, L. E., Bond, V. P., and Hughes, W. L. (1961a). *Exptl. Cell Res.* **25**, 627.

Feinendegen, L. E., Bond, V. P., and Hughes, W. L. (1961b). *Ann. Histochim.* **6**, 487.

Feinendegen, L. E., Bond, V. P., and Painter, R. B. (1961c). *Exptl. Cell Res.* **22**, 381.

Feinendegen, L. E., Bond, V. P., and Drew, R. M. (1961d). *Nature* **191**, 1398.

Feinendegen, L. E., Bond, V. P., and Hughes, W. L. (1966a). *Proc. Soc. Exptl. Biol. Med.* **122**, 448.

Feinendegen, L. E., Bond, V. P., and Hughes, W. L. (1966b). *Exptl. Cell Res.* **43**, 107.

Feldman, M., and Waddington, C. H. (1955). *J. Embryol. Exptl. Morphol.* **3**, 44.

Fell, H. B., Mellanby, E., and Pelc, S. R. (1956). *J. Physiol. (London)* **134**, 179.

Fettig, O., and Oehlert, W. (1964). *Arch. Gynaekol.* **199**, 649.

Fettig. O., and Sievers, R. (1966). *Beitr. Pathol. Anat. Allgem. Pathol.* **133**, 83.

Fichtelius, K. E., and Groth, O. (1963). *Nature* **200**, 587.

Ficq, A. (1953). *Experientia* **9**, 377.

Ficq, A. (1955a). *Exptl. Cell Res.* **9**, 286.

Ficq, A. (1955b). *Arch. Biol. (Liège)* **66**, 509.

Ficq, A. (1959a). *J. Histochem. Cytochem.* **7**, 215.

Ficq, A. (1959b). *In* "Problèmes d'Ultrastructures et de fonctions nucléaires, Exposés actuels de biologie cellulaire" p. 35. Lib. Acad. Med., Masson, Paris.

Ficq, A. (1959c). *In* "The Cell" (J. Brachet and A. E. Mirsky, eds.), Vol. 1, p. 67. Academic Press, New York.

Ficq, A., and Brachet, J. (1956). *Exptl. Cell Res.* **11**, 135.

Ficq, A., and Errera, M. (1955a). *Biochim. Biophys. Acta* **16**, 45.

Ficq, A., and Errera, M. (1955b). *Arch. Intern. Physiol. Biochim.* **63**, 259.

Ficq, A., and Errera, M. (1959). *Exptl. Cell Res. Suppl.* **7**, 145.

Ficq, A., and Pavan, C. (1957). *Nature* **180**, 983.

Ficq, A., Pavan, G., and Brachet, J. (1958). *Exptl. Cell Res.* **6**, 105.

Field, E. O., Dawson, K. B., and Gibbs, J. E. (1965). *Stain Technol.* **40**, 295.

Fink, K., Cline, R. E., Henderson, R. B., and Fink, R. M. (1956a). *J. Biol. Chem.* **221**, 425.

Fink, R. M., McGaughey, C., Cline, R. E., and Fink, K. (1956b). *J. Biol. Chem.* **218**, 1.

Fischer, J., Kolousek, J., and Lodin, Z. (1956). *Nature* **178**, 1122.

Fisher, E. R., Neering, J. C., Hazard, J. B., and Hays, R. A. (1952). *Am. J. Med. Sci.* **223**, 502.

Fiske, S., Courtecuisse, V., and Haguenau, F. (1966). *Compt. Rend. Acad. Sci.* **D262**, 126.

Fitzgerald, P. J. (1952a). *Cancer* **5**, 165.

Fitzgerald, P. J. (1952b). *Bull. N. Y. Acad. Sci.* **28**, 680.

Fitzgerald, P. J. (1955). *Brookhaven Symp. Biol.* **7**, 220.

Fitzgerald, P. J. (1959). In "Anatomical Cytology." McGraw-Hill, New York.

Fitzgerald, P. J. (1961). *Lab. Invest.* **10**, 846.

Fitzgerald, P. J. (1963). *Can. Med. Assoc. J.* **88**, 480.

Fitzgerald, P. J., and Engström, A. (1952). *Cancer* **5**, 643.

Fitzgerald, P. J., and Foote, F. W. (1949). *J. Clin. Endocrinol.* **9**, 1153.

Fitzgerald, P. J., and Vinijchaikul, K. (1959). *Lab. Invest.* **8**, 319.

Fitzgerald, P. J., Foote, F. W., and Hill, R. F. (1950). *Cancer* **3**, 86.

Fitzgerald, P. J., Eidinoff, M. L., Knoll, J. E., and Simmel, E. B. (1951). *Science* **114**, 494.

Fitzpatrick, T. B., and Kukita, A. (1956). *J. Invest. Dermatol.* **26**, 173.

Fleischmajer, R., and Witten, V. H. (1955). *J. Invest. Dermatol.* **25**, 223.

Fliedner, T. M., Kesse, M., Cronkite, E. P., and Robertson, J. S. (1964a). *Ann. N. Y. Acad. Sci.* **113**, 578.

Fliedner, T. M., Cronkite, E. P., Killmann, S. A., and Bond, V. P. (1964b). *Blood* **24**, 683.

Fliedner, T. M., Kretschmer, V., Hillen, M., and Wendt, F. (1965). *Schweiz. Med. Wochschr.* **95**, 1499.

Foot, E. C. (1963). *Nature* **198**, 297.

Forberg, S., Odeblad, E., Söremark, R., and Ullberg, S. (1964). *Acta Radiobiol.* **2**, 241.

Forbes, J. A. (1954). *Australasian Ann. Med.* **3**, 138.

Ford, D. H., Corey, K. R., and Gross, J. (1957). *Endocrinology* **61**, 426.

Ford, J. K., and Young, R. W. (1963). *Anat. Record* **146**, 125.

Fowler, J. H., Wu, A. M., Till, J. E., McCulloch, E. A., and Siminovitch, L. (1967). *J. Cell Physiol.* **69**, 65.

Fraccaro, M., Gustavsson, I., Hulten, M., Lindsten, J., Mannini, A., and Tiepolo, L. (1964). *Hereditas* **52**, 265.

Fraccaro, M., Hulten, M., Lindsten, J., and Tiepolo, L. (1965). *Exptl. Cell Res.* **38**, 675.

Frankfurt, O. S. (1967a). *Exptl. Cell Res.* **46**, 603.

Frankfurt, O. S. (1967b). *Tsitologiya* **9**, 1104.

Frankfurt, O. S., and Lipchina, L. P. (1964). *Dokl. Akad. Nauk SSSR, Otd. Cytol.* **154**, 207.

Franklin, R. M. (1963). *Biochim. Biophys. Acta* **72**, 555.

Franklin, R. M., and Granboulan, N. (1965). *J. Mol. Biol.* **14**, 623.

Fraser, R. C. (1964). *Exptl. Cell Res.* **33**, 473.

Freed, J. J. (1955). *Stain Technol.* **4**, 106.

Frenkel, E. P., Korst, D. R., and Zarafonetis, C. J. D. (1964). *Proc. 9th Congr. Intern. Soc. Hematol., Mexico, D. F., 1962* p. 119.

Fresco, J. R., and Bendich, A. (1960). *J. Biol. Chem.* **235**, 1124.

Fresco, J. R., Bendich, A., and Russell, P. J. (1955). *Federation Proc.* **14**, 214.

Freudenberg, K., Reznik, H., Fuchs, W., and Reichert, M. (1955). *Naturwissenschaften* **42**, 29.

Friberg, L., and Odeblad, E. (1957). *Acta Pathol. Microbiol. Scand.* **41**, 96.

Friberg, L., Odeblad, E., and Forssman, S. (1957). *A.M.A. Arch. Ind. Health* **16**, 163.

Friberg, U., and Ringertz, N. R. (1954). *Experientia* **10**, 67.

Friberg, U., and Ringertz, N. R. (1956). *J. Embryol. Exptl. Morphol.* **4**, 313.

Friedkin, M., Tilson, D., and Roberts, D. (1956). *J. Biol. Chem.* **220**, 627.

Frindel, E., Tubiana, M., and Vassort, F. (1967a). *Nature* **214**, 1017.

Frindel, E., Malaise, E. P., Alpen, E., and Tubiana, M. (1967b). *Cancer Res.* **27**, 1122.

Froland, A. (1965). *Stain Technol.* **40**, 42.

Froland, A. (1967). *Nature* **213**, 512.

Fromme, H. G. (1964). *Z. Naturforsch.* **19b**, 852.

Fry, R. J. M., Lesher, S., and Kohn, H. I. (1961a). *Nature* **191**, 290.

Fry, R. J. M., Lesher, S., and Kohn, H. I. (1961b). *Exptl. Cell Res.* **25**, 469.

Fry, R. J. M., Lesher, S., Sallese, A., and Staffeldt, E. (1963). *Radiation Res.* **19**, 628.

Fujita, S. (1967). *J. Cell Biol.* **32**, 277.

Fujita, S., and Takamoto, K. (1963). *Nature* **200**, 494.

Fujiwara, S., and Kaplan, A. S. (1967). *Virology* **32**, 60.

Furst, S. S., Roll, P. M., and Brown, G. B. (1950). *J. Biol. Chem.* **183**, 251.

Gabrieli, E. R., and Cutler, J. L. (1954). *Proc. Soc. Exptl. Biol. Med.* **87**, 661.

Gabrieli, E. R., Goulian, D., and Cutler, J. L. (1955). *Yale J. Biol. Med.* **28**, 63.

Gabrusewycz-Garcia, N. (1964). *Chromosoma* **15**, 312.

Gahan, P. B., and Rajan, A. K. (1966). *J. Exptl. Botany* **17**, 34.

Gall, J. G. (1959). *J. Biophys. Biochem. Cytol.* **5**, 295.

Gall, J. G., and Callan, H. G. (1962). *Proc. Natl. Acad. Sci. U.S.* **48**, 562.

Gall, J. G., and Johnson, W. W. (1960). *J. Biophys. Biochem. Cytol.* **7**, 657.

Gallimore, J. C., Boyd, G. A., and Stannard, J. N. (1954a). *Anat. Record.* **118**, 253.

Gallimore, J. C., Bauer, E. C., and Boyd, G. A. (1954b). *Stain Technol.* **29**, 95.

Galton, M., and Holt, S. F. (1965). *Exptl. Cell Res.* **37**, 111.

Garder, K. H., and Devik, F. (1963). *Intern. J. Radiation Biol.* **6**, 157.

Gaudecker, von B. (1966). *Z. Zellforsch. Mikroskop. Anat.* **72**, 281.

Gavosto, F. (1962). *Tritium Phys. Biol. Sci., Proc. Symp. Detection Use, Vienna, 1961*, **2**, 237.

Gavosto, F., and Rechenman, R. (1954). *Biochim. Biophys. Acta* **13**, 583.

Gavosto, F., Ficq, A., and Errera, M. (1954). *Exptl. Cell Res.* **6**, 238.

Gavosto, F., Pegoraro, L., Pileri, A., and Bernardelli, R. (1965). *Communaute Eur. Energ. At. EURATOM* **EUR 2451.e.**

Gelfant, S. (1963). *Symp. Intern. Soc. Cell Biol.* **2**, 229.

Gelfant, S. (1966). *In* "Methods in Cell Physiology" (D. M. Prescott, ed.), Vol. 2, p. 359. Academic Press, New York.

Gerbaulet, K., Brückner, J., and Maurer, W. (1961). *Naturwissenschaften* **48**, 526.

Gerbaulet, K., Maurer, W., and Brückner, J. (1963). *Biochim. Biophys. Acta* **68**, 462.

Gerber, G. (1963). *Communauté Eur. Energ. At. EURATOM* **EUR 308.e**, p. 3.

Gerber, G., Gerber, G., and Altman, K. I. (1960). *J. Biol. Chem.* **235**, 1433.

Gerbie, A. B., Hathaway, H. H., and Brewer, J. I. (1968). *Am. J. Obstetr. Gynecol.* **100**, 640.

German, J. (1964). *J. Cell Biol.* **20**, 37.

Geuskens, M., and Bernhard, W. (1966). *Exptl. Cell Res.* **44**, 579.

Ghiara, G. (1962). *Boll. Zool.* **29**, 73.

Gibor, A., and Granick, S. (1964). *Science* **145**, 890.

Gielink, A. J., Sauer, G., and Ringoet, A. (1966). *Stain Technol.* **41**, 281.

Gilbert, C. W., Muldal, S., Lajtha, L. G., and Rowley, J. (1962). *Nature* **195**, 869.

Gilbert, C. W., Muldal, S., and Lajtha, L. G. (1965). *Nature* **208**, 159.

Gilbert, C. W., Lajtha, L. G., Muldal, S., and Ockey, C. H. (1966). *Nature* **209**, 537.

Godman, G. C., and Lane, N. (1964). *J. Cell Biol.* **21**, 353.

Godwin, J. T., Duffy, B. J., Fitzgerald, P. J., Trunnell, J. B., and Rawson, R. W. (1951). *Cancer* **4**, 936.

Götte, H., Frimmer, M., and Hattemer, A. J. (1951). *Proc. Isotope Conf., Oxford* **1**, 283.

Goldfeder, A. (1965). *Nature* **207**, 612.

Goldfeder, A., and Miller, L. A. (1962). *Proc. Am. Assoc. Cancer Res.* **3**, 323.

Goldstein, L. (1958). *Exptl. Cell Res.* **15**, 635.

Goldstein, L. (1963). *In* "Cell Growth and Cell Division" (R. J. C. Harris, ed.), p. 129. Academic Press, New York.

Goldstein, L. (1965). *Symp. Intern. Soc. Cell Biol.* **4**, 79.

Goldstein, L., and Micou, J. (1959a). *J. Biophys. Biochem. Cytol.* **6**, 1.

Goldstein, L., and Micou, J. (1959b). *J. Biophys. Biochem. Cytol.* **6**, 301.

Goldstein, L., and Plaut, W. (1955). *Proc. Natl. Acad. Sci. U.S.* **41**, 874.

Goldstein, L., and Prescott, D. M. (1967). *J. Cell Biol.* **33**, 637.

Goldstein, L., Micou, J., and Crocker, T. T. (1960). *Biochem. Biophys. Acta* **45**, 82.

Gorbman, A. (1941). *Science* **94**, 192.

Gorbman, A., and Creaser, C. W. (1942). *J. Exptl. Zool.* **89**, 391.

Gorbman, A., and Evans, H. M. (1941). *Proc. Soc. Exptl. Biol. Med.* **47**, 103.

Gorbman, A., and Evans, H. M. (1943). *Endocrinology* **32**, 113.

Gorbman, A., Lissitzky, S., Michel, O., Michel, R., and Roche, J. (1952). *Endocrinology* **51**, 546.

Gothié, S., Moricard, R., and Cartier, R. (1963). *Compt. Rend. Soc. Biol.* **157**, 74.

Govaerts, J., Dallemagne, M. J., and Melon, J. (1951). *Endocrinology* **48**, 443.

Gowans, J. L. (1959). *J. Physiol. (London)* **146**, 54.

Gracheva, N. D. (1957). *Dokl. Akad. Nauk SSSR, Otd. Histol.* **113**, 688.

Gracheva, N. D. (1964a). *Radiobiologiya* **4**, 102.

Gracheva, N. D. (1964b). *Arch. Anat. Histol. Embriol.* **46**, 3.

Gracheva, N. D. (1964c). *Tsitologiya* **6**, 324.

Gracheva, N. D. (1964d). *In* "A Study of Cell Cycles and Metabolism of Nucleic Acids During Differentiation of the Cells" (L. N. Zhinkin and A. A. Zavarzin, eds.), p. 90. Nauka, Moscow and Leningrad.

Gracheva, N. D. (1966). *Arch. Anat. Histol. Embriol.* **50**, 38.

Graham, A. F., and Rake, A. V. (1963). *Ann. Rev. Microbiol.* **17**, 139.

Granboulan, N., and Franklin, R. M. (1966). *J. Bacteriol.* **91**, 849.

Granboulan, N., and Granboulan, P. (1964). *Proc. 3rd European Reg. Conf. Electron Microscopy, Prague* p. 31.

Granboulan, N., and Granboulan, P. (1965). *Exptl. Cell Res.* **38**, 604.

Granboulan, P. (1965). *Symp. Intern. Soc. Cell Biol.* **4**, 43.

Granboulan, P., and Audran, R. (1964). *Compt. Rend. Acad. Sci.,* D **259**, 3201.

Granboulan, P., Granboulan, N., and Bernhard, W. (1962). *J. Microscopie* **1**, 75.

Graul, E. H. (1953). *Strahlentherapie* **92**, 197.

Graul, E. H., and Hundeshagen, H. (1958). *Strahlentherapie* **106**, 405.

Graves, J. A. M. (1967). *Exptl. Cell Res.* **46**, 37.

Green, M., Pina, M., and Chagoya, V. (1964). *J. Biol. Chem.* **239**, 1188.

Greenberg, S. S., and Kopac, W. J. (1963). *Ann. N.Y. Acad. Sci.* **100**, 887.

Greulich, R. C. (1956). *J. Bone Joint Surg.* **38A**, 611.

Greulich, R. C. (1961). *Radiation Res.* **14**, 83.

Greulich, R. C., and Leblond, C. P. (1954). *J. Dental Res.* **33**, 859.

Greulich, R. C., and Slavkin, H. C. (1965). *Symp. Intern. Soc. Cell Biol.* **4**, 199.

Greulich, R. C., Cameron, I. L., and Thrasher, J. D. (1961). *Proc. Natl. Acad. Sci. U.S.* **47**, 743.

Grisham, J. W. (1960). *Proc. Soc. Exptl. Biol. Med.* **105**, 555.

Grisham, J. W. (1962). *Cancer Res.* **22**, 842.

Gross, J., and Leblond, C. P. (1947a). *Can. Med. Assoc. J.* **57**, 102.

Gross, J., and Leblond, C. P. (1947b). *J. Biol. Chem.* **171**, 309.

Gross, J., and Leblond, C. P. (1950). *J. Biol. Chem.* **184**, 489.

Gross, J., and Leblond, C. P. (1951). *Endocrinology* **48**, 714.

Gross, J., and Pitt-Rivers, R. (1952). *Brit. Med. Bull.* **8**, 136.

Gross, J., Bogoroch, R., Nadler, N. J., and Leblond, C. P. (1951). *Am. J. Roentgenol. Radium Therapy Nucl. Med.* **65**, 420.

Gross, J. D. (1957). *Nature* **180**, 440.

Gross, P. R., and Cousineau, G. H. (1963). *J. Cell Biol.* **19**, 260.

Grosse, A. V., and Snyder, J. C. (1947). *Science* **105**, 240.

Gude, W. D., Upton, A. C., and Odell, T. T. (1955). *Stain Technol.* **30**, 161.

Guidotti, G., and Setti, R. L. (1956). *Stain Technol.* **31**, 57.

Guttes, E. W., Hanawalt, P. C., and Guttes, S. (1967). *Biochem. Biophys. Acta* **142**, 181.

Haase, G., and Jung, G. (1964). *Naturwissenschaften* **51**, 404.

Hämmerling, J., and Stich, H. (1956a). *Z. Naturforsch.* **11b**, 158.

Hämmerling, J., and Stich, H. (1956b). *Z. Naturforsch.* **11b**, 162.

Hagmüller, K., and Hellauer, H. (1955). *Acta Histochem.* **2**, 16.

Hamilton, J. G. (1947). *Radiology* **49**, 325.

Hamilton, J. G. (1948). *Rev. Mod. Phys.* **20**, 718.

Hamilton, J. G. (1949). *New Engl. J. Med.* **240**, 863.

Hamilton, J. G., Soley, M. H., and Eichorn, K. B. (1940). *Univ. Calif. (Berkeley) Publ. Pharmacol.* **1**, 339.

Hammarsten, E., and Hevesy, G. (1946). *Acta Physiol. Scand.* **11**, 335.

Hammarsten, E., Reichard, P., and Saluste, E. (1949). *Acta Chem. Scand.* **3**, 432.

Hammarsten, E., Reichard, P., and Saluste, E. (1950). *J. Biol. Chem.* **183**, 105.

Hammarström, L., Appelgren, L.-E., and Ullberg, S. (1965a). *Exptl. Cell Res.* **37**, 608.

Hammarström, L., Nilsson, A., and Ullberg, S. (1965b). *Acta Radiol.* **63**, 183.

Hampton, J. C., and Quastler, H. (1961). *J. Biophys. Biochem. Cytol.* **10**, 140.

Hansborough, L. A., and Khan, M. (1951). *J. Exptl. Zool.* **116**, 447.

Hansborough, L. A., and Seay, H. (1951). *Proc. Soc. Exptl. Biol. Med.* **78**, 481.

Hansson, E. (1959). *Acta Physiol. Scand.* **46**, Suppl., 161.

Hara, H. (1966). *Beitr. Pathol. Anat. Allgem. Pathol.* **134**, 418.

Harbers, E. (1958). *In* "Handbuch d. Histochemie" (W. Graumann and K. Neumann, eds.), Vol. 1, p. 400. Fischer, Stuttgart.

Harbers, E., and Neumann, K. (1954). *Z. Naturforsch.* **9b**, 175.

Harbers, E., and Neumann, K. (1955). *Z. Naturforsch.* **10b**, 357.

Harding, C. V., and Srinivasan, B. D. (1961). *Exptl. Cell Res.* **25**, 326.

Harford, C. G., and Hamlin, A. (1965). *J. Bacteriol.* **89**, 1540.

Harford, C. G., Hamlin, A., and Rieders, E. (1966). *Exptl. Cell Res.* **42,** 50.

Harrington, H., and Lavik, P. S. (1955). *Arch. Biochem. Biophys.* **54,** 6.

Harris, H. (1959). *Biochem. J.* **73,** 362.

Harris, H. (1965). *Endeavour* **24,** 50.

Harris, H., and La Cour, L. F. (1963). *Nature* **200,** 227.

Harris, J. E., Slone, J. F., and King, D. T. (1950). *Nature* **166,** 25.

Harris, N. O., Dent, M. S., and Hayes, R. L. (1955). *J. Dental Res.* **34,** 470.

Harris, P. F., and Kugler, J. H. (1966). *Exptl. Cell Res.* **42,** 196.

Harrison, B. F., Thomas, M. D., and Hill, G. R. (1944). *Plant Physiol.* **19,** 245.

Harriss, E. B. (1956a). *Strahlentherapie, Sonderbaende 3,* **38,** 6.

Harriss, E. B. (1956b). *Advan. Radiobiol.* **38,** p. 333.

Harriss, E. B. (1956c). *Medica Mundi* **2,** No. 1.

Harwood, T. R., Putong, P. B., and Baserga, R. L. (1961). *Arch. Pathol.* **72,** 697.

Hauss, W. H., and Junge-Hülsing. G. (1961). *Deut. Med. Wochschr.* **86,** 763.

Hauss, W. H., Junge-Hülsing, G., and Schulze, W. (1960). *Z. Alternsforsch.* **14,** 259.

Hay, E. D. (1964). *In* "The Epidermis" (W. Montagna and W. C. Lobitz, eds.), p. 97. Academic Press, New York.

Hay, E. D., and Fischman, D. A. (1961). *Develop. Biol.* **3,** 26.

Hay, E. D., and Revel, J. P. (1963a). *J. Cell. Biol.* **16,** 29.

Hay, E. D., and Revel, J. P. (1963b). *Develop. Biol.* **7,** 152.

Healy, G. M., Siminovitch, L., Parker, R. C., and Graham, A. F. (1956). *Biochim. Biophys. Acta* **20,** 425.

Hecht, L. I., and Potter, V. R. (1956). *Cancer Res.* **16,** 988.

Heinonen, L., and Halkka, O. (1967). *Ann. Med. Exptl. Biol. Fenniae (Helsinki)* **45,** 101.

Hell, E. A., and Cruickshank, C. N. D. (1963). *Exptl. Cell Res.* **31,** 128.

Heller, D. A., and Hamilton, J. G. (1950). *In* "McCling's Handbook of Microscopical Technique" (R. Jones, ed.), p. 696. Harper & Row (Hoeber), New York.

Heller, M. (1948). *In* "Histopathology of Irradiation from External and Internal Sources" (W. Bloom, ed.), p. 70. McGraw-Hill, New York.

Helpap, B., and Maurer, W. (1967a). *Naturwissenschaften* **54,** 520.

Helpap, B., and Maurer, W. (1967b). *Verhandl. Deut. Ges. Pathol.* **51,** 262.

Hempel, K. (1963a). *Verhandl. Deut. Ges. Pathol.* **47,** 286.

Hempel, K. (1963b). *Exptl. Cell Res.* **31,** 594.

Hempel, K. (1965). *Histochemie* **4,** 507.

Hempel, K. (1966a). Habil.-Schrift, Universität Würzburg.

Hempel, K. (1966b). *Intern. Pigment Cell Conf., 6th, Sofia, 1965* p.162.

Hempel, K., and Erb, W. (1962). *Z. Zellforsch. Mikroskop. Anat.* **58,** 125.

Hempel, K., and Kraft, M. (1968). *Z. Zellforsch. Mikroskop. Anat.* **85,** 322.

Hempel, K., Lennartz, K.-J., and Maurer, W. (1962). *Beitr. Pathol. Anat. Allgem. Pathol.* **126,** 381.

Henderson, S. A. (1963). *Nature* **200,** 1235.

Henderson, S. A. (1964). *Chromosoma* **15,** 345.

Herrmann, W., Hartmann, G., and Brust, R. (1961). *Atompraxis* **7,** 315.

Herrmann, W., Hartmann, G., and Brust, R. (1962). *Atompraxis* **8,** 8.

Hershey, A. D. (1954). *J. Gen. Physiol.* **38,** 145.

Herve, A., and Closon, J. (1952). *Schweiz. Med. Wochschr.* **82,** 522.

Herve, A., and Govaerts, J. (1951). *Acta Radiol.* **35,** 257.

Herz, R. H. (1950). *Med. Radiography Phot.* **26,** 46.

Herz, R. H. (1951). *Nucleonics* **9,** No. 3, 24.

Herz, R. H. (1959). *Lab. Invest.* **8**, 71.

Hevesy, G. (1948). *Advan. Biol. Med. Phys.* **1**, 409.

Hibino, H., and Matsui, C. (1964). *Virology* **24**, 102.

Hicks, S. P., D'Amato, C. J., Coy, M. A., O'Brien, E. D., Thurston, J. M., and Joftes, D. L. (1961). *Brookhaven Symp. Biol.* **14**, 246.

Hill, D. K. (1959). *J. Physiol. (London)* **145**, 132.

Hill, D. K. (1962). *Nature* **194**, 831.

Hill, M. (1961a). *Nature* **189**, 916.

Hill, M. (1961b). *Exptl. Cell. Res.* **24**, 405.

Hill, M. (1962). *Exptl. Cell Res.* **28**, 21.

Hill, M. (1967). *Exptl. Cell Res.* **45**, 533.

Hill, M., and Drasil, V. (1960). *Exptl. Cell Res.* **21**, 569.

Hilscher, B., Hilscher, W., and Maurer, W. (1966). *Naturwissenschaften* **53**, 415.

Hilscher, W. (1964). *Beitr. Pathol. Anat. Allgem. Pathol.* **130**, 69.

Hilscher, W., and Makoski, H.-B. (1968). *Z. Zellforschg. Mikroskop. Anat.* **86**, 327.

Hilscher, W., and Maurer, W. (1962). *Naturwissenschaften* **49**, 352.

Hindley, J. (1963). *Biochem. Biophys. Res. Commun.* **12**, 175.

Hindmarsh, M., and Vaughan, J. (1957). *Brit. J. Radiol.* Suppl. 7, 71.

Hinrichs, H. R., Petersen, R. O., and Baserga, R. (1964). *Arch. Pathol.* **78**, 245.

Hirsch, H. M., Zelickson, A. S., and Hartmann, J. F. (1965). *Z. Zellforsch. Mikroskop. Anat.* **65**, 409.

Höbel, M., and Lehrnbecher, W. (1967). *Z. Ges. Exp. Med.* **144**, 24.

Hodge, H. C. (1950). *Arch. Ind. Hyg. Occupational Med.* **2**, 300.

Hodges, R. E., Evans, T. C., Bradbury, J. T., and Keettel, W. C. (1955). *J. Clin. Endocrinol. Metab.* **15**, 661.

Hoecker, F. E., and Roofe, P. G. (1949a). *Radiology* **52**, 856.

Hoecker, F. E., and Roofe, P. G. (1949b). *Res. Rev.* **10**.

Hoecker, F. E., and Roofe, P. G. (1951). *Radiology* **56**, 89.

Hoffman, J., and Post, J. (1967). *Cancer Res.* **27**, 898.

Hofmann, E., and Süss, A. (1954). *Naturwissenschaften* **41**, 506.

Hokin, L. E., and Huebner, D. (1967). *J. Cell Biol.* **33**, 521.

Holbrook, D. J., Evans, J. H., and Irvin, J. L. (1962). *Exptl. Cell Res.* **28**, 120.

Holland, N. D., and Nimitz, S. A. (1964). *Biol. Bull.* **127**, 280.

Holt, M. W., and Warren, S. (1950). *Proc. Soc. Exptl. Biol. Med.* **73**, 545.

Holt, M. W., and Warren, S. (1951). *Proc. Soc. Exptl. Biol. Med.* **76**, 4.

Holt, M. W., and Warren, S. (1952). *J. Natl. Cancer Inst.* **13**, 236.

Holt, M. W., and Warren, S. (1953a). *Lab. Invest.* **2**, 1.

Holt, M. W., and Warren, S. (1953b). *Lab. Invest.* **2**, 264.

Holt, M. W., Cowing, R. F., and Warren, S. (1949). *Science* **110**, 328.

Hood, S. L., and Comar, C. L. (1956). *U.S. At. Energy Comm.* **ORINS–12** (September), p. 280.

Hornsey, S., and Howard, A. (1956). *Ann. N.Y. Acad. Sci.* **63**, 915.

Horsley, R. J., Fucikovsky, L. A., and Banerjee, S. N. (1967). *Radiation Botany* **7**, 241.

Howard, A. (1956). *Ciba Found. Symp. Ionizing Radiations Cell Metab.* p. 196.

Howard, A., and Dewey, G. B. (1960). *In* "The Cell Nucleus" (J. S. Mitchell, ed.), p. 155. Academic Press, New York.

Howard, A., and Douglas, G. (1963). *Intern. J. Radiation Biol.* **6**, 405.

Howard, A., and Pelc, S. R. (1949). *Heredity* **3**, 383.

Howard, A., and Pelc, S. R. (1950). *Brit. J. Radiol.* **23**, 634.

Howard, A., and Pelc, S. R. (1951a). *Nature* **167**, 599.

Howard, A., and Pelc, S. R. (1951b). *Ciba Found. Conf. Isotopes Biochem.* p. 138.

Howard, A., and Pelc, S. R. (1951c). *Exptl. Cell Res.* **2**, 178.

Howard, A., and Pelc, S. R. (1953). *Heredity* **6**, Suppl., 261.

Hsu, T. C. (1962). *Exptl. Cell Res.* **27**, 332.

Hsu, T. C. (1964). *J. Cell Biol.* **23**, 53.

Hsu, T. C., and Lockhart, L. H. (1964). *Hereditas* **52**, 320.

Hsu, T. C., Dewey, W. C., and Humphrey, R. M. (1962). *Exptl. Cell Res.* **27**, 441.

Huang, T. (1960). *Intern. J. Appl. Radiation Isotopes* **8**, 234.

Hülser, D. F., and Rajewsky, M. F. (1966). *Biophysik* **3**, 123.

Huggert, A., Odeblad, E., Söremark, R., and Ullberg, S. (1961). *Acta Isotopica* **2**, 151.

Hughes, W. L. (1957). *Brookhaven Natl. Lab. Ann. Rept.*

Hughes, W. L. (1958). *Proc. Symp. Tritium Tracer Appl. N.Y., 1957.*

Hughes, W. L., Bond, V. P., Brecher, G., Cronkite, R. P., Painter, R. B., Quastler, H., and Sherman, F. G. (1958). *Proc. Natl. Acad. Sci. U.S.* **44**, 476.

Hughes, W. L., Commerford, S. L., Gitlin, D., Krueger, R. C., Schultze, B., Shah, V., and Reilly, P. (1964). *Federation Proc.* **23**, 640.

Hunt, W. L., and Foote, R. H. (1967). *Radiation Res.* **31**, 63.

Hurwitz, J., Furth, J. J., Malamy, M., and Alexander, M. (1962). *Proc. Natl. Acad. Sci. U.S.* **48**, 1222.

Hwang, W. S. S., Tonna, E. A., and Cronkite, E. P. (1962). *Nature* **193**, 896.

Hwang, W. S. S., Tonna, E. A., and Cronkite, E. P. (1963). *Arch. Oral Biol.* **8**, 377.

Hwang, W. S. S., Cronkite, E. P., and Tonna, E. A. (1966). *J. Dental. Res.* **45**, 350.

Iordansky, A. B. (1964). *Dokl. Akad. Nauk SSSR, Otd. Zytol.* **158**, 192.

Iordansky, A. B., and Matushina, H. D. (1966). *Genetika* **8**, 19.

Iordansky, A. B., Urbach, B. Y., and Matushina, H. D. (1966). *Dokl. Akad. Nauk SSSR, Otd. Biochim.* **167**, 1385.

Ives, D. H., Morse, P. A., and Potter, V. R. (1963). *J. Biol. Chem.* **238**, 1467.

Izawa, M., Allfrey, V. G., and Mirsky, A. E. (1963). *Proc. Natl. Acad. Sci. U.S.* **49**, 544.

Jackson, B., and Dessau, F. I. (1955). *Stain Technol.* **30**, 9.

Jacob, J., and Sirlin, J. L. (1964). *Nature* **202**, 622.

Jamienson, J. D., and Palade, G. E. (1967). *J. Cell Biol.* **34**, 597.

Jarabek, J. R., Kamins, M. M., and Vehe, K. L. (1953). *J. Am. Dental Assoc.* **47**, 639.

Jasinski, B., and Stiefel, G. E. (1954). *Schweiz. Med. Wochschr.* **84**, 947.

Jaskowetz, A. A. (1966). *Dokl. Akad. Nauk SSSR, Otd. Zytol.* **169**, 947.

Jennings, M. A., and Florey, H. W. (1956). *Quart. J. Exptl. Physiol.* **41**, 131.

Jennings, R. B., and Krakusin, J. S. (1952). *J. Lab. Clin. Med.* **40**, 815.

Jensen, W. A. (1957). *Proc. Natl. Acad. Sci. U.S.* **43**, 1038.

Jersild, R. A. (1966). *J. Cell Biol.* **31**, 413.

Jersild, R. A. (1968). *Anat. Rec.* **160**, 217.

Joftes, D. L. (1959). *Lab. Invest.* **8**, 131.

Joftes, D. L. (1963). *J. Nucl. Med.* **4**, 143.

Joftes, D. L., and Warren, S. (1955). *J. Biol. Phot. Assoc.* **23**, 145.

Johnson, H. A. (1961). *Cytologia (Tokyo)* **26**, 32.

Johnson, H. A., and Bond, V. P. (1961). *Cancer* **14**, 639.

Johnson, H. A., and Cronkite, E. P. (1959). *Radiation Res.* **11**, 825.

Johnson, H. A., and Cronkite, E. P. (1967). *Radiation Res.* **30**, 488.

Johnson, H. A., Haymaker, W. E., Rubini, J. R., Fliedner, T. M., Bond, V. P., Cronkite, E. P., and Hughes, W. L. (1960a). *Cancer* **13**, 636.

Johnson, H. A., Rubini, J. R., Cronkite, E. P., and Bond, V. P. (1960b). *Lab. Invest.* **9**, 460.

Johnson, N. W. (1967). *Arch. Oral Biol.* **12**, 901.

Jona, R. (1963). *Stain Technol.* **38,** 91.

Jonsson, N., and Lagerstedt, S. (1959). *Histochemie* **1,** 251.

Jorpes, E., Odeblad, E., and Boström, H. (1953). *Acta Haematol.* **9,** 273.

Jowsey, J. (1956). *U.S. At. Energy Comm.* **ORINS**–12 (September), p. 311.

Jowsey, J., Owen, M., and Vaughan, J. (1953). *Brit. J. Exptl. Med.* **34,** 661.

Jowsey, J., Owen, M., Tutt, M., and Vaughan, J. (1955). *Brit. J. Exptl. Pathol.* **36,** 22.

Jowsey, J., Sissons, H. A., and Vaughan, J. (1956). *J. Nucl. Energy* **2,** 168.

Jowsey, J., Rowland, R. E., Marshall, J. H., and McLean, F. C. (1958). *Endocrinology* **63,** 903.

Kaminski, E. J. (1955). *Stain Technol.* **30,** 139.

Kaplan, W. D., and Pelc, S. R. (1956). *Z. Induktive Abstammungs-Vererbungslehre* **87,** 356.

Kaplan, W. D., and Sisken, J. E. (1960). *Experientia* **16,** 67.

Kara, J., and Weil, R. (1967). *Proc. Natl. Acad. Sci. U.S.* **57,** 63.

Karasaki, S. (1965). *J. Cell Biol.* **26,** 937.

Karpishka, I., Leblond, C. P., and Carneiro, J. (1959). *Arch. Oral Biol.* **1,** 23.

Kasten, F. H., and Strasser, F. F. (1966a). *Natl. Cancer Inst. Monograph* **23,** 353.

Kasten, F. H., and Strasser, F. F. (1966b). *Nature* **211,** 135.

Kauffman, S. L. (1966). *Exptl. Cell Res.* **42,** 67.

Kauffman, S. L. (1968). *Exptl. Cell Res.* **49,** 420.

Kaufmann, B. P., Gay, H., and McDonald, M. R. (1949). *Cold Spring Harbor Symp. Quant. Biol.* **14,** 85.

Kaufmann, B. P., Gay, H., and McDonald, M. R. (1951a). *Am. J. Botany* **38,** 268.

Kaufmann, B. P., McDonald, M. R., and Gay, H. (1951b). *J. Cellular Comp. Physiol.* **38,** Suppl. 1, 71.

Kay, E. R. M. (1966). *Trans. N.Y. Acad. Sci.* **28,** 726.

Kayes, J., Maunsbach, A. B., and Ullberg, S. (1962). *J. Ultrastruct. Res.* **7,** 339.

Keiser, G., Cottier, H., Odartchenko, N., and Bond, V. P. (1964). *Blood* **24,** 254.

Keiser, G., Bryant, B. J., and Bond, V. P. (1966). *Radiation Res.* **28,** 166.

Kelly, L. S. (1957). *Progr. Biophys. Biophys. Chem.* **8,** 143.

Kemp, C. L. (1966). *Chromosoma* **19,** 137.

Kessler, D. (1967). *Exptl. Cell Res.* **45,** 676.

Keyl, H.-G., and Pelling, C. (1963). *Chromosoma* **14,** 347.

Khrushchov, N. G. (1963). *Dokl. Akad. Nauk SSSR, Otd. Zytol.* **151,** 1201.

Kidman, B., Rayner, B., Tutt, M., and Vaughan, J. (1952). *J. Pathol. Bacteriol.* **64,** 453.

Kihara, H. K., Amano, M., and Sibatani, A. (1956). *Biochim. Biophys. Acta* **21,** 489.

Kikuchi, Y., and Sandberg, A. A. (1965). *J. Natl. Cancer Inst.* **34,** 795.

Killander, D., and Zetterberg, A. (1965). *Exptl. Cell Res.* **38,** 272.

Killmann, S. A., Cronkite, E. P., Bond, V. P., and Fliedner, T. M. (1962a). *Proc. 8th Congr. European Soc. Haematol., Vienna, 1961,* 63.

Killmann, S. A., Cronkite, E. P., Fliedner, T. M., and Bond, V. P. (1962b). *Lab. Invest.* **11,** 845.

Killmann, S. A., Cronkite, E. P., Robertson, J. S., Fliedner, T. M., and Bond, V. P. (1963). *Lab. Invest.* **12,** 671.

Killmann, S. A., Cronkite, E. P., Fliedner, T. M., and Bond, V. P. (1964). *Blood* **24,** 267.

Kim, J., and Evans, T. G. (1964). *Radiation Res.* **21,** 129.

Kimball, R. F., and Perdue, S. W. (1962). *Exptl. Cell Res.* **27,** 405.

Kimball, R. F., and Prescott, D. M. (1964). *J. Cell Biol.* **21,** 496.

Kindler, H. (1962a). *Klin. Wochschr.* **40,** 60.

Kindler, H. (1962b). *Longenbecks Arch. Klin. Chir.* **301,** 79.

Kindler, H. (1963). *Klin. Wochschr.* **41,** 1059.

King, D. T., Harris, J. E., and Tkaczyk, S. (1951). *Nature* **167,** 273.

King, D. W., and Barnhisel, M. L. (1967). *J. Cell Biol.* **33,** 265.

King, R. C., and Falk, G. J. (1960). *J. Biochem. Biophys. Cytol.* **8,** 550.

Kishimoto, S., and Lieberman, I. (1964). *Exptl. Cell Res.* **36,** 92.

Kisieleski, W. E., Faraghan, W. G., Norris, W. P., and Arnold, J. S. (1952). *J. Pharmacol. Exptl. Therap.* **104,** 459.

Kisieleski, W. E., Baserga, R., and Lisco, H. (1961a). *Atompraxis* **7,** 81.

Kisieleski, W. E., Baserga, R., and Vaupotic, J. (1961b). *Radiation Res.* **15,** 341.

Kisieleski, W. E., Samuels, L. D., and Hiley, P. C. (1964). *Nature* **202,** 458.

Kit, S., Dubbs, D. R., and Frearson, P. M. (1965). *J. Biol. Chem.* **240,** 2565.

Kleihues, P., and Schultze, B. (1967). *Naturwissenschaften* **54,** 173.

Kleine, T. O. (1967). *Naunyn-Schmiedebergs Arch. Pharmak. U. Exp. Path.* **258,** 215.

Klinge, O., and Stöcker, E. (1965). *Beitr. Pathol. Anat. Allgem. Pathol.* **131,** 395.

Klinman, N. R., and Erslev, A. (1963). *Proc. Soc. Exptl. Biol. Med.* **112,** 338.

Knutson, F., and Norin, T. (1956). *Acta Pathol. Microbiol. Scand.* **38,** 447.

Knudtson, K. P., Priest, R. E., Sloop, R. D., and Jesseph, J. E. (1963). *Lab. Invest.* **12,** 606.

Koburg, E. (1961a). *Beitr. Pathol. Anat. Allgem. Pathol.* **124,** 108.

Koburg, E. (1961b). *Arch. Ohr.-Nas-ü. Kehlk.-Heilk.* **178,** 150.

Koburg, E. (1962a). *Ann. Histochim.* **7,** Suppl. 2, 97.

Koburg, E. (1962b). *Verhandl. Deut. Ges. Pathol.* **46,** 238.

Koburg, E. (1963a). *Ann. Histochim.* **8,** Suppl. 1, 249.

Koburg, E. (1963b). *In* "Cell Proliferation" (L. F. Lamerton and R. J. M. Fry, eds.), p. 62. Blackwell, Oxford.

Koburg, E., and Hempel, K. (1965). *Symp. Intern. Soc. Cell Biol.* **4,** 177.

Koburg, E., and Maurer, W. (1962). *Biochim. Biophys. Acta* **61,** 229.

Koburg, E., and Plester, D. (1962). *Acta Oto-Laryngol.* **54,** 319.

Koburg, E., and Schultze, B. (1961). *Verhandl. Deut. Ges. Pathol.* **45,** 103.

Koch, W. (1951). *Strahlentherapie* **85,** 253.

Kodicek, E., and Loewi, G. (1955). *Proc. Roy. Soc. (London)* **B144,** 100.

Koehler, J. K., Mühlethaler, K., and Freywyssling, A. (1963). *J. Cell Biol.* **16,** 73.

Komender, J., Koscianek-Malczewska, H., and Ostrowski, K. (1965). *Experientia* **21,** 249.

Konrad, C. G. (1963). *J. Cell Biol.* **19,** 267.

Kopriwa, B. M. (1967a). *J. Histochem. Cytochem.* **14,** 923.

Kopriwa, B. M. (1967b). *J. Histochem. Cytochem.* **15,** 501.

Kopriwa, B. M., and Leblond, C. P. (1962). *J. Histochem. Cytochem.* **10,** 269.

Korson, R. (1951). *Stain Technol.* **26,** 265.

Kotani, M., Yamashita, A., Rai, F., Seiki, K., and Horii, I. (1967). *Blood* **29,** 616.

Kowalewski, K. (1958). *Endocrinology* **63,** 759.

Kozuka, S., and Moore, G. E. (1966). *J. Natl. Cancer Inst.* **36,** 623.

Krakusin, J. S., and Jennings, R. B. (1955). *A. M. A. Arch. Pathol.* **59,** 471.

Kramsch, D., Beck, V., and Oehlert, W. (1963). *Beitr. Pathol. Anat. Allgem. Pathol.* **128,** 416.

Kraus, L. M., and Morrison, D. B. (1955). *Proc. Soc. Exptl. Biol. Med.* **89,** 598.

Krause, M., and Plaut, W. (1960). *Nature* **188,** 511.

Kreutzer, F. L., Miller, E. R., Soley, M. H., and Lindsay, S. (1950). *A. M. A. Arch. Surg.* **60,** 707.

Kuehl, L. (1967). *J. Biol. Chem.* **242,** 2199.

Kumamoto, Y. (1953). *Anat. Record* **115,** 339.

Kumamoto, Y., and Leblond, C. P. (1956). *J. Dental Res.* **35,** 147.

Kumamoto, Y., and Leblond, C. P. (1958). *J. Dental Res.* **37,** 147.

Kunz, J., and Braselmann, H. (1965). *Acta Biol. Med. Ger.* **14,** 570.

Kuper, S. W. A., and Pelc, S. R. (1952). *Parasitology* **42,** 269.

Kurita, Y., Moriwaki, K., and Yosida, T. H. (1964). *Gann* **55,** 397.

Kurnick, N. B. (1950). *Exptl. Cell Res.* **1,** 151.

Kurnick, N. B. (1952). *Stain Technol.* **27,** 233.

Kury, G., and Carter, H. W. (1965). *Arch. Pathol.* **80,** 38.

Kusanagi, A. (1964a). *Nippon Idengaku Zasshi* **39,** 254.

Kusanagi, A. (1964b). *Botan. Mag. (Tokyo)* **77,** 388.

Kutzim, H. (1962). *Nucl. Med.* **3,** 39.

Kuyper, C. M. A., Smets, L. A., and Pieck, A. C. M. (1962a). *Exptl. Cell Res.* **26,** 217.

Kuyper, C. M. A., Liebecq-Hutter, S., and Chèvremont-Comhaire, S. (1962b). *Exptl. Cell Res.* **28,** 459.

Kuzin, A. M., and Wainson, A. A. (1966). *Nature* **212,** 819.

Kyker, G. C., Christopherson, W. M., Berg, H. F., and Brucer, M. (1956). *Cancer* **9,** 489.

Kyogoku, M., Yagi, Y., Planinsek, J., Bernecky, J., and Pressman, D., (1964). *Cancer Res.* **24,** 268.

Laakso, L., Lindgren, I., and Rekonen, A. (1965). *Acta Radiol.* **3,** 305.

Lacassagne, A., and Lattès, J. (1924a). *Compt. Rend. Soc. Biol.* **90,** 485.

Lacassagne, A., and Lattès, J. (1924b). *Compt. Rend. Soc. Biol.* **90,** 487.

Lacassagne, A., and Lattès, J. (1924c). *Compt. Rend. Acad. Sci.* **178,** 488.

Lacassagne, A., and Lattès, J. (1924d). *Bull. d'Histol.* **1,** 279.

La Cour, L. F., and Crawley, J. W. C. (1965). *Chromosoma* **16,** 124.

La Cour, L. F., and Pelc, S. R. (1958). *Nature* **182,** 506.

La Cour, L. F., and Pelc, S. R. (1959a). *Proc. 10th Intern. Congr. Genet., Montreal, 1958* **2,** 156.

La Cour, L. F., and Pelc, S. R. (1959b). *Nature* **183,** 1455.

Lacroix, P. (1952). *Experientia* **8,** 426.

Lacroix, P. (1953). *Bull. Acad. Roy. Med. Belg.* **18,** 489.

Lacroix, P., and Ponlot, R. (1958). *Radioisotopes in Scientific Res.* **3.**

Lagerstedt, S. (1956). *Experientia* **12,** 425.

Lahtiharju, A., and Rytömaa, T. (1967). *Exptl. Cell Res.* **46,** 593.

Lahtiharju, A., and Teir, H. (1964). *Exptl. Cell Res.* **34,** 205.

Lajtha, L. G. (1952). *Exptl. Cell Res.* **3,** 696.

Lajtha, L. G. (1954). *J. Photogr. Sci.* **2,** 130.

Lajtha, L. G. (1959). *In* "The Kinetics of Cellular Proliferation" (F. Stohlman, ed.), p. 173. Grune & Stratton, New York.

Lajtha, L. G., and Oliver, R. (1959). *Lab. Invest.* **8,** 214.

Lajtha, L. G., and Oliver, R. (1960). *Ciba Found. Symp. Haemopoiesis: Cell Prod. Regulation* p. 289.

Lajtha, L. G., and Suit, H. D. (1955). *Brit. J. Haematol.* **1,** 55.

Lajtha, L. G., Ellis, F., and Oliver, R. (1953). *Brit. J. Cancer* **7,** 401.

Lajtha, L. G., Oliver, R., and Ellis, F. (1954a). *Radiol. Symp., London* p. 216.

Lajtha, L. G., Oliver, R., and Ellis, F. (1954b). *Brit. J. Cancer* **8,** 367.

Lala, P. K., and Patt, H. M. (1966). *Proc. Natl. Acad. Sci. U.S.* **56,** 1735.

Lala, P. K., Maloney, M. A., and Patt, H. M. (1965). *Exptl. Cell Res.* **38,** 626.

Lala, P. K., Patt, H. M., and Maloney, M. A. (1966). *Acta Haematol.* **35,** 311.

Lamerton, L. F., (1966). *Radiation Res.* **27,** 119.

Lamerton, L. F., and Harriss, E. B. (1951). *Brit. Med. J.* **ii,** 932.

Lamerton, L. F., and Harriss, E. B. (1954). *J. Phot. Sci.* **2,** 135.

Lamerton, L. F., Belcher, E. H., and Harriss, E. B. (1954). *Proc. 2nd Radioisotope Conf., Oxford, Engl.* p. 210.

Lane, N., Caro, L., Otero-Vilardebó, L. R., and Godman, G. C. (1964). *J. Cell Biol.* **21,** 339.

Lang, W. (1967). Personal communication.

Lang, W., and Maurer, W. (1965). *Exptl. Cell Res.* **39,** 1.

Lang, W., Müller, D., and Maurer, W. (1966a). *Exptl. Cell Res.* **44,** 645.

Lang, W., Pilgrim, C., and Maurer, W. (1966b). *Naturwissenschaften* **53,** 210.

Lang, W., Müller, D., and Maurer, W. (1968). *Exptl. Cell Res.* **49,** 558.

Lark, K. G., (1963). *In* "Molecular Genetics" (J. H. Taylor, ed.), Pt. I, p. 153. Academic Press, New York.

Larsson, K. S. (1960). *Exptl. Cell Res.* **21,** 498.

Larsson, K. S. (1962a). *Acta Odontol. Scand. Suppl.* **31.**

Larsson, K. S. (1962b). *Acta Morphol. Neerl. Scand.* **4,** 349.

Larsson, K. S. (1962c). *Acta Morphol. Neerl. Scand.* **4,** 369.

Lauf, P., Seemayer, N., and Oehlert, W. (1962). *Z. Krebsforsch.* **64,** 490.

Layton, L. L. (1951a). *Cancer* **4,** 198.

Layton, L. L. (1951b). *Proc. Soc. Exptl. Biol. Med.* **76,** 596.

Leak, L. V. (1965). *J. Ultrastruct. Res.* **12,** 135.

Lebedeva, G. S., and Zavarzin, A. A. (1964). *In* "A Study of Cell Cycles and Metabolism of Nucleic Acid During Differentiation of the Cells" (L. N. Zhinkin and A. A. Zavarzin, eds.), p. 60. Nauka, Moscow and Leningrad.

Lebedeva, G. S., and Zavarzin, A. A. (1966). *Arch. Anat. Histol. Embriol.* **50,** 21.

Leblond, C. P. (1943a). *J. Anat.* **77,** 149.

Leblond, C. P. (1943b). *Stain Technol.* **18,** 159.

Leblond, C. P. (1944). *Anat. Record* **88,** 285.

Leblond, C. P. (1948a). *Recent. Progr. Hormone Res.* **3,** 159.

Leblond, C. P. (1948b). *Advan. Biol. Med. Phys.* **1,** 353.

Leblond, C. P. (1949). *Ann. N.Y. Acad. Sci.* **50,** 444.

Leblond, C. P. (1951). *J. Am. Pharm. Assoc.* **40,** 595.

Leblond, C. P. (1965a). *Am. J. Anat.* **116,** 1.

Leblond, C. P. (1965b). *Symp. Intern. Soc. Cell Biol.* **4,** 321.

Leblond, C. P., and Amano, M. (1962). *J. Histochem. Cytochem.* **10,** 162.

Leblond, C. P., and Bélanger, L. F. (1946). *Anat. Record* **94,** 542.

Leblond, C. P., and Cameron, J. (1952). *Anat. Record* **112,** 455.

Leblond, C. P., and Gross, J. (1948). *Endocrinology* **43,** 306.

Leblond, C. P., and Gross, J. (1949). *J. Clin. Endocrinol.* **9,** 149.

Leblond, C. P., and Gross, J. (1951). (P. F. Hahn, ed.), p. 250. Academic Press, New York.

Leblond, C. P., Fertman, M. B., Puppel, I. D., and Curtis, G. M. (1946). *A. M. A. Arch. Pathol.* **41,** 510.

Leblond, C. P., Percival, W. L., and Gross, J. (1948a). *Proc. Soc. Exptl. Biol. Med.* **67,** 74.

Leblond, C. P., Stevens, C. E., and Bogoroch, R. (1948b). *Science* **108,** 531.

Leblond, C. P., Wilkinson, G. W., Bélanger, L. F., and Robichon, J. (1950). *Am. J. Anat.* **86,** 289.

Leblond, C. P., Bélanger, L. F., and Greulich, R. C. (1955). *Ann. N.Y. Acad. Sci.* **60,** 630.

Leblond, C. P., Everett, N. B., and Simmons, B. (1957). *Am. J. Anat.* **101,** 225.

Leblond, C. P., Lacroix, P., Ponlot, R., and Dhom, A. (1959a). *Bull. Acad. Roy. Med. Belg.* **24,** 421.

Leblond, C. P., Messier, B., and Kopriwa, B. (1959b). *Lab. Invest.* **8**, 296.

Leblond, C. P., Kopriwa, B., and Messier, B. (1963). *Intern. Congr. Histochem. Cytochem., 1st, Paris, 1960* p. 1.

Leblond, C. P., Greulich, R. C., and Pereira, J. P. M. (1964). *Advan. Biol. Skin* **5**, 39.

Lederer, B., and Lennartz, K.-J. (1968). *Z. Krebsforschg.* **70**, 230.

Ledoux, L. (1965). *Progr. Nucleic Acid Res. Mol. Biol.* **4**, 231.

Ledoux, L., Gerber, G. B., Charles, P., Remy, J., and Remy-Defraigne, J. (1967). *Experientia* **23**, 16.

Leevy, C. M. (1963). *Ann. N.Y. Acad. Sci.* **104**, 939.

Leevy, C. M., George, W., Deysine, M., and Gnassi, A. M. (1962). *Exptl. Mol. Biol.* **1**, 457.

Lennartz, K.-J., and Maurer, W. (1964). *Z. Zellforsch.* **63**, 478.

Lennartz, K.-J., Hempel, K., and Maurer, W. (1961). *Naturwissenschaften* **48**, 529.

Lennartz, K.-J., Maurer, W., and Eder, M. (1968a). *Z. Krebsforschg.* **71**, 267.

Lennartz, K.-J., Maurer, W., and Eder, M. (1968c). *Histochemie* **13**, 84.

Lennartz, K.-J., Maurer, W., and Schümmelfeder, N. (1964). *Verhandl. Deut. Ges. Pathol.* **48**, 280.

Lennartz, K.-J., Schümmelfeder, N., and Maurer, W. (1966). *Naturwissenschaften* **53**, 21.

Lennartz, K.-J., Eder, M., and Maurer, W. (1968b). *Acta Histochem. Suppl.* 8, 89.

Lesch, R., Schiessle, W., and Oehlert, W. (1964). *Beitr. Pathol. Anat. Allgem. Pathol.* **129**, 296.

Lesher, S. (1966). *In* "Radiation and Ageing" (P. J. Lindop and G. A. Sacher, eds.), p. 183. Taylor & Francis, London.

Lesher, S., Stroud, A. N., and Brues, A. M. (1960). *Cancer Res.* **20**, 1341.

Lesher, S., Fry, R. J. M., and Kohn, H. I. (1961a). *Exptl. Cell Res.* **24**, 334.

Lesher, S., Fry, R. J. M., and Sacher, G. A. (1961b). *Exptl. Cell Res.* **25**, 398.

Lesher, S., Walburg, H. E., and Sacher, G. A. (1964). *Nature* **202**, 884.

Lesher, S., Lamerton, L. F., Sacher, G. A., Fry, R. J. M., Steel, G. G., and Roylance, P. J. (1966). *Radiation Res.* **29**, 57.

Leslie, I. (1955). *In* "Nucleic Acids" (E. Chargaff and J. N. Davidson, eds.), Vol. 2, p. 1. Academic Press, New York.

Lettré, H., and Paweletz, N. (1966). *Naturwissenschaften* **53**, 268.

Levi, H. (1951). *Biochim. Biophys. Acta* **7**, 198.

Levi, H. (1953). *Nature* **171**, 123.

Levi, H. (1954). *Exptl. Cell Res.* **7**, 44.

Levi, H., and Hogben, A. S. (1955). *Kgl. Danske Videnskab. Selskab Mat. Fys. Medd.* **30**, 3.

Levi, H., and Nielsen, A. (1959). *Lab. Invest.* **8**, 82.

Levina, L. J., and Shapiro, I. M. (1967). *Genetika* **3**, 154.

Levina, L. J., Polikarpova, S. I., and Shapiro, I. M. (1966). *Dokl. Akad. Nauk SSSR, Otd. Zytol.* **171**, 988.

Levine, B., Hoffman, H., and Freedlander, S. O. (1957). *Cancer* **10**, 164.

Levy, H. B. (1963). *Proc. Soc. Exptl. Biol. Med.* **113**, 886.

Lewin, R., Hart, H. E., Greenberg, J., Spencer, H., Stern, K. G., and Laszlo, D. (1954a). *Science* **119**, 880.

Lewin, R., Hart, H. E., Greenberg, J., Spencer, H., Stern, K. G., and Laszlo, D. (1954b). *Proc. 2nd Radioisotope Conf., Oxford, Engl.* **1**, 125.

Lieb, L. M., and Lisco, H. (1966). *Cancer Res.* **26**, 733.

Lima-de-Faria, A. (1959a). *Science* **130**, 503.

Lima-de-Faria, A. (1959b). *J. Biophys. Biochem. Cytol.* **6**, 457.

Lima-de-Faria, A. (1961). *Hereditas* **47**, 674.

Lima-de-Faria, A. (1962a). *Chromosoma* **13**, 47.

Lima-de-Faria, A. (1962b). *Progr. Biophys. Biophys. Chem.* **12**, 281.

Lima-de-Faria, A. (1964). *Intern. Congr. Biol. 11th, Providence, Rhode Island.*

Lima-de-Faria, A. (1965). *Hereditas* **53**, 1.

Lima-de-Faria, A., and Moses, M. J. (1964). *Hereditas* **52**, 367.

Lima-de-Faria, A., and Reitalu, J. (1963). *J. Cell Biol.* **16**, 315.

Lima-de-Faria, A., Reitalu, J., and Bergman, S. (1961). *Hereditas* **47**, 695.

Lima-de-Faria, A., Reitalu, J., and O'Sullivan, M. A., (1965). *Chromosoma* **16**, 152.

Lin, T. P., and Goldberg, E. D. (1951). *Endocrinology* **48**, 485.

Lindenbaum, A., and Alper, R. E. (1966). *Atompraxis* **12**, 127.

Linnartz-Niklas, A., Hempel, K., and Maurer, W. (1964). *Z. Zellforsch. Mikroskop. Anat.* **62**, 443.

Lipchina, L. P. (1967). *Tsitologiya* **9**, 1093.

Lipkin, M. (1965). *Federation Proc.* **24**, 10.

Lipkin, M., and Quastler, H. (1962). *J. Clin. Invest.* **41**, 141.

Lipkin, M., Quastler, H., and Muggia, F. (1963a). *Radiation Res.* **19**, 277.

Lipkin, M., Bell, B., and Sherlock, P. (1963b). *J. Clin. Invest.* **42**, 767.

Lipkin, M., Sherlock, P., and Bell, B. (1963c). *Gastroenterology* **45**, 721.

Lippman, R. W., Finkle, R. D., and Gillette, D. (1951). *Proc. Soc. Exptl. Biol. Med.* **77**, 68.

Liquier-Milward, J. (1954). *Biochim. Biophys. Acta* **14**, 459.

Liquier-Milward, J. (1956). *Nature* **177**, 619.

Lisco, H., Nishimura, E. T., Baserga, R., and Kisieleski, W. E. (1961a). *Lab. Invest.* **10**, 435.

Lisco, H., Baserga, R., and Kisieleski, W. E. (1961b). *Nature* **192**, 571.

Littau, V. C., Allfrey, V. G., Frenster, J. H., and Mirsky, A. E. (1964). *Proc. Natl. Acad. Sci. U.S.* **52**, 93.

Little, J. R., Brecher, G., Bradley, T. R., and Rose, S. (1962). *Blood* **19**, 236.

Littlefield, J. E. (1966). *Biochim. Biophys. Acta* **114**, 398.

Litvak, R. M., and Baserga, R. (1964). *Exptl. Cell Res.* **33**, 540.

Löbbecke, E.-A., Schultze, B., and Maurer, W. (1969). *Exptl. Cell Res.* (in press).

Logan, R. (1959). *Biochim. Biophys. Acta* **35**, 251.

Logan, R., Errera, M., and Ficq, A. (1959a). *Biochim. Biophys. Acta* **32**, 147.

Logan, R., Ficq, A., and Errera, M. (1959b). *Biochim. Biophys. Acta* **31**, 402.

Lomakina, L. J., Zhilina, M. V., and Sagdeeva, L. G. (1967). *Tsitologiya* **9**, 1155.

Looney, W. B. (1953). *Federation Proc.* **12**, 395.

Looney, W. B. (1965a). *Nature* **205**, 1334.

Looney, W. B. (1965b). *Radiol. Clin. North Am.* **3**, 209.

Looney, W. B. (1966a). *Intern. J. Radiation Biol.* **10**, 97.

Looney, W. B. (1966b). *Nature* **210**, 111.

Looney, W. B., and Woodruff, L. A. (1953). *A. M. A. Arch. Pathol.* **56**, 1.

Looney, W. B., Pardue, M. L., and Banghart, F. W. (1963). *Nature* **198**, 804.

Looney, W. B., Chang, L. O., Williams, S. S., Forster, J., Haydock, I. C., and Banghart, F. W. (1965). *Radiation Res.* **24**, 312.

Lord, B. I. (1964). *Brit. J. Haematol.* **10**, 496.

Lord, B. I. (1965). *Brit. J. Haematol.* **11**, 130.

Lüttge, U., and Weigl, J. (1965). *Planta* **64**, 28.

Lupulescu, A., and Petrovici, A. (1965). *Arch. Anat. Microscop. Morphol. Exptl.* **54**, 895.

Lupulescu, A., and Petrovici, A. (1966). *Acta Biol. Med. Ger.* **16**, 86.

Lupulescu, A., Merculiev, E., and Nicolae, M. (1964). *Acta Anat.* **57**, 37.

McCarter, J. A., and Quastler, H. (1962a). *Biochim. Biophys. Acta* **55**, 552.

McCarter, J. A., and Quastler, H. (1962b). *Nature* **194**, 873.

MacDonald, A. M., Cobb, J., Solomon, A. K., and Steinberg, D. (1949). *Proc. Soc. Exptl. Biol. Med.* **72**, 117.

McElligott, T. F., (1962). *J. Pathol. Bacteriol.* **83**, 347.

McFall, E., and Stent, G. S. (1959). *Biochim. Biophys. Acta* **34**, 580.

McGrath, R. A., Leach, W. M., and Carlson, J. G. (1965). *Exptl. Cell Res.* **37**, 39.

Machemer, R., and Oehlert, W. (1964). *Endocrinology* **46**, 77.

McIsaac, R. J. (1955). *Endocrinology* **57**, 571.

McLaughlin, W. L., and Ehrlich, M. (1954). *Nucleonics* **12**, No 10, 34.

MacLeod, R. D. (1968). *Chromosoma (Berl.)* **24**, 177.

McMaster-Kaye, R. (1960). *J. Biophys. Biochem. Cytol.* **8**, 365.

McMaster-Kaye, R. (1962). *J. Histochem. Cytochem.* **10**, 154.

McMaster-Kaye, R., and Taylor, J. H. (1958). *J. Biophys. Biochem. Cytol.* **4**, 5.

McQuade, H. A., and Friedkin, M. (1960). *Exptl. Cell Res.* **21**, 118.

McQuade, H. A., Friedkin, M., and Atchison, A. A. (1956a). *Exptl. Cell Res.* **11**, 249.

McQuade, H. A., Friedkin, M., and Atchison, A. A. (1956b). *Exptl. Cell Res.* **11**, 256.

Magnusson, G., Bergström, I., and Odeblad, E. (1955). *Acta Radiol.* **43**, 227.

Mahaley, M. S., Mahaley, J. L., and Day, E. D. (1965). *Cancer Res.* **25**, 779.

Maisin, J. R., and Lambiet-Collier, M. (1967). *Int. J. Radiat. Biol.* **13**, 35.

Mak, S. (1965). *Exptl. Cell Res.* **39**, 286.

Malaise, E., Frindel, E., and Tubiana, M. (1967). *Compt. Rend. Acad. Sci.* **D264**, 1104.

Malmon, A. G., (1965). *J. Theoret. Biol.* **9**, 77.

Manasek, F. J., Adelstein, S. J., and Lyman, C. P. (1965). *J. Cellular Comp. Physiol.* **65**, 319.

Mancini, R. E., and de Lustig, E. S. (1954). *Rev. Soc. Arg. Biol.* **30**, 67.

Mancini, R. E., Vilar, O., Stein, E., and Fiorini, H. (1961). *J. Histochem. Cytochem.* **9**, 278.

Mangan, J., Miki-Noumura, T., and Gross, P. R. (1965). *Science* **147**, 1575.

Mantyeva, V. L., Rapaport, M. A., Tulykas, S. Y., and Zbarsky, I. B. (1966). *Vopr. Med. Khim.* **12**, 407.

Marin, G., and Bender, M. A. (1963a). *Intern. J. Radiation Biol.* **7**, 221.

Marin, G., and Bender, M. A. (1963b). *Intern. J. Radiation Biol.* **7**, 235.

Marinelli, L. D., and Hill, R. F. (1948). *Am. J. Roentgenol. Radium Therapy Nucl. Med.* **59**, 396.

Marinelli, L. D., Foote, F. W., Hill, R. F., and Hocker, A. F. (1947). *Am. J. Roentgenol. Radium Therapy Nucl. Med.* **58**, 17.

Marsh, J. C., and Perry, S. (1964a). *J. Clin. Invest.* **43**, 267.

Marsh, J. C., and Perry, S. (1964b). *Arch. Biochem. Biophys.* **104**, 146.

Maruyama, Y. (1964). *Nature* **201**, 93.

Mattingly, S. A. (1963). *Exptl. Cell Res.* **29**, 314.

Mauer, A. M. (1965). *Blood* **26**, 1.

Mauer, A. M., and Fisher, V. (1966). *Blood* **28**, 428.

Maurer, W. (1960). *Colloq. Ges. Physiol. Chem. 10, Mosbach, 1959.* Springer, Berlin.

Maurer, W. (1961). Unpublished observations.

Maurer, W., and Koburg, E. (1964). *In* "Biochemie des Hörorgans" (S. Rauch, ed.), p. 430. Thieme, Stuttgart.

Maurer, W., and Primbsch, E. (1964). *Exptl. Cell Res.* **33**, 8.

Maurer, W., Koburg, E., and Schultze, B. (1961). Unpublished observations.

Maurer, W., Lennartz, K.-J., and Hempel, K. (1963). *Radioaktive Isotope Klin. Forsch.*, *Strahlentherapie, Sonderbaende* **53,** 512.

Maurer, W., Pilgrim, C., Wegener, K., Hollweg, S., and Lennartz, K.-J. (1965). *Radioaktive Isotope Klin. Forsch.*, *Strahlentherapie, Sonderbaende*, **60,** 96.

Mazia, D., and Bucher, N. L. R. (1960). *Experientia* **16,** 215.

Mazia, D., Hayashi, T., and Yudowitch, K. (1947). *Cold Spring Harbor Symp. Quant. Biol.* **12,** 122.

Mazia, D., Plaut, W. S., and Ellis, G. W. (1955). *Exptl. Cell Res.* **9,** 305.

Meachim, G., and Collins, D. H. (1962). *Ann. Rheumatic Diseases* **21,** 45.

Mellgren, J. (1952). *Exptl. Cell Res.* **3,** 689.

Mellgren, J., Knutsson, F., and Norin, T. (1954). *Acta Pathol. Microbiol. Scand.* **34,** 393.

Mendelsohn, M. L. (1960a). *Science* **132,** 1496.

Mendelsohn, M. L. (1960b). *J. Natl. Cancer Inst.* **25,** 485.

Mendelsohn, M. L. (1962a). *Science* **135,** 213.

Mendelsohn, M. L. (1962b). *J. Natl. Cancer Inst.* **28,** 1015.

Mendelsohn, M. L. (1963). *In* "Cell Proliferation" (L. F. Lamerton and R. J. M. Fry, eds.), p. 190. Blackwell, Oxford.

Mendelsohn, M. L. (1964a). *Acta. Unio Intern. Contra Cancrum* **20,** 1400.

Mendelsohn, M. L. (1964b). *In* "Cellular Radiation Biology" Univ. of Texas Press, Austin, Texas.

Miller, O. L., Stone, G. E., and Prescott, D. M. (1964b). *J. Cell Biol.* **23,** 654.

Miller, O. J., Breg, W. R., Warburton, D., Miller, D. A., Firschein, I. L., and Hirschhorn, K. (1966). *Cytogenetics* **5,** 137.

Milyutina, N. A. (1967). *Zh. Obshch. Biol.* **28,** 335.

Mitchell, J. (1966). *Aust. J. Exp. Biol. Med. Sci.* **44,** 225.

Mitchell, J. P. (1967). *Ann. Bot.* **31,** 427.

Mitchison, J. M., and Lark, K. G. (1962). *Exptl. Cell Res.* **28,** 452.

Mitroiu, P., Lang, W. and Maurer, W. (1968). *Z. Zellforschg. Mikroskop. Anat.* **90,** 68.

Monesi, V. (1962). *J. Cell Biol.* **14,** 1.

Monesi, V. (1964). *J. Cell Biol.* **22,** 521.

Monesi, V. (1965a). *Exptl. Cell Res.* **39,** 197.

Monesi, V. (1965b). *Chromosoma* **17,** 11.

Monesi, V., and Crippa, M. (1964). *Z. Zellforsch. Mikroskop. Anat.* **62,** 807.

Monesi, V., Crippa, M., and Zito-Bignami, R. (1967). *Chromosoma* **21,** 369.

Montagna, W., and Hill, C. R. (1957). *Anat. Record* **127,** 163.

Monti, A., Maloney, M. A., and Patt, H. M. (1963). Rept. No. TID–17632. U.S. At. Energy Comm.

Moore, A. C. (1951). *Brit. J. Appl. Phys.* **2,** 20.

Moorhead, P. S., and Defendi, V. (1963). *J. Cell Biol.* **16,** 202.

Morishima, A., Grumbach, M. M., and Taylor, J. H. (1962). *Proc. Natl. Acad. Sci. U.S.* **48,** 756.

Mortreuil-Langlois, M. (1961). *Exptl. Cell Res.* **24,** 46.

Moses, M. J. (1964). *J. Histochem. Cytochem.* **12,** 115.

Moyson, F. (1956). *Rev. Belge Pathol. Med. Exptl.* **25,** 190.

Muckenthaler, F. A. (1964). *Exptl. Cell Res.* **35,** 531.

Müller, D. (1963). *Verhandl. Deut. Ges. Pathol.* **47,** 352.

Müller, D., and Maurer, W. (1965). *Beitr. Pathol. Anat. Allgem. Pathol.* **131,** 121.

Müller, H. G. (1961). *In* "Der Eiweisstoffwechsel der Weiblichen Genitalorgane" (H. Meyer and J. Becker, eds.), Urban & Schwarzenberg, Munich.

Müller, H. G. (1964). *In* "Der Zelleiweisstoffwechsel während der Nidation, Plazentation und Keimentwicklung" (H. Meyer and F. Becker, eds.). Urban & Schwarzenberg, Munich.

Mukherjee, B. B., Burkholder, G. D., Sinha, A. K., and Ghosal, S. K. (1966). *Can. J. Genet. Cytol.* **8,** 631.

Mukherjee, B. B., Sinha, A. K., Mann, K. E., Ghosal, S. K., and Wright, W. C. (1967). *Nature* **214,** 710.

Murray, R. G., and Murray, A. (1964). *Anat. Record* **150,** 95.

Murray, R. G., and Woods, P. A. (1964). *Anat. Record* **150,** 113.

Muth, H. (1959). Sonderausschuss Radioaktivität, Kolloquium über radioactive Partikel, Schriftenreihe des Bundesministers f. Atomkernenergie und Wasserwirtschaft, Heft 12, 173.

Nadler, N. J. (1951). *Can. J. Med. Sci.* **29,** 182.

Nadler, N. J. (1953a). *J. Histochem. Cytochem.* **1,** 377.

Nadler, N. J. (1953b). *Am. J. Roentgenol. Radium Therapy Nucl. Med.* **70,** 814.

Nadler, N. J. (1965). *Symp. Intern. Soc. Cell Biol.* **4,** 303–319.

Nadler, N. J., and Bogoroch, R. (1951). *Anat. Record* **109,** 329.

Nadler, N. J., Leblond, C. P., and Bogoroch, R. (1954). *Endocrinology* **54,** 154.

Nadler, N. J., Leblond, C. P., and Carneiro, J. (1960). *Proc. Soc. Exptl. Biol. Med.* **105,** 38.

Nadler, N. J., Young, B. A., Leblond, C. P., and Mitmaker, B. (1964). *Endocrinology* **74,** 333.

Nagata, I., Sutou, K., Misonou, Y., and Miura, Y. (1965). *Gann* **56,** 59.

Nagata, T., and Nawa, T. (1966). *Histochemie* **7,** 370.

Nakai, T. (1964). *J. Cell Biol.* **21,** 63.

Nakai, T., and Shubik, P. (1964). *J. Invest. Dermatol.* **43,** 267.

Nakamura, R. M., Miyada, D. S., and Moyer, D. L. (1963). *Nature* **199,** 707.

Nandi, S., Poddar, R. K., and Pyne, C. K. (1956). *J. Endocrinol.* **13,** 125.

Narahara, H. T., Everett, N. B., Simmons, B. S., and Williams, R. H. (1958). *Am. J. Pathol.* **192,** 227.

Nass, M. M. K., Nass, S., and Afzelius, B. A. (1965). *Exptl. Cell Res.* **37,** 516.

Natarajan, A. T. (1961). *Exptl. Cell Res.* **22,** 275.

Neubert, D., Helge, H., and Bass, R. (1965). *Arch. Exptl. Pathol. Pharmakol.* **252,** 258.

Neukomm, S., Rivier, J., and Lerch, P. (1954). *Schweiz. Med. Wochschr.* **18,** 512.

Neustein, H. B., and Maunsbach, A. B. (1966). *J. Ultrastruct. Res.* **16,** 141.

Neutra, M., and Leblond, C. P. (1966). *J. Cell Biol.* **30,** 119.

Nevmivaka, G. A. (1964). *In* "A Study of Cell Cycles and Metabolism of Nucleic Acids During Differentiation of the Cells" (L. N. Zhinkin and A. A. Zavarzin, eds.), p. 107. Nauka, Moscow and Leningrad.

Niklas, A., and Maurer, W. (1955). *Hoppe-Seyler/Thierfelder, Handbuch Physiol.-Pathol.-Chem. Analyse* **2,** 734.

Niklas, A., and Oehlert, W. (1956). *Beitr. Pathol. Anat. Allgem. Pathol.* **116,** 92.

Niklas, A., Quincke, E., Maurer, W., and Neyen, H. (1958). *Biochem. Z.* **330,** 1.

Nilsson, A., and Ullberg, S. (1962a). *Acta Radiol.* **58,** 81.

Nilsson, A., and Ullberg, S. (1962b). *Acta Radiol.* **58,** 168.

Nilsson, A., and Ullberg, S. (1962c). *Acta Radiol.* **58,** 275.

Nilsson, G., and Cederlund, J. (1966). *Nature* **212,** 1381.

Noltenius, H., Miyasaki, K., and Oehlert, W. (1962). *Beitr. Pathol. Anat. Allgem. Pathol.* **127,** 232.

Noltenius, H., Kempermann, H., and Oehlert, W. (1964). *Naturwissenschaften* **51,** 63.

Noorduyn, N. J. A., and de Man, J. C. H. (1966). *J. Cell Biol.* **30**, 655.
Norris, W. P., and Woodruff, L. A. (1954). *Ann. Rev. Nucl. Sci.* **5**, 297.
Nougarède, A., and Bronchart, R. (1967). *Compt. Rend. Acad. Sci.* **D264**, 1844.
Novek, J. (1962). *Intern. J. Appl. Radiation Isotopes* **13**, 187.
Nover, A., and Schultze, B. (1960). *Arch. Ophthalmol.* **161**, 554.
Nunez, E. A., Money, W. L., and Becker, D. V. (1966). *Acta Endocrin.* **51**, 369.
Nygaard, O. F., and Potter, R. L. (1959). *Radiation Res.* **10**, 462.
O'Brien, R. T., and George, L. A., II (1959). *Nature* **183**, 1461.
Odeblad, E. (1952). *Acta Radiol. Suppl.* **93**.
Odeblad, E. (1953). *Acta Radiol.* **39**, 192.
Odeblad, E., and Boström, H. (1952). *Acta Pathol. Microbiol. Scand.* **31**, 339.
Odeblad, E., and Boström, H. (1953a). *Acta Pathol. Microbiol. Scand.* **32**, 448.
Odeblad, E., and Boström, H. (1953b). *Acta Chem. Scand.* **7**, 233.
Odeblad, E., and Magnusson, G. (1954). *Acta Endocrinol.* **17**, 290.
Odeblad, E., and Ziliotto, D. (1955). *Acta Radiol.* **44**, 313.
Odeblad, E., Dobson, E. L., Odeblad, A.-M., and Jones, H. B. (1955). *Am. J. Physiol.* **181**, 210.
Oehlert, W. (1959). *Acta Histochem.* **6**, 315.
Oehlert, W. (1961). *Beitr. Pathol. Anat. Allgem. Pathol.* **124**, 311.
Oehlert, W. (1966). *Verhandl. Deut. Ges. Pathol.* **50**, 90.
Oehlert, W. (1968). *In* "Handbuch der allgemeine Pathologie," (F. Büchner, ed.), Vol. II/5, p. 671. Springer, Berlin.
Oehlert, W., and Büchner, T. (1961). *Beitr. Pathol. Anat. Allgem. Pathol.* **125**, 374.
Oehlert, W., and Coté, J. (1961). *Deut. Med. Wochschr.* **86**, 403.
Oehlert, W., and Hartje, J. (1963a). *Naturwissenschaften* **50**, 358.
Oehlert, W., and Hartje, J. (1963b). *Beitr. Pathol. Anat. Allgem. Pathol.* **128**, 376.
Oehlert, W., and Lesch, R. (1965). *European J. Cancer* **1**, 295.
Oehlert, W., and Schultze, B. (1960). *Beitr. Pathol. Anat. Allgem. Pathol.* **123**, 101.
Oehlert, W., and Schultze, B. (1962). *Ann. Histochim.* **7**, Suppl. 2, 111.
Oehlert, W., and von Pein, B. (1963). *Beitr. Pathol. Anat. Allgem. Pathol.* **128**, 300.
Oehlert, W., Schultze, B., and Maurer, W. (1958). *Beitr. Pathol. Anat. Allgem. Pathol.* **119**, 343.
Oehlert, W., Schultze, B., and Maurer, W. (1960). *Beitr. Pathol. Anat. Allgem. Pathol.* **122**, 289.
Oehlert, W., Coté, J., and Büchner, F. (1961). *Beitr. Pathol. Anat. Allgem. Pathol.* **125**, 280.
Oehlert, W., Hämmerling, W., and Büchner, F. (1962a). *Beitr. Pathol. Anat. Allgem. Pathol.* **126**, 91.
Oehlert, W., Seemayer, N., and Lauf, P. (1962b). *Beitr. Pathol. Anat. Allgem. Pathol.* **127**, 63.
Oehlert, W., Nettesheim, P., and Machemer, R. (1962c). *Histochemie* **3**, 99.
Oehlert, W., Lesch, R., and Dörmer, P. (1963a). *Naturwissenschaften* **50**, 713.
Oehlert, W., Dörmer, P., and Lesch, R. (1963b). *Beitr. Pathol. Anat. Allgem. Pathol.* **128**, 468.
Oehlert, W., Karasek, J., and Bertelmann, H. (1966). *Beitr. Pathol. Anat. Allgem. Pathol.* **134**, 395.
Oja, H. K., Oja, S. S., and Hasan, J. (1966). *Exptl. Cell Res.* **45**, 1.
Öktay, M., and Sengün, A. (1963). *Nature* **197**, 613.
Okazaki, R., and Kornberg, A. (1964). *J. Biol. Chem.* **239**, 275.
Olszewska, M. J. (1964). *Exptl. Cell Res.* **33**, 571.

Olszewska, M. J., and Brachet, J. (1960). *Arch. Intern. Physiol. Biochim.* **68,** 693.

Olszewska, M. J., and Brachet, J. (1961). *Exptl. Cell Res.* **22,** 370.

Oppenheimer, E. T., Fishman, M. M., Stout, A. P., Willhite, M., and Danishefsky, I. (1960). *Cancer Res.* **20,** 654.

Ord, M. G., and Stocken, L. A. (1956). *Biochem. J.* **63,** 3.

Osgood, E. E. (1959). *In* "The Kinetics of Cellular Proliferation" (F. Stohlman, ed.), p. 184. Grune & Stratton, New York.

Osmond, D. G., and Everett, N. B. (1964). *Blood* **23,** 1.

Oster, H., Kundt, H.-W., and Taugner, R. (1955). *Arch. Exptl. Pathol. Pharmakol. Naunyn-Schmiedebergs* **224,** 476.

Ostrowski, K., and Sawicki, W. (1961). *Exptl. Cell Res.* **24,** 625.

Ostrowski, K., Komender, J., and Kwarecky, K. (1961). *Experientia* **17,** 183.

Ostrowski, K., Barnard, E. A., Stocka, Z., and Darzynkiewicz, Z. (1963). *Exptl. Cell Res.* **31,** 89.

Ostrowski, K., Barnard, E. A., Darzynkiewicz, Z., and Rymaszewska, D. (1964). *Exptl. Cell Res.* **36,** 43.

Owen, M., Jowsey, J., and Vaughan, J. (1955). *J. Bone Joint Surg.* **37B,** 324.

Owen, M., Sissons, H. A., and Vaughan, J. (1957). *Brit. J. Cancer* **11,** 229.

Painter, R. B., and Drew, R. M. (1959). *Lab. Invest.* **8,** 278.

Painter, R. B., and Rasmussen, R. E. (1964). *Nature* **201,** 162.

Painter, R. B., and Robertson, J. S. (1959). *Radiation Res.* **11,** 206.

Painter, R. B., Drew, R. M., and Hughes, W. L. (1958). *Science* **127,** 1244.

Painter, R. B., Drew, R. M., and Rasmussen, R. E. (1964). *Radiation Res.* **21,** 355.

Palade, G. R., and Caro, L. G., (1964). *Intern. Congr. Cell Biol., 11th, Providence, Rhode Island.*

Pallas, J. E., Jr., and Crafts, A. S. (1957). *Science* **125,** 192.

Pantelouris, E. M. (1958). *Exptl. Cell Res.* **14,** 584.

Parsons, J. A. (1964). *J. Cell Biol.* **23,** 70A.

Parsons, J. A. (1965). *J. Cell Biol.* **25,** 641.

Passalacqua, F. (1953). *Biol. Latina* **6,** 390.

Passalacqua, F. (1954a). *Arch. Ital. Anat. Istol. Patol.* **28,** 269.

Passalacqua, F. (1954b). *Biol. Latina* **7,** 935.

Patel, G., and Wang, T. Y. (1965). *Biochim. Biophys. Acta* **95,** 314.

Patt, H. M., and Maloney, M. A. (1959). *In* "The Kinetics of Cellular Proliferation" (F. Stohlman, ed.), p. 201. Grune & Stratton, New York.

Patt, H. M., and Maloney, M. A. (1963). *In* "Cell Proliferation" (L. F. Lamerton and R. J. M. Fry, eds.), p. 157. Blackwell, Oxford.

Patt, H. M., and Quastler, H. (1963). *Physiol. Rev.* **43,** 357.

Pavlovic, M. R. (1955). *J. Endocrinol.* **12,** 227.

Payne, A. H., Kelly, L. S., and Entenman, C. (1952). *Proc. Soc. Exptl. Biol. Med.* **81,** 698.

Peacock, W. J. (1963). *Proc. Natl. Acad. Sci. U.S.* **49,** 793.

Pecher, C. (1941). *Proc. Soc. Exptl. Biol. Med.* **46,** 86.

Pecher, C. (1942). *Univ. Calif. (Berkeley) Publ. Pharmacol.* **2,** 117.

Pelc, S. R. (1947). *Nature* **160,** 749.

Pelc, S. R. (1956). *Intern. J. Appl. Radiation Isotopes* **1,** 172.

Pelc, S. R. (1957). *Exptl. Cell Res.* **4,** 231.

Pelc, S. R. (1958). *Exptl. Cell Res.* **14,** 301.

Pelc, S. R. (1959). *Lab. Invest.* **8,** 225.

Pelc, S. R. (1962). *Nature* **193,** 793.

Pelc, S. R. (1963a). *In* "Cell Proliferation" (L. F. Lamerton and R. J. M. Fry, eds.), p. 94. Blackwell, Oxford.

Pelc, S. R. (1963b). *Exptl. Cell Res.* **29**, 194.

Pelc, S. R. (1964). *J. Cell Biol.* **22**, 21.

Pelc, S. R. (1967). *Symp. Ges. Histochem., 12th, Gent, Belgium, 1967.*

Pelc, S. R. (1968a). *Acta Histochem* Suppl. **8**, 41.

Pelc, S. R. (1968b). *Nature* **219**, 162.

Pelc, S. R. (1968c). *J. Cell Sci.* **3**, 263.

Pelc, S. R., and Appleton, T. C. (1965). *Nature* **205**, 1287.

Pelc, S. R., and Glücksmann, A. (1955). *Exptl. Cell Res.* **8**, 336.

Pelc, S. R., and Howard, A. (1952). *Brit. Med. Bull.* **8**, 132.

Pelc, S. R., and Howard, A. (1955). *Radiation Res.* **3**, 135.

Pelc, S. R., and Howard, A. (1956). *In* "Progress in Radiobiology" p. 8. Kynoch Press, Birmingham, England.

Pelc, S. R., and La Cour, L. F. (1959). *Experientia* **15**, 131.

Pelc, S. R., Coombes, J. D., and Budd, G. C. (1961). *Exptl. Cell Res.* **24**, 192.

Pellerin, P. (1961). *Pathol. Biol. Semaine Hop.* **9**, 233.

Pelling, C. (1959). *Nature* **184**, 655.

Pelling, C. (1964). *Chromosoma* **15**, 71.

Pentel, L., and Tonna, E. A. (1965). *Lab. Invest.* **14**, 169.

Percival, W. L., and Leblond, C. P. (1948). *Rev. Can. Biol.* **7**, 217.

Perrotta, C. A. (1966). *Radiation Res.* **28**, 232.

Perry, R. P. (1960). *Exptl. Cell Res.* **20**, 216.

Perry, R. P. (1962a). *Congr. Nucl., 6, Rome, 1961.*

Perry, R. P. (1962b). *Proc. Natl. Acad. Sci. U.S.* **48**, 2179.

Perry, R. P. (1963). *Exptl. Cell Res.* **29**, 400.

Perry, R. P. (1964a). *Natl. Cancer Inst. Monograph* **14**, 73.

Perry, R. P. (1964b). *In* "Methods in Cell Physiology" (D. M. Prescott, ed.), Vol. 1, p. 305. Academic Press, New York.

Perry, R. P. (1966). *Natl. Cancer Inst. Monograph* **23**, 527.

Perry, R. P., and Errera, M. (1960). *In* "The Cell Nucleus" (J. S. Mitchell, ed.), p. 24. Butterworth, London and Washington, D.C.

Perry, R. P., Hell, A., and Errera, M. (1961a). *Biochim. Biophys. Acta* **49**, 47.

Perry, R. P., Errera, M., Hell, A., and Dürwald, H. (1961b). *J. Biophys. Biochem. Cytol.* **11**, 1.

Perry, R. P., Srinivasan, P. R., and Kelly, D. E. (1964). *Science* **145**, 504.

Person, S., and Osborn, M. (1964). *Science* **143**, 44.

Peters, T., and Ashley, C. A. (1967). *J. Cell Biol.* **33**, 53.

Petersen, A. J. (1964). *J. Cell Biol.* **23**, 651.

Petersen, R. O., and Baserga, R. (1964). *Arch. Pathol.* **77**, 582.

Pfeiffer, R. A., and Büchner, T. (1964). *Nature* **204**, 804.

Pfeiffer, R. A., Büchner, T., and Scharfenberg, W. (1965). *Klin. Wochschr.* **43**, 521.

Pfeiffer, R. A., Keuth, U., Stupperich, E., and Büchner, T. (1966). *Beitr. Pathol. Anat. Allgem. Pathol.* **133**, 249.

Pflueger, O. H., and Yunis, J. J. (1966). *Exptl. Cell Res.* **44**, 413.

Philipp, K. (1955). *Strahlentherapie, Sonderbaende* **33**, 21.

Phillips, T. L., and Leong, G. F. (1967). *Cancer Res.* **27**, 286.

Pickworth, J. W., Cotton, K., and Skyring, A. P. (1963). *Stain Technol.* **38**, 237.

Pilgrim, C., and Maurer, W. (1962). *Naturwissenschaften* **49**, 544.

Pilgrim, C., and Maurer, W. (1965). *Exptl. Cell Res.* **37**, 183.

Pilgrim, C., Erb, W., and Maurer, W. (1963). *Nature* **199**, 863.

Pilgrim, C., Lennartz, K.-J., Wegener, K., Hollweg, S., and Maurer, W. (1965). *Z. Zellforsch. Mikroskop. Anat.* **68**, 138.

Pilgrim, C., Lang, W., and Maurer, W. (1966). *Exptl. Cell Res.* **44**, 129.

Pinheiro, P., Leblond, C. P., and Droz, B. (1963). *Exptl. Cell Res.* **31**, 517.
Pitt-Rivers, R., and Trotter, W. R. (1953). *Lancet* **265**, 918.
Plaut, W. (1958). *Nature* **182**, 399.
Plaut, W. (1960). *Biochem. Pharmacol.* **4**, 79.
Plaut, W. (1963). *J. Mol. Biol.* **7**, 632.
Plaut, W., and Mazia, D. (1956). *J. Biophys. Biochem. Cytol.* **2**, 573.
Plaut, W., and Mazia, D. (1957). *Texas Rept. Biol. Med.* **15**, 181.
Plaut, W., and Sagan, L. A. (1958). *J. Biophys. Biochem. Cytol.* **4**, 843.
Plentl, A. A., and Schoenheimer, R. (1944). *J. Biol. Chem.* **153**, 203.
Plester, D., Koburg, E., and Hempel, K. (1962). *Ann. Histochim.* 7 *Suppl.* **2**, 91.
Pogo, A. O., Littau, V. C., Allfrey, V. G., and Mirsky, A. E. (1967). *Proc. Natl. Acad. Sci. U.S.* **57**, 743.
Pollister, A. W. (1952). *Exptl. Cell Res. Suppl.* **2**, 59.
Pollister, A. W. (1965). *J. Morphol.* **116**, 89.
Pollister, A. W., and Ris, H. (1947). *Cold Spring Harbor Symp. Quant. Biol.* **12**, 147.
Ponlot, R. (1958). *Arch. Biol. (Liege)* **69**, 441.
Post, J., and Hoffman, J. (1961). *Radiation Res.* **14**, 713.
Post, J., and Hoffman, J. (1964). *J. Cell Biol.* **22**, 341.
Post, J., and Hoffman, J. (1967). *Radiation Res.* **30**, 748.
Post, J., and Hoffman, J. (1968). *Radiation Res.* **34**, 570.
Post, J., Huang, C., and Hoffman, J. (1963). *J. Cell Biol.* **18**, 1.
Potter, R. L., and Nygaard, O. F. (1963). *J. Biol. Chem.* **238**, 2150.
Potter, V. R. (1959). *In* "The Kinetics of Cellular Proliferation" (F. Stohlman, ed.), p. 104. Grune & Stratton, New York and London.
Potter, V. R. (1960). *In* "Nucleic Acid Outlines" (R. H. Burris and H. C. Lichstein, eds.), Vol. 1. Burgess, Minneapolis, Minnesota.
Prensky, W., and Smith, H. H. (1964). *Exptl. Cell Res.* **34**, 525.
Prescott, D. M. (1959). *J. Biophys. Biochem. Cytol.* **6**, 203.
Prescott, D. M. (1960). *Exptl. Cell Res.* **19**, 29.
Prescott, D. M. (1962). *J. Histochem. Cytochem.* **10**, 145.
Prescott, D. M. (1963). *In* "Cell Growth and Cell Division" (R. J. C. Harris, ed.), p. 111. Academic Press, New York.
Prescott, D. M. (1964a). *In* "Methods in Cell Physiology" (D. M. Prescott, ed.), Vol. 1, p. 365. Academic Press, New York.
Prescott, D. M. (1964b). *Natl. Cancer Inst. Monograph* **14**, 57.
Prescott, D. M. (1966). *J. Cell Biol.* **31**, 1.
Prescott, D. M., and Bender, M. A. (1962). *Exptl. Cell Res.* **26**, 260.
Prescott, D. M., and Bender, M. A. (1963a). *Exptl. Cell Res.* **29**, 430.
Prescott, D. M., and Bender, M. A. (1963b). *J. Cellular Comp. Physiol.* **62**, Suppl. 1, 175.
Prescott, D. M., and Kimball, R. F. (1961). *Proc. Natl. Acad. Sci. U.S.* **47**, 686.
Przelecka, A., and Dutkowski, A. (1965). *Bull. Acad. Polon. Sci. Ser. Sci. Biol.* **13**, 573.
Przybylski, R. J. (1961). *Exptl. Cell Res.* **24**, 181.
Puck, T. T. (1964). *Cold Spring Harbor Symp. Quant. Biol.* **29**, 167.
Puck, T. T., and Steffen, J. (1963). *Biophys. J.* **3**, 5.
Puck, T. T., Sanders, P., and Petersen, D. (1964). *Biophys. J.* **4**, 441.
Quastler, H. (1963). *In* "Cell Proliferation" (L. F. Lamerton and R. J. M. Fry, eds.), p. 18. Blackwell, Oxford.
Quastler, H., and Sherman, F. G. (1959). *Exptl. Cell Res.* **17**, 420.
Quay, W. B. (1957). *Stain Technol.* **32**, 175.
Rabinovitch, M., and Plaut, W. (1962a). *J. Cell Biol.* **15**, 525.

Rabinovitch, M., and Plaut, W. (1962b). *J. Cell Biol.* **15**, 535.

Racadot, J., Oliver, L., Porcile, E., and Droz, B. (1965). *Compt. Rend. Acad. Sci.* **D261**, 2972.

Rajewsky, M. F. (1965). *European J. Cancer* **1**, 281.

Rajewsky, M. F. (1966). *Biophysik* **3**, 65.

Ramfjord, S. P., Engler, W. O., and Hiniker, J. J. (1966). *J. Periodontol.* **37**, 179.

Rao, M. V. N., and Prescott, D. M. (1967). *J. Cell Biol.* **33**, 281.

Ray, P. M. (1967). *J. Cell Biol.* **35**, 659.

Ray, R. C., and Stevens, G. W. W. (1953). *Brit. J. Radiol.* **26**, 362.

Rayner, B., Tutt, M., and Vaughan, J. (1953). *Brit. J. Exptl. Pathol.* **34**, 138.

Rechenmann, R. V. (1967a). *Atompraxis* **13**, 30.

Rechenmann, R. V. (1967b). *J. Nucl. Biol. Med.* **11**, 111.

Reich, E., Franklin, R. M., Shatkin, A. J., and Tatum, E. L. (1961). *Science* **134**, 556.

Reichard, P., and Estborn, B. (1951). *J. Biol. Chem.* **188**, 839.

Reichard, P., Canellakis, Z. N., and Canellakis, E. S. (1961). *J. Biol. Chem.* **236**, 2514.

Reinholz, E., Belloch-Zimmermann, V., and Wirth, C. (1960). *Experientia* **16**, 286.

Reiskin, A. B., and Berry, R. J. (1968). *Cancer Res.* **28**, 898.

Reiskin, A. B., and Mendelsohn, M. L. (1962). *Proc. Am. Assoc. Cancer Res.* **3**, 253.

Reiskin, A. B., and Mendelsohn, M. L. (1964). *Cancer Res.* **24**, 1131.

Reiter, J. M., and Littlefield, J. W. (1964). *Biochim. Biophys. Acta* **80**, 562.

Reiter, R. J. (1965). *Lab. Invest.* **14**, 1636.

Reiter, R. J., and Pizzarello, D. J. (1966). *Texas Rept. Biol. Med.* **24**, 189.

Revel, J. P. (1965). *Symp. Intern. Soc. Cell Biol.* **4**, 293.

Revel, J. P., and Hay, E. D. (1961). *Exptl. Cell Res.* **25**, 475.

Revel, J. P., and Hay, E. D. (1963a). *Z. Zellforsch. Mikroskop. Anat.* **61**, 110.

Revel, J. P., and Hay, E. D. (1963b). *Anat. Record* **145**, 367.

Revesz, L., Forssberg, A., and Klein, G. (1956). *J. Natl. Cancer Inst.* **17**, 37.

Rho, J. H., and Bonner, J. (1961). *Proc. Natl. Acad. Sci. U.S.* **47**, 1611.

Rhodes, A., Ford, D., and Rhines, R. (1964). *Exptl. Neurol.* **10**, 251.

Riddiford, L. M. (1960). *J. Exptl. Zool.* **144**, 25.

Rieke, W. O. (1962). *J. Cell Biol.* **13**, 205.

Ris, H., Tolmach, L. J., Lajtha, L. G., Smith, C. L., Das, N. K., and Zeuthen, E. (1963). *J. Cellular Comp. Physiol.* **62**, Suppl. 1, 141.

Robbins, E., and Borun, T. W. (1967). *Proc. Natl. Acad. Sci. U.S.* **57**, 409.

Robertson, J. S., Bond, V. P., and Cronkite, E. P. (1959). *Intern. J. Appl. Radiation Isotopes* **7**, 33.

Robinson, S. H., and Brecher, G. (1963). *Science* **142**, 392.

Robinson, S. H., Brecher, G., Lourie, I. S., and Haley, J. E. (1965). *Blood* **26**, 281.

Roche, J., and Yagi, Y. (1952). *Compt. Rend. Soc. Biol.* **146**, 642.

Rogers, A. W. (1967). *In* "Techniques of Autoradiography" Elsevier, Amsterdam.

Rohr, H. (1965). *Arch. Pathol. Anat. Physiol.* **338**, 342.

Rohr, H. P., Schmalbeck, J., and Feldhege, A. (1967). *Z. Zellforsch. Mikroskop. Anat.* **80**, 183.

Rohr, H., Seutter, U., and Schmalbeck, J. (1968). *Z. Zellforschg. Mikroskop. Anat.* **85**, 376.

Roll, K., and Killmann, S. A. (1965). *Nature* **205**, 1235.

Rose, S., and Nelson, J. (1956). *Australian J. Exptl. Biol. Med. Sci.* **34**, 105.

Ross, R. (1964). *In* "Advances in Biology of Skin. Vol. V: Wound Healing" (W. Montagna and R. E. Billingham, eds.), p. 144. Macmillan (Pergamon), New York.

Ross, R. (1965a). *Symp. Intern. Soc. Cell Biol.* **4**, 273.

Ross, R. (1965b). *Atomlight* **46**, 1.

Ross, R., and Benditt, E. P. (1962). *J. Cell Biol.* **15**, 99.

Ross, R., and Benditt, E. P. (1965). *J. Cell Biol.* **27**, 83.

Rotblat, J., and Ward, G. (1956). *Phys. Med. Biol.* **1**, 125.

Roth, E., Noltenius, H., and Oehlert, W. (1963). *Frankfurter Z. Pathol.* **73**, 40.

Roth, L. J., and Barlow, C. F. (1961). *Science* **134**, 22.

Rotherham, J., and Schneider, W. C. (1958). *J. Biol. Chem.* **232**, 853.

Rothstein, H., Fortin, J., and Sonneborn, D. (1966). *Experientia* **22**, 294.

Rowden, G., and Budd, G. C. (1967). *J. Develop. Dermatol.* **48**, 571.

Rubin, E. (1966). *J. Histochem. Cytochem.* **14**, 688.

Rubin, E., Masuko, K., Goldfarb, S., and Zak, F. G. (1964). *Proc. Soc. Exptl. Biol. Med.* **115**, 381.

Rubini, J. R., Cronkite, E. P., Bond, V. P., and Fliedner, T. M. (1960). *J. Clin. Invest.* **39**, 909.

Rubini, J. R., Cronkite, E. P., Bond, V. P., and Keller, B. S. (1961). *J. Nucl. Med.* **2**, 223.

Rubini, J. R., Keller, S., Eisentraut, A., and Cronkite, E. P. (1962). *Tritium Phys. Biol. Sci., Proc. Symp. Detection Use, Vienna, 1961* **2**, 247.

Rubini, J. R., Westcott, E., and Keller, S. (1966). *J. Lab. Clin. Med.* **68**, 566.

Ruf, F. (1955). *Radioaktive Isotope Klin. Forsch., Strahlentherapie, Sonderbaende* **33**, 212.

Ruf, F., and Philipp, K. (1950). *Umschau* **50**, 539.

Ruf, F., and Philipp, K. (1951). *Med. Monatsschr.* **5**, 248.

Russell, R. S., Sanders, F. K., and Bishop, O. N. (1949). *Nature* **163**, 639.

Sacerdote, M., and Pennisi, F. (1965). *Z. Zellforsch. Mikroskop. Anat.* **68**, 589.

Sado, T., and Makinodan, T. (1964). *J. Immunol.* **93**, 696.

Sakuma, K., and Terayama, H. (1967). *J. Biochem. (Tokyo)* **61**, 504.

Salpeter, M. M. (1967). *J. Cell Biol.* **32**, 379.

Salpeter, M. M., and Bachmann, L. (1964). *J. Cell Biol.* **22**, 469.

Salter, W. T., and Johnston, MacA. W. (1948). *Trans. Assoc. Am. Physicians* **61**, 210.

Sampson, M., and Davies, D. D. (1966). *Life Sci.* **5**, 1239.

Sampson, M., Katoh, A., Hotta, Y., and Stein, H. (1963). *Proc. Natl. Acad. Sci. U.S.* **50**, 459.

Samuels, L. D., and Kisieleski, W. E. (1963). *Radiation Res.* **18**, 620.

Samuels, L. D., Kisieleski, W. E., and Baserga, R. (1964). *Atompraxis* **10**, 144.

Sandborn, E. (1963). *Anat. Record* **145**, 280.

Sander, S., and Attramadal, A. (1968). *Acta Endocrinolog.* **58**, 235.

Sano, Y., Kawamoto, M., and Takahashi, S. (1957). *Arch. Histol. Japon.* **11**, 573.

Savchuck, W. B. (1957). *J. Bone Joint Surg.* **39A**, 140.

Sawicki, W. (1964). *Postepy. Biochem.* **10**, 503.

Sawicki, W., and Pawinska, M. (1965). *Stain Technol.* **40**, 67.

Sawicki, W., Kieler, J., and Briand, P. (1967a). *Intern. J. Cancer* **2**, 153.

Sawicki, W., Kieler, J., and Briand, P. (1967b). *Stain Technol.* **42**, 143.

Schaechter, M., Bentzon, M. W., and Maaloe, O. (1959). *Nature* **183**, 1207.

Schaefer, H. J., and Golden, A. (1955). *Yale J. Biol. Med.* **27**, 432.

Scheer, K. E. (1951). *Fortschr. Gebiete Roentgenstrahlen* **76**, 65.

Scherbaum, O. H. (1960). *Ann. N.Y. Acad. Sci.* **90**, 565.

Scheuermann, W. (1964). *Z. Naturforsch.* **19b**, 434.

Scheving, L. E., and Chiakulas, J. J. (1965). *Exptl. Cell Res.* **39**, 161.

Scheving, L. E., and Pauly, J. E. (1967). *J. Cell Biol.* **32**, 677.

Schmalbeck, J., and Rohr, H. (1967). *Z. Zellforsch. Mikroskop. Anat.* **80**, 329.

Schmid, W. (1963). *Cytogenetics* **2**, 175.

Schmidt, G. (1955). *In* "The Nucleic Acids" (E. Chargaff and J. N. Davidson, eds.), Vol. 1, p. 583. Academic Press, New York.

Schmidt, G., and Thannhäuser, S. J. (1945). *J. Biol. Chem.* **161**, 83.

Schneider, G., and Maurer, W. (1963). *Acta Histochem.* **15**, 171.

Schneider, L. K., and Rieke, W. O. (1967). *J. Cell Biol.* **33**, 497.

Schneider, W. C. (1945). *J. Biol. Chem.* **161**, 293.

Schneider, W. C. (1956). *J. Biol. Chem.* **216**, 287.

Schneider, W. C. (1957). *J. Natl. Cancer Inst.* **18**, 569.

Schneider, W. C., and Brownell, L. W. (1957). *J. Natl. Cancer Inst.* **18**, 579.

Schooley, J. C., Bryant, B. J., and Kelly, L. S. (1959). *In* "The Kinetics of Cellular Proliferation" (F. Stohlman, ed.), p. 208. Grune & Stratton, New York.

Schraub, A., Rajewsky, B., Reinholz, E., Wirth, C., and Belloch-Zimmermann, V. (1960). *Intern. Congr. Radiol., Trans., 9th, Munich, 1959* p. 1269.

Schultze, B. (1968). *In* "Handbuch der allgemeinen Pathologie" (F. Büchner, ed.), Vol. II/5, p. 466, Springer, Berlin.

Schultze, B., and Hughes, W. L. (1965). Radioakt. Isotope Klin. Forsch., Vol. VI, p. 287; Sonderbaende Strahlenbehandlung, Vol. 60.

Schultze, B., and Kleihues, P. (1967). *Experientia* **23**, 941.

Schultze, B., and Maurer, W. (1962). *Tritium Phys. Biol. Sci. Proc. Symp. Detection Use, Vienna, 1961* **2**, 229.

Schultze, B., and Maurer, W. (1963). *Z. Zellforsch. Mikroskop. Anat.* **60**, 387.

Schultze, B., and Maurer, W. (1967). *In* "The Control of Nuclear Activity" (L. Goldstein, ed.), p. 319. Prentice-Hall, Englewood Cliffs, New Jersey.

Schultze, B., and Nover, A. (1959). *Anat. Anz.* **106**, 393.

Schultze, B., and Oehlert, W. (1960). *Science* **131**, 737.

Schultze, B., Oehlert, W., and Maurer, W. (1959). *Beitr. Pathol. Anat. Allgem. Pathol.* **120**, 58.

Schultze, B., Oehlert, W., and Maurer, W. (1960). *Beitr. Pathol. Anat. Allgem. Pathol.* **122**, 406.

Schultze, B., Oehlert, W., and Maurer, W. (1961). *Biochim. Biophys. Acta* **49**, 35.

Schultze, B., Citoler, P., Hempel, K., Citoler, K., and Maurer, W. (1965). *Symp. Intern. Soc. Cell Biol.* **4**, 107.

Schwarz, M. R., and Rieke, W. O. (1963). *Lab. Invest.* **12**, 92.

Schwarzacher, H. G., and Schnedl, W. (1965). *Z. Zellforsch. Mikroskop. Anat.* **67**, 165.

Schweiger, H. G. (1964). *Naturwissenschaften* **51**, 521.

Schweiger, H. G., and Bremer, H. J. (1960). *Exptl. Cell Res.* **20**, 617.

Schweiger, H. G., and Bremer, H. J. (1961). *Biochim. Biophys. Acta* **51**, 50.

Scott, A., and Kalz, F. (1956). *J. Invest. Dermatol.* **26**, 149.

Scott, J. F., and Taft, E. B. (1958). *Biochim. Biophys. Acta* **28**, 45.

Scott, K. G., Axelrod, D. J., Fisher, H., Crowley, J. F., and Hamilton, J. G. (1948a). *J. Biol. Chem.* **176**, 283.

Scott, K. G., Copp, D. H., Axelrod, D. J., and Hamilton, J. G. (1948b). *J. Biol. Chem.* **175**, 691.

Scott, K. G., Axelrod, D. J., Crowley, J. F., and Hamilton, J. G. (1949a). *A.M.A. Arch. Pathol.* **48**, 31.

Scott, K. G., Axelrod, D. J., and Hamilton, J. G. (1949b). *J. Biol. Chem.* **177**, 325.

Scullica, L., Grimes, P., and McElvain, N. (1963). *Arch. Ophthalmol.* **70**, 659.

Seed, J. (1966a). *J. Cell Biol.* **28**, 233.

Seed, J. (1966b). *J. Cell Biol.* **28**, 249.

Seed, J. (1966c). *J. Cell Biol.* **28**, 257.

Seed, J. (1966d). *J. Cell Biol.* **28**, 263.

Sekeris, C. E., Schmid, W., Gallwith, D., and Lukacs, I. (1966). *Life Sci.* **5**, 969.

Shaw, M., and MacLachlan, G. A. (1954). *Nature* **173**, 29.

Sheldon, H., McKenzie, J. M., and van Nimwegan, D. (1964). *J. Cell Biol.* **23**, 200.

Sherman, F. G., and Quastler, H. (1960). *Exptl. Cell Res.* **19**, 343.

Sherman, F. G., Quastler, H., and Wimber, D. R. (1961). *Exptl. Cell Res.* **25**, 114.

Shimotori, N., and Morgan, A. F. (1943). *J. Biol. Chem.* **147**, 201.

Shoup, G. D., Prescott, D. M., and Wykes, J. R. (1966). *J. Cell Biol.* **31**, 295.

Showacre, J. L., Cooper, W. G., and Prescott, D. M. (1967). *J. Cell Biol.* **33**, 273.

Sibatani, A., De Kloet, S. R., Allfrey, V. G., and Mirsky, A. E. (1962). *Proc. Natl. Acad. Sci. U.S.* **48**, 471.

Siegel, E., Graig, F. A., Crystal, M. M., and Siegel, E. P. (1961). *Brit. J. Cancer* **15**, 647.

Sigel, B., Pechet, G., Que, M. Y., and MacDonald, R. A. (1965). *J. Surg. Res.* **5**, 72.

Silk, M. H., Hawtrey, A. O., Spence, I. M., and Gear, J. H. S. (1961). *J. Biophys. Biochem. Cytol.* **10**, 577.

Siminovitch, L., and Graham, A. F. (1956). *Can. J. Microbiol.* **2**, 585.

Simmel, E. B., Fitzgerald, P. J., and Godwin, J. T. (1951). *Stain Technol.* **26**, 25.

Simpson-Herren, L., Blow, J. G., and Brown, P. H. (1968). *Cancer Res.* **28**, 724.

Sims, R. T. (1965). *Quart. J. Microscop. Sci.* **106**, 229.

Sinclair, N. R., and McCarter, J. A. (1964). *Nature* **203**, 521.

Sinclair, W. K., and Morton, R. A. (1966). *Radiation Res.* **29**, 450.

Singer, M., and Salpeter, M. M. (1966a). *Nature* **210**, 1225.

Singer, M., and Salpeter, M. M. (1966b). *J. Morphol.* **120**, 281.

Sirlin, J. L. (1960a). *In* "The Cell Nucleus" (J. S. Mitchell, ed.), p. 35. Butterworth, London and Washington, D.C.

Sirlin, J. L. (1960b). *Exptl. Cell Res.* **19**, 177.

Sirlin, J. L. (1962a). *Progr. Biophys. Biophys. Chem.* **12**, 25.

Sirlin, J. L. (1962b). *Biochem. J.* **85**, 26.

Sirlin, J. L., and Elsdale, T. R. (1959). *Exptl. Cell Res.* **18**, 268.

Sirlin, J. L., and Jacob, J. (1964). *Nature* **204**, 545.

Sirlin, J. L., and Knight, G. R. (1958). *Chromosoma* **9**, 119.

Sirlin, J. L., and Schor, N. A. (1962a). *Exptl. Cell Res.* **27**, 363.

Sirlin, J. L., and Schor, N. A. (1962b). *Exptl. Cell Res.* **27**, 165.

Sirlin, J. L., and Waddington, C. H. (1956). *Exptl. Cell Res.* **11**, 197.

Sirlin, J. L., Jacob, J., and Kato, K.-I. (1962). *Exptl. Cell Res.* **27**, 355.

Sirlin, J. L., Tandler, C. J., and Jacob, J. (1963). *Exptl. Cell Res.* **31**, 611.

Sirlin, J. L., Jacob, J., and Birnstiel, M. L. (1965). *Biochim. Biophys. Acta* **108**, 716.

Sisken, J. E. (1959). *Exptl. Cell Res.* **16**, 602.

Sisken, J. E. (1964). *In* "Methods of Cell Physiology" (D. M. Prescott, ed.), Vol. 1, p. 387. Academic Press, New York.

Sisken, J. E., and Kinosita, R. (1961a). *J. Biophys. Biochem. Cytol.* **9**, 509.

Sisken, J. E., and Kinosita, R. (1961b). *Exptl. Cell Res.* **24**, 168.

Sisken, J. E., and Morasca, L. (1965). *J. Cell Biol.* **25**, 179.

Sisken, J. E., Morasca, L., and Kibby, S. (1965). *Exptl. Cell Res.* **39**, 103.

Sjöstrand, J. (1965a). *Experientia* **21**, 142.

Sjöstrand, J. (1965b). *Z. Zellforsch. Mikroskop. Anat.* **68**, 481.

Sjöstrand, J. (1966). *Acta Physiol. Scand.* 67, *Suppl.* **270.**

Skalko, R. G. (1965). *J. Exptl. Zool.* **160**, 171.

Skougaard, M. R., and Stewart, P. A. (1966). *Exptl. Cell Res.* **45**, 158.

Sky-Peck, H. H., and Hendrickson, F. R. (1962). *Presby.-St. Luke's Hosp. Bull.* **1**, 19.

Smets, L. A. (1966). *Nature* **211**, 527.

Smith, A. H., Reck, D. G., and Luick, J. R. (1957). *Am. J. Physiol.* **190**, 455.

Smith, C. L. (1961). *Proc. Roy. Soc. (London)* **B154**, 557.

Smith, C. L. (1963). *Strahlenschutz Forsch. Praxis* **3**, 15.

Smith, J. R., and Fozzard, H. A. (1963). *Nature* **197**, 562.

Smith, S. H., and Schlegel, D. E. (1964). *Science* **145**, 1058.

Smitherman, T. C., Debons, A. F., Pittman, J. A., and Stephens, V. (1963). *Nature* **198**, 499.

Smoliar, V. (1966). *Intern. J. Radiation Biol.* **11**, 21.

Sognnaes, R. F., and Shaw, H. (1952). *J. Am. Dental Assoc.* **44**, 489.

Sommers, S. C., Geyer, B. S., Geyer, S., and Chute, R. N. (1953). *Proc. Soc. Exptl. Biol. Med.* **84**, 234.

Sonenberg, M., Keston, A. S., and Money, W. L. (1951a). *Endocrinology* **48**, 148.

Sonenberg, M., Money, W. L., Keston, A. S., Fitzgerald, P. J., and Godwin, J. T. (1951b). *Endocrinology* **49**, 709.

Sparvoli, E., Gay, H., and Kaufmann, B. P. (1966). *Caryologia* **19**, 65.

Sporn, M. B., and Dingman, W. (1963). *Biochim. Biophys. Acta* **68**, 387.

Sprey, B. (1967). *Z. Pflanzenphysiol.* **58**, 108.

Srinivasan, B. D. (1964). *Nature* **203**, 100.

Srinivasan, P. R., Miller-Faurès, A., Brunfaut, M., and Errera, M. (1963). *Biochim. Biophys. Acta* **72**, 209.

Stafford, D. W., and Iverson, R. M. (1964). *Science* **143**, 580.

Stanners, C. P., and Till, J. E. (1960). *Biochim. Biophys. Acta* **37**, 406.

Staroscik, R. N., Jenkins, W. H., and Mendelsohn, M. L. (1964). *Nature* **202**, 456.

Steel, G. G. (1962). *Tritium Phys. Biol. Sci. Proc. Symp. Detection Use, Vienna, 1961* **2**, 349.

Steel, G. G. (1966). *Nature* **210**, 806.

Steel, G. G., and Bensted, J. P. M. (1965). *European J. Cancer* **1**, 275.

Steel, G. G., and Lamerton, L. F. (1965). *Exptl. Cell Res* **37**, 117.

Steel, G. G., Adams, K., and Barrett, J. C. (1966). *Brit. J. Cancer* **20**, 784.

Steffensen, D. M., and Bergeron, J. A. (1959). *J. Biophys. Biochem. Cytol.* **6**, 339.

Steffensen, D. M., and Sheridan, W. F. (1965). *J. Cell Biol.* **25**, 619.

Stein, O., and Gross, J. (1963). *Exptl. Cell Res.* **31**, 208.

Stein, O., and Quastler, H. (1964). *Radiation Res.* **21**, 212.

Stein, O., and Stein, Y. (1966a). *Exptl. Cell Res.* **42**, 198.

Stein, O., and Stein, Y. (1966b). *Israel J. Med. Sci.* **2**, 239.

Stein, O., and Stein, Y. (1967). *J. Cell Biol.* **33**, 319.

Stembridge, V. A., Kniseley, R. M., and Gibbs, W. (1953). *Lab. Invest.* **2**, 349.

Stenram, U. (1962a). *Stain Technol.* **37**, 231.

Stenram, U. (1962b). *Exptl. Cell Res.* **26**, 485.

Stenram, U. (1964). *Exptl. Cell Res.* **36**, 242.

Stenram, U., and Hirschman, R. (1965). *Acta Anat.* **61**, 445.

Stenram, U., and Willén, R. (1966). *Cancer Res.* **26**, 765.

Sterling, C., and Chichester, C. O. (1956). *Stain Technol.* **31**, 227.

Stevens, G. W. W. (1948). *Nature* **161**, 432.

Stevens, G. W. W. (1950). *Brit. J. Radiol.* **23**, 723.

Stewart, P. A., Quastler, H., Skougaard, M. R., Wimber, D. R., Wolfsberg, M. F., Perrotta, C. A., Ferbel, B., and Carlough, M. (1965). *Radiation Res.* **24**, 521.

Stillström, J. (1963). *Intern. J. Appl. Radiation Isotopes* **14**, 113.

Stillström, J. (1965). *Intern. J. Appl. Radiation Isotopes* **16**, 357.

Stirling, C. E., and Kinter, W. B. (1967). *J. Cell Biol.* **35**, 585.

Stocking, C. R., and Gifford, E. M. (1959). *Biochem. Biophys. Res. Commum.* **1**, 159.

Stöcker, E. (1962a). *Z. Zellforsch. Mikroskop. Anat.* **57**, 145.

Stöcker, E. (1962b). *Verhandl. Deut. Ges. Pathol.* **46**, 330.

Stöcker, E. (1962c). *Z. Zellforsch. Mikroskop. Anat.* **57**, 47.

Stöcker, E. (1963a). *Naturwissenschaften* **50**, 130.

Stöcker, E. (1963b). *Naturwissenschaften* **50**, 44.

Stöcker, E. (1963c). *Z. Zellforsch. Mikroskop. Anat.* **58**, 790.

Stöcker, E. (1964a). *Z. Zellforsch. Mikroskop. Anat.* **62**, 80.

Stöcker, E. (1964b). *Beitr. Pathol. Anat. Allgem. Pathol.* **129**, 247.

Stöcker, E. (1966a). *Fortschr. Med.* **84**, 202.

Stöcker, E. (1966b). *Verhandl. Deut. Ges. Pathol.* **50**, 53.

Stöcker, E., and Altmann, H.-W. (1963). *Z. Krebsforsch.* **65**, 351.

Stöcker, E., and Altmann, H.-W. (1964). *Naturwissenschaften* **51**, 15.

Stöcker, E., and Bach, G. (1965). *Naturwissenschaften* **52**, 264.

Stöcker, E., and Heine, W.-D. (1965a). *Naturwissenschaften* **52**, 212.

Stöcker, E., and Heine, W.-D. (1965b). *Beitr. Pathol. Anat. Allgem. Pathol.* **131**, 410.

Stöcker, E., and Pfeifer, U. (1965). *Naturwissenschaften* **52**, 663.

Stöcker, E., and Pfeifer, U. (1967). *Z. Zellforsch. Mikroskop. Anat.* **79**, 374.

Stöcker, E., Maurer, W., and Altmann, H.-W. (1961a). *Klin. Wochschr.* **39**, 926.

Stöcker, E., Maurer, W., and Altmann, H.-W. (1961b). *Naturwissenschaften* **48**, 582.

Stöcker, E., Teubner, E., and Rosenbusch, G. (1964a). *Verhandl. Deut. Ges. Pathol.* **48**, 295.

Stöcker, E., Cain, H., and Heine, W.-D. (1964b). *Naturwissenschaften* **51**, 195.

Stöcker, E., Kabus, K., and Dhom, G. (1965a). *Z. Zellforsch. Mikroskop. Anat.* **65**, 206.

Stöcker, E., Hauswaldt, C., and Klinge, O. (1965b). *Experientia* **21**, 511.

Stöcker, E., Hauswaldt, C., and Klinge, O. (1966a). *Beitr. Pathol. Anat. Allgem. Pathol.* **133**, 1.

Stöcker, E., Höper, V., Plato, S., and Heine, W.-D. (1966b). *Klin. Wochschr.* **44**, 657.

Stöcker, E., Altmann, H.-W., and Bödefeld, P. (1967). *Naturwissenschaften* **54**, 371.

Stone, G. E., and Miller, O. L. (1964). *J. Cell Biol.* **23**, 89A.

Stone, G. E., and Miller, O. L. (1965). *J. Exptl. Zool.* **159**, 33.

Stone, G. E., and Prescott, D. M. (1965). *Symp. Intern. Soc. Cell Biol.* **4**, 95.

Stone, G. E., Prescott, D. M., and Miller, O. L. (1964). *J. Protozool.* **11**, Suppl., 24.

Stone, G. E., Miller, O. L., and Prescott, D. M. (1965). *J. Cell Biol.* **25**, 171.

Stowell, R. E. (1946). *Stain Technol.* **21**, 137.

Stowell, R. E., and Zorzoli, A. (1947). *Stain Technol.* **22**, 51.

Stryckmans, P., Ramos, J., Fliedner, T. M., and Cronkite, E. P. (1964). *Blood* **24**, 851.

Stryckmans, P., Cronkite, E. P., and Fliedner, T. M. (1966). *Schweiz. Med. Wochschr.* **96**, 1278.

Stuart, A. E. (1955). *Australian J. Exptl. Biol. Med. Sci.* **33**, 429.

Stubblefield, E. (1965). *J. Cell Biol.* **25**, 137.

Stumpf, W. E. (1967). *Proc. Oak Ridge Sympos. Med.*, AEG Symp. Ser. No. 13, CONF No. 671111.

Stumpf, W. E., and Lester, R. (1966). *Lab. Invest.* **15**, 1156.

Stumpf, W. E., and Roth, L. J. (1964). *Stain Technol.* **39**, 219.

Stumpf, W. E., and Roth, L. J. (1965a). *Nature* **205**, 712.

Stumpf, W. E., and Roth, L. J. (1965b). *Cryobiology* **1**, 227.

Stumpf, W. E., and Roth, L. J. (1966). *J. Histochem. Cytochem.* **14**, 274.

Stumpf, W. E., and Roth, L. J. (1967). *J. Histochem. Cytochem.* **15**, 243.

Stumpf, W. E., and Roth, L. J. (1968). *Advan. Tracer Methodology* **4**, 113.

Suckow, E. E., Honeger, G. C., and Baserga, R. (1961). *Am. J. Pathol.* **38**, 663.

Sugino, Y., Frenkel, E. P., and Potter, R. L. (1963). *Radiation Res.* **19,** 682.

Suit, H. D., Lajtha, L. G., Oliver, R., and Ellis, F. (1957). *Brit. J. Haematol.* **3,** 165.

Sutter, R. P., Whitman, S. L., and Webster, G. (1961). *Biochim. Biophys. Acta* **49,** 233.

Swartzendruber, D. C., and Hanna, M. G. (1965). *J. Cell Biol.* **25,** 109.

Swierstra, E. E., and Foote, R. H. (1965). *Am. J. Anat.* **116,** 401.

Szollosi, D. (1966). *Anat. Record* **154,** 209.

Taft, P. D., and Brooks, S. E. H. (1963). *Lancet* 1069.

Takats, S. T. (1960). *Proc. 10th Intern. Congr. Cell Biol.* p. 13.

Takats, S. T., and Smellie, R. M. S. (1963). *J. Cell Biol.* **17,** 59.

Tannenbaum, A., Silverstone, H., and Koziol, J. (1951). *In* "Toxicology of Uranium" (A. Tannenbaum, ed.), p. 128. McGraw-Hill, New York.

Tanzer, M. L., and Hunt, R. D. (1964). *J. Cell Biol.* **22,** 623.

Taugner, R., and Wagenmann, U. (1958). *Arch. Exptl. Pathol. Pharmakol.* **234,** 336.

Taugner, R., Hole, H., Grigoleit, G., and Wagenmann, U. (1958). *Arch. Exptl. Pathol. Pharmakol.* **234,** 330.

Taxi, J., and Droz, B. (1966a). *Compt. Rend. Acad. Sci.* **D263,** 1237.

Taxi, J., and Droz, B. (1966b). *Compt. Rend. Acad. Sci.* **D263,** 1326.

Taylor, A. C., and Weiss, P. (1965). *Proc. Natl. Acad. Sci. U.S.* **54,** 1521.

Taylor, J. H. (1953). *Science* **118,** 555.

Taylor, J. H. (1956). *In* "Physical Techniques in Biological Research" (G. Oster and A. W. Pollister, eds.), Vol. 3, p. 545. Academic Press, New York.

Taylor, J. H. (1958a). *Exptl. Cell Res.* **15,** 350.

Taylor, J. H. (1958b). *Am. J. Botany* **45,** 123.

Taylor, J. H. (1959). *Am. J. Botany* **46,** 477.

Taylor, J. H. (1960a). *In* "Cell Physiology of Neoplasma" p. 547. Univ. of Texas Press, Austin, Texas.

Taylor, J. H. (1960b). *Ann. N. Y. Acad. Sci.* **90,** 409.

Taylor, J. H. (1960c). *Advan. Biol. Med. Phys.* **7,** 107.

Taylor, J. H. (1960d). *J. Biophys. Biochem. Cytol.* **7,** 455.

Taylor, J. H. (1961). Conference on Molecular and Radiation Biology. *Natl. Acad. Sci.—Natl. Res. Council, Publ.* **823,** 12.

Taylor, J. H. (1962a). *In* "Tritium in the Physical and Biological Sciences," IAEA, Vienna, Vol. II, p. 221.

Taylor, J. H. (1962b). *Intern. Rev. Cytol.* **13,** 39.

Taylor, J. H. (1963a). *Symp. Intern. Soc. Cell Biol.* **2,** 161.

Taylor, J. H. (1963b). *J. Cellular Comp. Physiol. Suppl.* **1,** 62, No. 2, 73.

Taylor, J. H. (1963c). *In* "Molecular Genetics" (J. H. Taylor, ed.), Pt. 1, p. 65. Academic Press, New York.

Taylor, J. H. (1963d). *Exptl. Cell Res. Suppl.* **9,** 99.

Taylor, J. H. (1964a). *J. Cell Biol.* **21,** 286.

Taylor, J. H. (1964b). *Symp. Intern. Soc. Cell Biol.* **3.**

Taylor, J. H. (1965). *J. Cell Biol.* **25,** 57.

Taylor, J. H., and McMaster, R. D. (1954). *Chromosoma* **6,** 489.

Taylor, J. H., and McMaster, R. D. (1955). *Genetics* **40,** 600.

Taylor, J. H., and Taylor, S. H. (1953). *J. Heredity* **44,** 128.

Taylor, J. H., Woods, P. S., and Hughes, W. L. (1957). *Proc. Natl. Acad. Sci. U.S.* **43,** 122.

Taylor, J. H., Haut, W. F., and Tung, J. (1962). *Proc. Natl. Acad. Sci. U.S.* **48,** 190.

Tencer, R. (1958). *J. Embryol. Exptl. Morphol.* **6,** 117.

Tencer, R., and Brachet, J. (1958). *Arch. Intern. Physiol. Biochim.* **66,** 443.

Teranishi, N. (1957). *Kyoto Furitsu Ika Daigaku Zasshi* **61,** 67.

Terasima, T. (1964). J. Genet. **40**, 162.

Terasima, T., and Tolmach, L. J. (1961). Nature **190**, 1210.

Terasima, T., and Tolmach, L. J. (1963a). Science **140**, 490.

Terasima, T., and Tolmach, L. J. (1963b). Biophys. J. **3**, 11.

Terasima, T., and Tolmach, L. J. (1963c). Exptl. Cell Res. **30**, 344.

Terasima, T., and Yasukawa, M. (1966). Exptl. Cell Res. **44**, 669.

Terskikh, V. V. (1965). Izv. Akad. Nauk SSSR **5**, 776.

Thomson, D. S., Pirie, A., and Overall, M. (1962). Arch. Ophthalmol. **67**, 464.

Thrasher, J. D. (1967). Anat. Record **157**, 621.

Thrasher, J. D., and Greulich, R. C. (1965). J. Exptl. Zool. **159**, 39.

Thrasher, J. D., Clark, F. I., and Clarke, D. R. (1966). Exptl. Cell Res. **45**, 232.

Thurston, J. M., and Joftes, D. L. (1963). Stain Technol. **38**, 231.

Tiepolo, L., Fraccaro, M., Hultin, M., Lindsten, J., Mannini, A., and Ming, P.-M. (1967). Cytogenetics **6**, 51.

Till, J. E. (1961). Ann. N. Y. Acad. Sci. **95**, 911.

Till, J. E., Whitmore, G. F., and Gulyas, S. (1963). Biochim. Biophys. Acta **72**, 277.

Tischendorf, F., and Linnartz-Niklas, A. (1958a). Anat. Anz. **105**, 400.

Tischendorf, F., and Linnartz-Niklas, A. (1958b). Experientia **14**, 379.

Tischendorf, F., and Linnartz-Niklas, A. (1961). Biochim. Biol. Sper. **1**, 258.

Tischendorf, F., and Linnartz-Niklas, A. (1962). Acta Anat. **48**, 7.

Titus, J. L., and Shorter, R. G. (1965). Arch. Pathol. **79**, 324.

Tixier-Vidal, A., Fiske, S., Picart, R., and Haguenau, P. (1965). Compt. Rend. Acad. Sci. **261**, 1133.

Toledo, J.-D. (1965). Beitr. Pathol. Anat. Allgem. Pathol. **131**, 63.

Toliver, A., and Simon, E. H. (1967). Exp. Cell Res. **45**, 603.

Tolles, W. E. (1959). Lab. Invest. **8**, 99.

Tolmach, L. J. (1961). Ann. N. Y. Acad. Sci. **95**, 743.

Tolmach, L. J. (1963). J. Cellular Comp. Physiol. **62**, Suppl. 1, 141.

Tolnai, S. (1965). Lab. Invest. **14**, 701.

Tomlin, D. H., Henry, K. M., and Kon, S. K. (1952). J. Anat. **86**, 475.

Tomlin, D. H., Henry, K. M., and Kon, S. K. (1953). Brit. J. Nutr. **7**, 235.

Tomlin, D. H., Henry, K. M., and Kon, S. K. (1955). Brit. J. Nutr. **9**, 144.

Tonna, E. A. (1960a). Anat. Record **136**, 292.

Tonna, E. A. (1960b). Anat. Record **137**, 251.

Tonna, E. A. (1961). J. Gerontol. **16**, 392.

Tonna, E. A. (1962). Nature **193**, 1301.

Tonna, E. A. (1964a). Lab. Invest. **13**, 1238.

Tonna, E. A. (1964b). J. Gerontol. **19**, 198.

Tonna, E. A. (1965). Symp. Intern. Soc. Cell Biol. **4**, 215.

Tonna, E. A., and Cronkite, E. P. (1958). Stain Technol. **33**, 255.

Tonna, E. A., and Cronkite, E. P. (1959). J. Biophys. Biochem. Cytol. **6**, 171.

Tonna, E. A., and Cronkite, E. P. (1960). J. Gerontol. **15**, 377.

Tonna, E. A., and Cronkite, E. P. (1962a). J. Gerontol. **17**, 353.

Tonna, E. A., and Cronkite, E. P. (1962b). J. Bone Joint Surg. **44A**, 1557.

Tonna, E. A., and Pentel, L. (1967). Arch. Oral Biol. **12**, 183.

Tonna, E. A., Cronkite, E. P., and Pavelec, M. (1962). J. Histochem. Cytochem. **10**, 601.

Tonna, E. A., Cronkite, E. P., and Pavelec, M. (1963a). J. Histochem. Cytochem. **11**, 720.

Tonna, E. A., Brecher, G., Cronkite, E. P., and Schwartz, I. L. (1963b). Arch. Rheumatism **6**, 1.

Torelli, U., Grossi, G., Artusi, T., and Emilia, G. (1963). Acta Haematol. **30**, 129.

Torelli, U., Grossi, G., Artusi, T., Emilia, G., Attiya, I. R., and Mauri, C. (1964). *Acta Haematol.* **32,** 271.

Torelli, U., Artusi, T., Grossi, G., Emilia, G., and Mauri, C. (1965). *Nature* **207,** 755.

Toto, P. D., and Dhawan, A. S. (1966). *J. Dental Res.* **45,** 948.

Toto, P. D., and Ojha, G. (1962). *J. Dental Res.* **41,** 388.

Trelstad, R. L. (1965). *Exptl. Cell Res.* **39,** 318.

Trepel, F., Rastetter, J., Theml, H., and Stockhusen, G. (1966). *Med. Klin. (Munich)* **61,** 618.

Trip, P., and Gotham, P. R. (1967). *Canad. J. Bot.* **45,** 1567.

Tschermak-Woess, E. (1960). *Chromosoma* **11,** 25.

Tzschaschel, R. (1958a). *Atompraxis* **4,** 49.

Tzschaschel, R. (1958b). *Atompraxis* **4,** 265.

Tzschaschel, R. (1959). *Atompraxis* **5,** 224.

Ullberg, S., and Söremark, R. (1961). *Gastroenterology* **40,** 109.

Ulrich, F., Reinhardt, W. O., and Li, C. H. (1951a). *Endocrinology* **49,** 213.

Ulrich, F., Copp, D. H., Asling, C. W., Li, C. H., and Reinhardt, W. O. (1951b). *Endocrinology* **48,** 245.

Upton, A. C., and Odell, T. T. (1956). *A. M. A. Arch. Pathol.* **62,** 194.

Utakoji, T., and Hsu, T. C. (1965). *Cytogenetics* **4,** 295.

Van den Broek, C. J. H., and Tates, A. D. (1961). *Exptl. Cell Res.* **24,** 201.

Van Heyningen, H. (1964). *Anat. Record* **148,** 485.

Van Heyningen, H. (1965). *Symp. Intern. Soc. Cell Biol.* **4,** 261.

Van Middlesworth, L. (1947). *U.S. At. Energy Comm.* **MDDC. 1022.**

Van't Hof, J. (1963). *Cytologia (Tokyo)* **28,** 30.

Van't Hof, J. (1965). *Exptl. Cell Res.* **39,** 48.

Van't Hof, J. (1966). *Am. J. Botany* **53,** 246.

Van't Hof, J. (1967). *Exptl. Cell Res.* **46,** 335.

Van't Hof, J. (1968). *Exptl. Cell Res.* **51,** 167.

Van't Hof, J., and Sparrow, A. H. (1963a). *Proc. Natl. Acad. Sci. U.S.* **49,** 897.

Van't Hof, J., and Sparrow, A. H. (1963b). *Radiation Botany* **3,** 239.

Van't Hof, J., and Sparrow, A. H. (1965). *J. Cell Biol.* **26,** 187.

Van't Hof, J., Wilson, G. B., and Colon, A. (1960). *Chromosoma* **11,** 313.

Van Tubergen, R. P. (1961). *J. Biophys. Biochem. Cytol.* **9,** 219.

Varga, L., and Varteresz, V. (1968). *Acta Biochim. Biophys. Acad. Sci. Hung.* **3,** 217.

Vasiliev, J. M. (1967). *Tsitologiya* **9,** 1121.

Veenema, R. J., Fingerhut, B., and Girgis, A. S. (1963). *J. Urol.* **90,** 736.

Vendrely, C., Tournier, P., Wicker, R., Grange, M. T., and Kasten, F. (1964). *Bull. Cancer* **51,** 447.

Verly, W. G., and Hunebelle, G. (1957). *Bull. Soc. Chim. Belges* **66,** 640.

Verly, W. G., Firket, H., and Hunebelle, G. (1958a). *Proc. Intern. Conf. Peaceful Uses At. Energy, Geneva* 2nd Unit, **25,** 181.

Verly, W. G., Hunebelle, G., and Firket, H. (1958b). *Arch. Intern. Physiol. Biochim.* **66,** 130.

Veselý, J., (1963). *Neoplasma* **10,** 483.

Vincent, W. S. (1954). *Biol. Bull.* **107,** 325.

Vincent, W. S. (1955a). *Biol. Bull.* **109,** 353.

Vincent, W. S. (1955b). *Intern. Rev. Cytol.* **4,** 269.

Vincent, W. S. (1957a). *Science* **126,** 306.

Vincent, W. S. (1957b). *In* "The Beginnings of Embryonic Development" (A. Tyler, R. V. Borstel, and C. B. Metz, eds.). Publ. No. 48, p. 1. *Am. Assoc. Advance. Sci.*, Washington, D. C.

Vincent, W. S., and Baltus, E. (1960). *Biol. Bull.* **119,** 299.

Vorbrodt, A. (1962). *Bull. Acad. Polon. Sci. Ser. Sci. Biol.* **10,** 111.

Waddington, C. H., and Sirlin, J. L. (1959). *Exptl. Cell Res.* **17,** 582.

Wagner, H. P., Cottier, H., Cronkite, E. P., Cunningham, L., Jansen, C. R., and Rai, K. R. (1967). *Exptl. Cell Res.* **46,** 441.

Wainson, A. A., and Kuzin, A. M. (1965). *Dokl. Akad. Nauk SSSR, Otd. Biophys.* **165,** 933.

Wainwright, W. W., Anderson, E. C., Hammer, P. C., and Lehman, C. A. (1954). *Nucleonics* **12,** No. 1, 19–21.

Walker, B. E. (1959). *Texas Rept. Biol. Med.* **17,** 375.

Walker, B. E., and Leblond, C. P. (1958). *Exptl. Cell Res.* **14,** 510.

Walker, P. M. B., and Yates, H. B. (1952). *Proc. Roy. Soc. (London)* **B140,** 274.

Warner, G. F., and Dobson, E. L. (1954). *Am. J. Physiol.* **179,** 93.

Warren, S., and Dixon, F. J. (1948). *Am. J. Med. Sci.* **216,** 136.

Warshawsky, H., and Leblond, C. P. (1961). *Anat. Record* **139,** 284.

Warshawsky, H., Leblond, C. P., and Droz, B. (1963). *J. Cell Biol.* **16,** 1.

Waser, P. G. (1958). *Helv. Physiol. Acta* **16,** 171.

Waser, P. G., and Lüthi, U. (1956). *Nature* **178,** 981.

Waser, P. G., and Lüthi, U. (1957). *Arch. Intern. Pharmacodyn.* **112,** 272.

Wasserman, R. H., and Bélanger, L. F. (1961). *J. Histochem. Cytochem.* **9,** 452.

Wegener, K., Hollweg, S., and Maurer, W. (1964). *Z. Zellforsch. Mikroskop. Anat.* **63,** 309.

Weiss, P. (1967). *Proc. Natl. Acad. Sci. U.S.* **57,** 1239.

Weiss, P., and Holland, Y. (1967). *Proc. Natl. Acad. Sci. U.S.* **57,** 258.

Weissman, S. M., Smellie, R. M. S., and Paul, J. (1960). *Biochim. Biophys. Acta* **45,** 101.

Welling, W., Bootsma, D., Van Muiswinkel, E., and Berghegen, C. A. P. (1965). *Biochim. Biophys. Acta* **95,** 262.

Wellings, S. R., and Philp, J. R. (1964). *Z. Zellforsch. Mikroskop. Anat.* **61,** 871.

Werner, G., Werner, H., Bosque, P. G., and Quevedo, J. C. (1966). *Z. Naturforsch.* **21b,** 238.

Whang-Peng, J., Tjio, J. H., and Cason, J. C. (1967). *Proc. Soc. Exptl. Biol. Med.* **125,** 260.

Wheeler, B. M. (1947). *Proc. Natl. Acad. Sci. U.S.* **33,** 298.

Wheeler, G. P., Bowdon, B. J., Wilkoff, L. J., and Dulmadge, E. A. (1967). *Proc. Soc. Exp. Biol. Med.* **126,** 903.

Whitmore, G. F., Stanners, C. P., Till, J. E., and Gulyas, S. (1961). *Biochim. Biophys. Acta* **47,** 66.

Whitmore, G. F., Till, J. E., and Gulyas, S. (1967). *Radiation Res.* **30,** 155.

Whittle, E. D. (1966). *Biochim. Biophys. Acta* **114,** 44.

Wilkinson, G. W., and Leblond, C. P. (1953). *Surg. Gynecol. Obstet.* **97,** 143.

Williams, A. I. (1951). *Nucleonics* **8,** No. 6, 10.

Williamson, M. B., and Guschlbauer, W. (1963). *Arch. Biochem. Biophys.* **100,** 245.

Wilske, K. R., and Ross, R. (1965). *J. Histochem. Cytochem.* **13,** 38.

Wilson, W. L., Harding, C. V., and Wilson, J. R. (1967). *Exp. Eye Res.* **6,** 343.

Wimber, D. E. (1959). *Proc. 9th Intern. Botan. Congr.* **2,** 432.

Wimber, D. E. (1960). *Amer. J. Botany* **47,** 828.

Wimber, D. E. (1963). *In* "Cell Proliferation" (L. F. Lamerton and R. J. M. Fry, eds.), p. 1. Blackwell, Oxford.

Wimber, D. E. (1966a). *Am. J. Botany* **53**, 21.

Wimber, D. E. (1966b). *Exptl. Cell Res.* **42**, 296.

Wimber, D. E., and Lamerton, L. F. (1963). *Radiation Res.* **18**, 137.

Wimber, D. E., and Lamerton, L. F. (1965). *Nature* **207**, 432.

Wimber, D. E., and Lamerton, L. F. (1966). *Radiation Res.* **28**, 694.

Wimber, D. E., and Quastler, H. (1963). *Exptl. Cell Res.* **30**, 8.

Wimber, D. E., Quastler, H., Stein, O. L., and Wimber, D. R. (1960). *J. Biochem. Biophys. Cytol.* **8**, 327.

Winteringham, F. P. W., Harrison, A., and Hammond, J. H. (1950). *Nature* **165**, 149.

Witten, V. H., and Sulzberger, M. B. (1955). *Am. J. Roentgenol. Radium Therapy Nucl. Med.* **74**, 90.

Wolberg, W. H., and Brown, R. R. (1962). *Cancer Res.* **22**, 1113.

Wolfart, W. (1964). *Beitr. Pathol. Anat. Allgem. Pathol.* **129**, 436.

Wolfe, H. J., and Vickery, A. L. (1964). *Lab. Invest.* **13**, 743.

Wolfsberg, M. F. (1964). *Exptl. Cell Res.* **35**, 119.

Wollgiehn, R., and Mothes, K. (1963). *Naturwissenschaften* **50**, 95.

Wollgiehn, R., and Mothes, K. (1964). *Exptl. Cell Res.* **35**, 52.

Wolstenholme, D. R. (1966). *Chromosoma* **19**, 449.

Wolstenholme, D. R., and Plaut, W. (1964). *J. Cell Biol.* **22**, 505.

Woodard, J., Rasch, E., and Swift, H. (1961). *J. Biophys. Biochem. Cytol.* **9**, 445.

Woods, P. S. (1957). *J. Biophys. Biochem. Cytol.* **3**, 71.

Woods, P. S. (1959). *Brookhaven Symp. Biol.* **12**, 153.

Woods, P. S. (1962). *Tritium Phys. Biol. Sci., Proc. Symp. Detection Use, Vienna, 1961* **2**, 335.

Woods, P. S., and Schairer, M. U. (1959). *Nature* **183**, 303.

Woods, P. S., and Taylor, J. H. (1959). *Lab. Invest.* **8**, 309.

Woods, P. S., and Zubay, G. (1965). *Proc. Natl. Acad. Sci. U.S.* **54**, 1705.

Wrba, H., Rabes, H., and Brändle, H. (1964). *Naturwissenschaften* **51**, 42.

Yagoda, H. (1955). *Rev. Sci. Instr.* **26**, 263.

Yamada, T., and Takata, C., (1963). *Develop. Biol.* **8**, 358.

Yang, S.-J., Hahn, G. M., and Bagshaw, M. A. (1966). *Exptl. Cell Res.* **42**, 130.

Yankee, R. A., De Vita, V. T., and Perry, S. (1967). *Cancer Res.* **27**, 2381.

Yoon, C. H., and Sabo, J. (1964). *Exptl. Cell Res.* **34**, 599.

Young, B. A., and Kopriwa, B. M. (1964). *J. Histochem. Cytochem.* **12**, 438.

Young, R. W. (1962a). *Anat. Record* **142**, 335.

Young, R. W. (1962b). *Anat. Record* **143**, 1.

Young, R. W. (1962c). *J. Bone Joint Surg.* **44A**, 1025.

Young, R. W. (1962d). *Exptl. Cell Res.* **26**, 562.

Young, R. W. (1963). *Clin. Orthopaed.* **26**, 147.

Zadjela, F., and Moreno, G. (1963). *Nouvelle Rev. Franc. Hematol.* **3**, 65.

Zajicek, G., Bernstein, N., Rosin, A., and Gross, J. (1963). *Exptl. Cell Res.* **31**, 390.

Zalik, S. E., and Yamada, T. (1967). *J. Exp. Zool.* **165**, 385.

Zalkind, S. Y., Poberiy, I. A., and Deryabina, I. S. (1965). *Zh. Obshch. Biol.* **26**, 113.

Zalokar, M. (1959). *Nature* **183**, 1330.

Zalokar, M. (1960a). *Exptl. Cell Res.* **19**, 559.

Zalokar, M. (1960b). *Exptl. Cell Res.* **19**, 184.

Zavarzin, A. A. (1964). *In* "A Study of Cell Cycles and Metabolism of Nucleic Acids During Differentiation of the Cells" (L. N. Zhinkin and A. A. Zavarzin, eds.), p. 37. Nauka, Moscow and Leningrad.

272   REFERENCES

Zavarzin, A. A. (1967). *Tsitologiya* **9**, 1072.
Zavarzin, A. A., and Lebedeva, G. S. (1964). *In* "A Study of Cell Cycles and Metabolism of Nucleic Acids During Differentiation of the Cells" (L. N. Zhinkin and A. A. Zavarzin, eds.), p. 126. Nauka, Moscow and Leningrad.
Zavarzin, A. A., and Stroeva, O. G. (1964). *In* "A Study of Cell Cycles and Metabolism of Nucleic Acids During Differentiation of the Cells" (L. N. Zhinkin and A. A. Zavarzin, eds.), p. 116. Nauka, Moscow and Leningrad.
Zavarzin, A. A., Orlova, G. N., and Zhorno, L. J. (1964). *In* "A Study of Cell Cycles and Metabolism of Nucleic Acids During Differentiation of the Cells" (L. N. Zhinkin and A. A. Zavarzin, eds.), p. 51. Nauka, Moscow and Leningrad.
Zavarzin, A. A., Samoshkina, N. A., and Dondua, A. K. (1966). *Zh. Obshch. Biol.* **27**, 697.
Zetterberg, A. (1966). *Exptl. Cell Res.* **42**, 500.
Zetterberg, A., and Killander, D. (1965a). *Exptl. Cell Res.* **39**, 22.
Zetterberg, A., and Killander, D. (1965b). *Exptl. Cell Res.* **40**, 1.
Zhdanov, V. M., Klisenko, G. A., Stakhanova, V. M., and Zhantieva, Y. M. (1964). *Nature* **202**, 1028.
Zhinkin, L. N. (1966). *Arch. Anat. Histol. Embrhol.* **50**, 9.
Zhinkin, L. N., and Andreeva, L. F. (1963). *J. Embryol. Exptl. Morphol.* **11**, 353.
Ziliotto, D., and Odeblad, E. (1955). *Acta Med. Patavina* **15**, 207.

ADDITIONAL REFERENCES

Mendelsohn, M. L., Dohan, F. C., and Moore, N. A. (1960). *J. Nat. Cancer Inst.* **25**, 477.
Meneghelli, V. (1960). *Acta Anat.* **43**, 231.
Merriam, R. W. (1958). *J. Histochem. Cytochem.* **6**, 43.
Messier, B., and Leblond, C. P. (1957). *Proc. Soc. Exptl. Biol. & Med.* (*N. Y.*) **96**, 7.
Messier, B., and Leblond, C. P. (1960). *Amer. J. Anat.* **106**, 247.
Metcalf, D., and Wiadrowski, M. (1966). *Cancer Res.* **26**, 483.
Meyer, R. R., (1966). *Biochem. Biophys. Res. Comm.* **25**, 549.
Meyer, R. R. (1967). *J. Cell. Biol.* **31**, 151A.
Meyer, R. R., and Ris. H. (1967). *J. Cell Biol.* **31**, 76A.
Meyer-Arendt, J. R. (1962). *Acta Histochem.* **13**, 47.
Meyer-Schützmeister, L., and Vincent, D. *In* "Landolt-Börnstein Zahlenwerte und Funktionen aus Physik, Chemie, Astronomie, Geophysik, Technik," (A. Eucken, ed.), Vol. 1, p. 350. Springer-Verlag, Berlin, 1952.
Meyer zum Gottesberge, A. (1961). *Acta-oto-laryng.* Suppl. **163**, 46.
Meyer zum Gottesberge, A., and Plester, D. (1961). Archiv Ohren-Heilk. u. Z. Hals-Heilk. **178**, 145.
Michelson, A. M., (1963). *In* "The Chemistry of Nucleosides and Nucleotides," Academic Press, New York,
Miller, A., and Maunsbach, A. B. (1966). *Science* **151**, 1000.
Miller, O. L., Stone, G. E., and Prescott, D. M. (1964a). *In* "Methods in Cell Physiology" (D. M. Prescott, ed.), Vol. I, p. 371. Academic Press, New York.

Author Index

Numbers in italics refer to the pages on which the complete references are listed.

A

Abraham, S., 155, *229*
Adams, J. E., 95, *229*
Adams, K., 150, *265*
Adelstein, S. J., 92, 109, *229, 254*
Adolphe, M., 140, *229*
Adrian, E. K., 106, *229*
Afzelius, B. A., 79, *256*
Aghajanian, G. K., 226, *229*
Albou, G., 6, *229*
Albouy, G., 6, *229*
Alexander, M., 174, *247*
Alfert, M., 27, 157, 179, 180, *229, 237*
Allfrey, V. G., 166, 167, 172, 174, 175, 188, 223, 224, *229, 247, 253, 260, 264*
Alpen, E., 112, 138, *242*
Alper, R. E., *253*
Altman, E., 198, *229*
Altman, J., 106, 198, 215, *229, 237*
Altman, K. I., 93, *242*
Altmann, H.-W., 103, 104, 107, 108, 171, 172, 182, 200, 210, 214, *266*
Amano, M., 27, 28, 77, 92, 168, 171, 189, *229, 248, 251*
Ames, I. H., 98, *229*
Amprino, R., 53, 58, 65, 66, 73, *229*
Anderson, E. C., 39, *270*
André, T., 19, *230*
Andreeva, L. F., 131, 150, *272*
Andreeva, L. P., 131, *230*
Andresen, N., 43, *230*
Andrews, G. A., 74, *230*
Andros, G., 43, 46, *230*
Antipova, M. P., 107, *230*
Anton, H. J., 213, *230*
Antoni, F., 25, *230*
Appelgren, L.-E., 44, 46, 67, 70, 218, 219, 226, *230, 238, 239, 244*
Appleton, T. C., 45, 85, 87, *230, 259*
Archambeau, J. O., 104, 113, *233*

Archibald, R. M., 68, *239*
Arnold, G., 23, 170, 174, *230*
Arnold, J. S., 31, 65, 70, 73, *230, 249*
Artusi, T., 181, 199, *268, 269*
Ashley, C. A., 26, *259*
Asling, C. W., 68, 71, *230, 269*
Atchison, A. A., 77, 101, *254*
Atkins, L., 154, *230*
Atkinson, W. B., 29, *230*
Atlas, M., 128, *230*
Attramadal, A., 44, *262*
Audran, R., 219, *243*
Austoni, M. E., 62, 63, *230*
Axelrod, D. J., 18, 19, 31, 69, 71, *230, 236, 263*
Ayvazian, J. H., 95, *239*

B

Bach, G., 105, *266*
Bachmann, L., 20, 219, 220, 221, 222, *230, 231, 262*
Bachmann, R., 73, *231*
Bade, E. G., 105, *231*
Baeckeland, E., 78, 171, *231, 235*
Bagshaw, M. A., 99, *271*
Baldwin, R. R., 19, *238*
Ball, C. R., 139, *231*
Baltus, E., 167, *270*
Banerjee, M. R., 124, 137, 144, *231*
Banerjee, S. N., 160, *246*
Banghart, F. W., 157, *253*
Banks, D., 42, *231*
Barigozzi, C., 154, *231*
Barker, A. N., 54, 55, 56, *239*
Barlow, C. F., 59, *262*
Barnard, E. A., 226, 227, *231, 258*
Barnhisel, M. L., 178, *249*
Barnum, C. P., 156, *231*
Barr, H. J., 98, *231*
Barrett, J. C., 150, *265*

273

M

Subject Index

A

Actinomycin D
  in DNA synthesis, 107, 108
  in nucleolus, 215
  in protein synthesis, 215
  in RNA synthesis, 174
  in tumor cells, 108
Adenine-^{14}C, 94, 167, 181
Adenine-^{3}H, 79
Adenine-^{15}N, 94
Algae, iodine uptake, 52
Alpha particles, 1
Americium-241, 71
Amino acids
  free, 184
  incorporation into proteins, 193
    into tumors, 215
  incorporation scheme, 205
  labeled, 184, 201
  specific activity, 184
  turnover rate, 184
β-Aminoisobutyric acid (BAIBA), 81
Aminopterin, 163
Application of emulsions, 32
Arsenic-73, 73
Arsenic-74, 73
Artifacts, 15
Auger electrons, 46
Availability time of thymidine-^{3}H, 87

B

Background, 14
  determination of, 15
  factors influencing, 14
Bacteria, DNA synthesis in, 165
Beta absorption, 23
Beta particles, 1
Beta self-absorption, 21
  in RNA synthesis studies, 170
Bones
  DNA synthesis in bone fracture, 106

incorporation of phosphorus-32, 57
  of sulfur-35, 52
mineralization of, 64
protein synthesis in, 197
Bromide-80, 75
Bromide-82, 75

C

Cadmium-115, 74
Calcium-45, 64
  mineralization of bones, 64
    of teeth, 66
  uptake in different tissues, 67
Carbon-14
  glucose, 59
  hydrocortisone, 60
  labeled substances, 59
  lactose, 60
  in plants, 61
  tyrosinase, 60
Carcinogenesis
  DNA synthesis in, 109
  RNA synthesis in, 181
Catabolism of thymidine-^{3}H, 81
CCl$_4$
  cell proliferation after, 105, 108
  protein synthesis after, 213
Cell cycle, see also DNA synthesis
  determination of, 114
    methods, 115
      double labeling with thymidine-^{3}H
        and -^{14}C, 116
  percentage of labeled mitosis, 115
  irradiation effects on, 158
  radiosensitivity, 159
  subphases of, 120
    G$_1$ phase, 133
    G$_2$ phase, 133
    mitosis, 121
    radiosensitivity, 159
    (S + G$_2$ + M), 133
    S phase, 120